The Antenna Experimenter's Guide

SECOND EDITION

Peter Dodd, G3LDO

Radio Society of Great Britain

Published by the Radio Society of Great Britain, Cranborne Road, Potters Bar, Herts
EN6 3JE.

First published 1991
Second edition 1996
Reprinted 2000

ISBN 1 872309 36 4

Cover design: Jennifer Crocker.
Illustrations: Roy Pettit, Derek Cole and Bob Ryan.
Production and typography: Ray Eckersley, Seven Stars Publishing.

Printed in Great Britain by Bell & Bain Ltd, Glasgow.

Contents

Chapter 3: Measurement of resonance 31

Chapter 4: Measurement of field strength 41

Chapter 5: Measuring antenna performance 58

Preface

"How unfit, and how unworthy a choice I have made of myself, to undertake a work of this mixture."– Sir Walter Raleigh, preface to The History of the World

This book is about experimenting with antennas. It is not an antenna book in the normal sense, that is to say it does not have antenna designs to suit particular requirements. What it does do is to encourage you to make antennas, to measure the performance of them and to know what it is that you are measuring.

The objectives of this book are:

- To encourage experimenting with, and construction of, antennas.
- To describe construction and use of simple RF measuring equipment.
- To explain how to adjust any antenna, home-made or commercial, for maximum efficiency using this test equipment.
- To describe how to overcome some of the problems of supporting an antenna at a sufficient height to allow the antenna to be effective.

There have been many changes regarding the assessment of antenna performance since the first edition of this book in 1991. Most of the change has occured in antenna analysis computer programs. At the time I noted that "if the recent history of computers is anything to go on then these antenna analysis programs can only become more accurate, easier to use and cheaper". This turned out to be the case so the chapter on mathematical modelling had to be extensively rewritten.

In general the subject matter covered by this book is as follows. Chapter 1 is an introduction to antennas and measurement with a few words about safety. Chapters 2, 3 and 4 are devoted the measurement of impedance, resonance and field strength respectively. Chapter 5 is concerned with the assessment of an antenna's performance in its environment using the measuring instruments described. Chapter 6 is all about the building of antennas and masts with methods of measuring coaxial cable resonance and loss. Chapter 7 covers the construction and adjustment of a range of experimental antennas. Chapter 8 describes mathematical modelling and computer analysis of antennas.

Although this book has been written mainly for radio amateurs, this interesting and absorbing subject is open to anyone with an interest in the subject. My early experiments with antennas were associated with television DX.

The only prerequisites to understanding the material are a basic knowledge of electricity, magnetism and Ohm's Law, a knowledge of simple AC theory and the characteristics of inductors and capacitors. The Radio Amateurs' Examination (RAE) level is perfectly adequate. Just enough antenna theory is included to illustrate how a particular RF measuring instrument functions.

Peter Dodd, G3LDO
West Sussex, 1996

Acknowledgements

I am indebted to the following people and organisations for assistance and material. Other sources of information are credited in the the text.

Peter Swallow, G8EZE, for providing valuable technical advice and constructive criticism.

Derek Pearson, G3ZOM, who did further development work on the noise bridge and FET dip meter, and made kits of these projects available.

Bert Weller, WD8KBW, for help and advice on the measurement of impedance and for locating the original papers by Harold A Wheeler and L J Chu on the limitations of small antennas.

The ARRL for permission to use copyright material from their publications, and particularly for their consent to use the *QST* article by W2WAM in Appendix 1.

Barney Wilmott, G8TGH, who made available a modern signal generator so that I could make make comparative signal strength checks.

Allen Grey, G8LCO, who introduced me to the Hewlett Packard 4815A RF vector impedance meter.

James Corum, K1AON, for supplying additional information on his toroid antennas.

Eric Knowles, G2XK, for photographs and information on his lightweight fold-over mast.

Byron C Weaver, WU2J, for the information on the W1QP/W8CPC compact beam.

Bob Carter, G4VSO, for permission to use his FSM circuit in Chapter 4.

1 Experimenting and measurement

MOST radio amateurs experiment with antennas to some degree or other. Even if you put up a simple end-fed antenna, then try changing the length or its shape, or try a different arrangement using a different counterpoise or a different feed method; all this is experimenting with antennas. The objective is always to improve the signal-to-noise ratio of the received signal or to increase the strength of the transmitted signal.

To achieve an optimum design normally takes a good deal of time and patience. This is because of the time taken to evaluate the latest change to see if it resulted in an improvement. If direct measurements can be performed then a lot more can be learned regarding the design in a shorter time. For this reason a great deal of space is devoted in this book to the construction of simple test equipment.

Not everyone is interested in antenna construction and experimenting as such. However, all active radio amateurs use antennas, and there are very few who would not be interested in knowing how to improve the performance of an existing antenna or being assured that the performance of their latest commercial antenna was optimum.

The key to constructive experimentation or antenna optimisation is measurement. Measurement and recording of data makes the subject more interesting and comprehensible. Analysis of data from one experiment can reduce the number of unproductive experiments.

RF MEASURING INSTRUMENTS

Antenna measuring equipment is often regarded as expensive and beyond the reach of most of us. While this may be true in the case of commercial equipment, it is relatively easy to make

simple measuring equipment. All test equipment has limitations in range and accuracy of the parameter being measured. While simple equipment may not be as accurate as an item of expensive commercial equipment, the measurements can still be valid provided that you are aware of the limitations of the instrument that you are using. In the descriptions of the test equipment in the following chapters the limitations of each instrument will be explained.

Take, for example, the simple diode field-strength meter. It is insensitive and has a limited range when used with a simple analogue meter. Nevertheless, as will be described in Chapter 4, this instrument can be valuable for checking the performance of the antenna.

Accuracy

Some people have an obsession with high accuracy when it comes to measurements. While this might be commendable, it may not be necessary. Take, for example, the receiver noise bridge for measuring impedance shown in Fig 1.1. The resolution of the scales is very coarse but is perfectly adequate for the purposes for which it was designed. It is small, rugged and suitable for carrying aloft to adjust the gamma match on a beam antenna. On the other hand, it may be necessary to measure the impedance

Fig 1.1. Commercial Paloma receiver bridge. Note that the resolution of the scales is very coarse, but is perfectly adequate for the purposes for which it was designed

Fig 1.2. Commercial General Radio 1606 impedance bridge. Note that the resolution of the scales is fine, enabling accurate measurement of impedance

of an antenna fairly accurately if you wish to set up a phased array. An example of an instrument suitable for this is shown in Fig 1.2.

Note that there is a difference between *accuracy* and *resolution*. Accuracy is the ability of the instrument to measure the absolute value of the parameter being measured within a given percentage. Resolution is the ability of the instrument readout to distinguish one value from another. You could, for example, have an instrument that has a poor accuracy but high resolution – you then finish up with precise inaccuracy.

However, don't be intimidated into not constructing measuring equipment because you cannot achieve a specified degree of accuracy. Just be aware of the general accuracy of the measuring instrument and remember that is better to measure to an accuracy of only 25% than not to measure at all. Methods of dealing with errors in measurements are described later under 'Errors'.

UNITS

Before considering measurements we need to establish what it is that we are trying to measure and what units are to be used. This turned out to be more difficult than I imagined. For example, when it came to measuring signal strength there was a whole range of units that had to be reconciled before I could even start.

When it came to measuring impedance the situation was even worse. Why did some instruments measure impedance and others measure admittance? Relatively recently I discovered the concept of duality, even though it has been around for a long time; a whole chapter is devoted to the subject in *Second Thoughts on Radio Theory* [1], published in 1955. More recently Dr H Paul Shuch, N6TX, addressed the subject in a comprehensible and comprehensive way [2] as follows:

"What we call technological progress is merely our ever-increasing ability to convert one sort of energy into another – at will and under complete control. It is a modification of the environment we call work. Of course, no energy conversion is 100% efficient, and the Laws of Thermodynamics tell us that in any energy conversion we are going to 'spill' some along the way – usually in the form of heat.

"Just as matter can exist in various states (solid, liquid, gaseous), so energy can occupy two possible states: potential and kinetic. We generally define potential energy as energy of position or location and kinetic energy as that of a mass in motion. Since potential and kinetic energy are duals, any manipulation we perform on one has its dual, or equivalent manipulation for the other. It is this duality that interrelates the various reciprocal electronics parameters with which we are all familiar.

"Electrical potential energy per unit charge (V or E) we recognise as electromotive force (EMF) or potential difference, measured in volts. Since electrical current (I) is measured in amperes, which specifies the rate of motion of charged particles (that exhibit mass), current is a manifestation of electrical kinetic energy per unit flux. Just how much mass do charged particles have? Precious little. A single electron weighs about a billionth of a gram. Yet mass in motion, no matter how minute, exhibits kinetic energy. And current is measured in coulombs per second (amperes), a coulomb being six billion billion electrons worth of charge. Hence the kinetic energy represented by each ampere of current is not insignificant.

"Our harnessing of electrical energy involves the ability to convert it from the potential to the kinetic state, and back again at will. Resistance (R) represents the conversion of electrical potential to kinetic energy. Its value, measured on ohms, is merely an expression of the ratio of potential energy per unit charge (EMF) applied to the resulting kinetic energy per unit flux (current). We call the mathematical expression of this ratio 'Ohm's Law' and it merely quantifies the conversion of potential to kinetic energy.

"I know, you've probably been taught that resistance is the opposition to current flow, and as far as that statement goes, it's correct. But opposition defines one of the things resistance *does,* not what resistance is. The dual of resistance, conductance (G) represents the conversion of electrical kinetic to potential energy. Its value, measured in mhos or siemens, is an expression of the ratio of kinetic energy (in amperes), applied to the resulting kinetic energy (in volts) appearing across the circuit.

"The ability of a capacitor to store potential energy (in the form of electrostatic lines of force) should be familiar to you. Capacitance (C) is defined as the ratio of potential energy to stored charge. Similarly, an inductor (which is the dual of a capacitor) stores kinetic energy in the form of a magnetic field. Thus inductance (L) can be defined as the ratio of kinetic energy (current) to stored flux.

"As you will recall, both capacitors and inductors exhibit reactance (X) measured in ohms, that involves both stored energy and angular velocity. Thus we can consider reactance as involving stored per unit of time. The dual of reactance is susceptance, measured in mhos or siemens, which can relate to the energy *released* from storage over a period of time.

"We define impedance (Z) as the combination of resistance and reactance occurring in a series circuit. It is important to note that the term 'impedance' is properly applied to series circuits only, and if any other configuration exists, it must be converted to its series equivalent before impedance can be specified. Mathematically, impedance is the vector sum of resistance (the conversion of potential to kinetic energy) and reactance (energy stored over time).

"The dual of impedance is admittance (Y), measured in mhos or siemens. This we define as a combination of conductance and susceptance found in a parallel circuit. It is important to note that the term 'admittance' is applied to parallel circuits only, and if any other configuration exists, it must be converted to its parallel equivalent before admittance can be specified. Mathematically, admittance is the vector sum of conductance (the conversion of kinetic energy) and susceptance (energy released from storage over time)."

The mathematical purist will deem the above definitions simplistic, and rightly so. They do, however provide us with a framework for all the units described in the following chapters.

HANDLING EXPERIMENTAL DATA
Recording experimental data

The results of your experimental work will be expressed in a series of numbers, otherwise known as 'data'.

Plotting polar diagrams, or making several comparative gain readings, involves recording lots of data. Keep all this data together in one notebook and label each test, together with any other relevant information. Leave room on the page for correction factors.

All comments, observations and calculation etc should also go into this notebook. It is bad practice to record anything on loose scraps of paper – they only get lost. Make a note of the date on which you take the measurements. When taking a reading, record the data directly as it is presented, eg 5.1 volts should be entered as '5.1 volts' without any correction factors. Any correction factors and their effect on the data should be entered on a separate column or line. It is never a waste of time to jot down all manner of notes as to the way the experiment is progressing, for example, the reason you decided to repeat some measurements or a suspicion that some of the equipment is not functioning correctly. Early experimental work recorded in my notebook is rather a mess in this respect. It is quite remarkable how a few cryptic comments, so self-explanatory when written, become utterly meaningless after a period of time.

Errors

A significant aspect of experimental work is identifying sources of error, reducing their effects and assessing the reliability of the final result.

Never be satisfied with a single reading, no matter which measurement you are making – repeat it. This procedure will improve the precision of the final result; it can also show up careless mistakes. All measurements are subject to *random errors* and these spread the readings about the true value. Sometimes the readings are too high, sometimes too low. With repeated readings these errors tend to cancel.

By taking a sufficiently large number of readings the random errors can be made as small as you like.

Not all errors behave in this way; some errors cause all measurements to be systematically shifted in one direction. If a *systematic error* is present, a random spread of readings will no longer be spread around a true mean value but another value. Under these experimental conditions, no matter how many readings are taken, the result will not 'home in' on the true value. These types of errors, and methods of avoiding them, are described in Chapter 5 – 'Method of measuring absolute antenna gain at VHF'.

This method of measuring gain is achieved by measuring comparative gain using a reference antenna of known gain. Because of the effects of ground, any change in the position of any of the antennas used in the test can affect the recorded gain.

Random errors are reduced, as described above, by making several measurements and taking the average. Systematic errors are overcome by making several gain measurements with the antennas in different positions to overcome the shift caused by ground reflections.

A good deal of experimental work is concerned not so much with the measurement of a particular value of some quantity, as with the study of how one quantity varies as the result of a change in another. There are several types of such dependence. For example, the direction headings of a beam antenna and the signal-strength readings on a nearby field-strength meter.

All measurements are subject to inaccuracy. You can never be sure of the exact value for a measured voltage. The digital voltmeter can lull us into a sense of security by giving a reading like '3.756V' but this probably a case of precise inaccuracy. This voltage may have been derived from current flowing through a resistor with 2% accuracy; the current may be the result of an RF waveform detected by a diode.

Calculations

Calculations may be involved with some of the data. The data may be normalised, a process of applying a factor so that the data fits a graph or chart (see Chapter 5). This process involves multiplication and this can lead to data with strings of meaningless digits. For example, if a correction factor is applied to an item of data, as shown in Fig 5.9 of Chapter 5:

$$12 \times 0.7272 = 8.7264$$

a number with four decimal points emerges. How many of these digits are meaningful? If the results are to be used to plot a polar diagram then there is no reason for the data to have more than one figure after the decimal point.

Graphs

A graph is a visual aid. A measurement, the scatter of the readings, interpolation or the point of departure from a curve *can* all be determined by a list of readings, but it is a lot easier to see what is happening when the results are shown in the form of a graph – see Fig 1.1. Extrapolation of data may also be possible, and is easier with a graph.

I sometimes find it useful to make a temporary graph from squared paper just to see if the data is well behaved or if one of the readings is the result of an inaccurate measurement.

In an experiment it is usual to change one quantity (the *independent variable*) by given amounts and see what effect is produced on the other quantity (the *dependent variable*). It is conventional to plot the independent variable along the horizontal axis and the dependent variable along the vertical axis.

In the case of the polar diagram the graph uses polar (circular) co-ordinates. In this case the antenna heading, in degrees, is the independent variable and is plotted on the radial axis. The signal strength is the dependent variable and is plotted on the circular axis.

Take enough readings to show the general trend of the data. Choose scales such that the points are spread over the area of the graph. When plotting a graph through the points, draw a smooth curve through the average of the plotted values rather than joining up the points; this is more likely to correspond to reality. A value that is some distance from the average, as shown at 1m height in Fig 1.3, is probably caused by faulty data or by a mistake in recording the data, and should be plotted again.

The graph in Fig 1.4 shows coaxial cable length measurements made using a MFJ-249 active SWR meter. Because of the poor accuracy of this instrument at low SWRs the exact length cannot be defined and is estimated using graphical interpolation.

DOCUMENTATION

It is good practice to document your experimental work. This is useful because it is a record of the work you have done. Furthermore, the act of writing up experimental work usually highlights gaps in the series of experiments that you may have carried out.

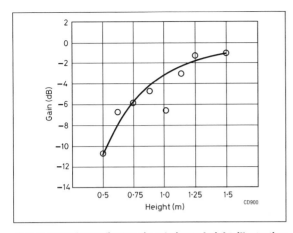

Fig 1.3. Plot of VHF dipole gain relative to height, illustrating how the graph should be drawn and plotted

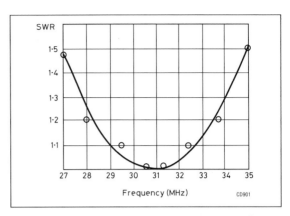

Fig 1.4. Resonant length of a length of coaxial cable estimated using graphical interpolation

This documentation can also form the basis of an antenna article for a magazine; editors are always on the look-out for good antenna or RF measuring equipment articles.

Henry Cavendish, the eighteenth-century British physicist, developed a deep understanding of electrical phenomena through his experimental work. Unfortunately he rarely took the time and trouble to write up his findings. The result was that others continued working on problems he had already solved. For example, he discovered Ohm's Law of electrical resistance 50 years before Ohm did. The law is rightly ascribed to Ohm because he made the information available to others.

THE DIODE

This is something of a diversion. Nearly all the RF measuring devices described in this book make use of the diode so it is necessary to consider the characteristics of this device and be aware of its limitations.

Diodes used for measuring RF are usually point-contact or Schottky-barrier types.

A point-contact diode is formed by bringing a pointed metal wire into contact with a piece of semiconductor material.

A Schottky-barrier diode is constructed using a planar process, where a thin layer of insulating material is grown over a small hole in the insulator, depositing a metal film onto the semiconductor through the window formed. This type of construction is more rugged, with a lower series resistance. However, it has a higher capacitance which may be a disadvantage for some applications.

Ideally the diode should rectify the RF waveform to produce a DC voltage proportional to the peak of the RF waveform. How well the diode voltmeter does this depends on several factors.

Choice of filter components following the diode

Consider the half-wave, peak-reading circuit of a field-strength meter shown in Fig 1.5.

The waveforms associated with this circuit are shown in Fig 1.6. The diode conducts on the positive

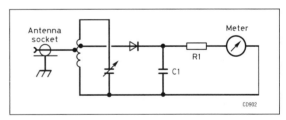

Fig 1.5. Field-strength meter using a half-wave, peak-reading RF voltmeter

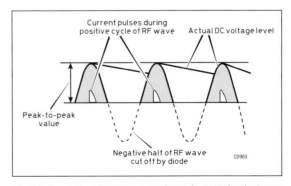

Fig 1.6. Current and voltage waveforms in FSM circuit shown in Fig 1.5

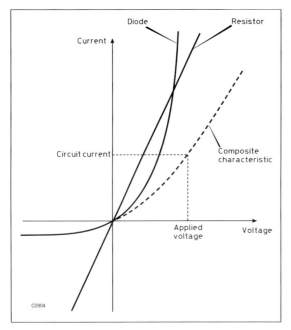

Fig 1.7. Compound characteristics of a diode and resistor

half-cycles of the RF waveform. The current through the diode charges capacitor C1. During the non-conducting phase C1 discharges through R1 and the meter.

Provided the time constant of C1, R1 is large compared with the RF waveform, then the degree of discharge will be small, and the difference between the true peak value and the measured value will be insignificant.

Linearity

The current/voltage characteristic of the resistor is a straight line over its working range. The slope of the characteristic is constant, the resistor current is equal to the voltage across it and Ohm's Law applies, ie $I = V/R$.

In the case of a diode the device is non-linear. If the diode is in the reverse-biased condition its resistance is very large. In the forward-biased condition the resistance varies with the magnitude of the applied voltage. It is this characteristic that allows the device to rectify an AC or RF waveform.

A diode with negligible load has a square-law characteristic, ie the current through the diode varies as the square of the applied voltage. In any practical application the diode is in series with a load such as a meter or an amplifier. In this case the characteristic will be a composite of the diode and

load. If the value of the resistive load is increased, the gradient of the slope will be reduced but the slope will become more linear as the load component of the composite characteristic predominates – see Fig 1.7. The reduction of gradient also means that the sensitivity, ie current flow/applied voltage, is reduced.

If the diode is followed by a high-impedance amplifier, it results in an increased load resistance and instrument linearity, and of course greater sensitivity because of the gain of the amplifier.

For most measurement purposes the requirement is for the output to be directly proportional to the applied AC voltage, ie that the circuit is linear. From the discussion above it can be seen that linearity is achieved by using a relatively large load for the diode, large enough so that this resistance, rather than the resistance of the diode, governs the current flow.

Detection of small RF voltages

The voltage/current characteristics of various diodes that can be used for detecting RF voltages are shown in Fig 1.8. As you can see, the RF voltage has to exceed a certain threshold before the diode conducts.

This limitation can be overcome by amplifying the RF voltage before detection or else forward biasing the diode to conduction so that it only operates over the linear part of the diode curve. Both of these measures are used in the design of a field-strength meter shown in Chapter 4 (Fig 4.14).

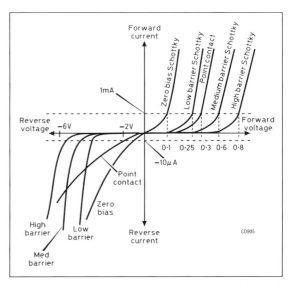

Fig 1.8. Voltage/current characteristics of various diodes used for detecting RF voltages

SAFETY

Many accidents are caused by trying to rush the work, possibly because it is getting dark and the job must be finished, or trying to obtain maximum antenna optimisation just before a contest in a few hours time. An accident results in this work not being done anyway, so a few notes regarding safety are relevant.

Ladders

All antenna work, particularly on HF antennas, involves the use of a ladder or a step-ladder. I am personally aware of more accidents due to misuse of ladders and step-ladders than any other cause. It is important that a ladder is set at a safe angle and fixed as firmly in place as the situation will allow. A step-ladder should be fully open with all four feet in contact with the ground. This can be difficult on uneven ground; wooden or concrete slabs may be used as packing under one or two of the legs to stabilise it.

AC mains supplies

It is sometimes necessary to use power tools or test equipment powered from the AC mains supply. Never use AC mains-powered equipment in wet weather or if the ground is wet; use an earth leakage trip – this device is simply connected into the extension lead at the mains supply socket. I have has found the rechargeable battery-operated electric drill a boon to the antenna constructor and experimenter.

Working with antenna masts

NEVER erect an antenna and mast that could possibly come in contact with electric power lines. Steel mast sections can be very heavy – ensure that adequate lifting tackle and a gin-pole is available. Always stop to consider the implications of the next move, particularly when dealing with heavy sections of steel.

MAINTENANCE

All fixings, including U-bolts and hose clamps, should be given a protective layer of grease. All metal surfaces forming a joint should also be protected this way. This is particularly important where copper wire is fixed to the aluminium on the elements. The effect of clamping dissimilar metals can result is a film of oxide on the joints within a few weeks of construction, resulting in antenna inefficiency and the danger of EMC problems, if this protection is not carried out.

The end, or any joints, of the coaxial cable should be sealed against the ingress of moisture. How this is done depends on the degree of permanency required. I use a general-purpose grease normally used for wheel bearings. This keeps PL-259 plugs and sockets, and the screw connectors, free from corrosion. It also appears to prevent moisture entering the coaxial cable.

Self-amalgamating tape or silicone rubber sealant can be used for sealing the end of coaxial cable if a more permanent job is required. Rubber sealant that generates acetic acid (vinegar smell) as it cures should be avoided.

REFERENCES

[1] *Second Thoughts on Radio Theory*, 'Cathode Ray', *Wireless World*.

[2] Chapter 5 – 'Transmission Media', Dr H Paul Shuch, N6TX, in *The ARRL UHF/Microwave Experimenters Manual*, ARRL.

2 Measuring impedance

ANTENNA IMPEDANCE

An antenna is a device that converts RF power from a transmitter into electromagnetic radiation or electromagnetic radiation into RF power. Many amateur radio antennas are, or are a derivative of, a resonant half-wave ($\lambda/2$) dipole so this antenna will be used as an example. Such an antenna is basically a tuned circuit having inductance, capacitance and resistance (see Fig 2.1).

When the antenna is resonant, the capacitive and inductive reactances are equal and opposite, and only a resistive component remains. If the antenna has no other losses, this resistor represents the element through which power fed into the antenna is lost from the circuit as electromagnetic radiation, and it is known as the *radiation resistance* of the antenna. In electrical circuit terms, this 'loss' is analogous to the conversion of electric power into heat in an electric fire, which is essentially a high-power resistor. In practical antennas, some energy is dissipated as heat due to the resistance of the conductors which can be represented in the equivalent circuit as a second, usually small, resistor in series with the radiation resistance. The antenna designer's aim is to minimise this unwanted resistance while maximising the radiation resistance by choosing suitably sized conductors and connections as explained later in this book.

Returning to the lossless antenna, the radiation resistance is dependent on the size of the antenna in terms of its operating wavelength. For short dipole antennas the radiation resistance is proportional to the square of the physical length in wavelengths. An infinitesimally short dipole has zero resistance. A linear dipole with uniform current distribution and 0.1λ long has a radiation resistance of 2.5Ω; and a $\lambda/2$ dipole has a radiation resistance of around 70Ω.

Radiation resistance is determined solely by the size and shape of the antenna, whether it is a simple

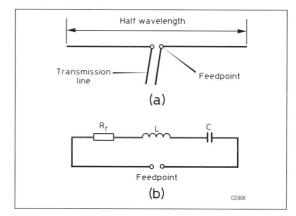

Fig 2.1. Centre-fed $\lambda/2$ dipole and equivalent circuit

dipole or a more complex structure. The resistance presented to the antenna feeder is dependent on where and how the feed is connected to the antenna. In the case of a centre-fed dipole less than $\lambda/2$ long, the input or feed-point resistance is the same as the radiation resistance if the dipole is lossless.

The input resistance of the same $\lambda/2$ dipole fed near one end is very high. Its equivalent, a parallel-tuned circuit, is shown in Fig 2.2.

However, antennas only exhibit pure resistance at resonance; at any other frequency there is always inductive or capacitive reactance present. When transmitter power is fed to the antenna the current in the resistive part is in phase with the applied voltage, while the current in the inductive or capacitive part (reactance) is 90° out of phase with the applied voltage. The combination of resistance and reactance occurring in a series circuit (see Fig 2.2) is *impedance* (Z). The impedance of a circuit can be defined as the ratio of the driving voltage to the current it produces.

Because impedance is derived from resistance and reactance it is always expressed in two parts, $Z = R + jX$. An impedance having a resistance of 75Ω

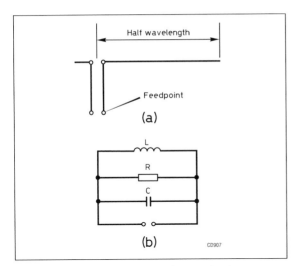

Fig 2.2. End-fed λ/2 dipole and equivalent circuit

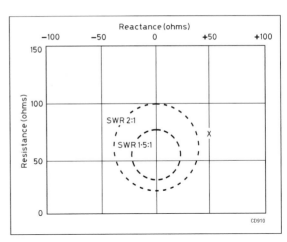

Fig 2.3. Impedance chart, with X showing an impedance of 75R +50jX. The circles represent SWRs of 1.5:1 and 2:1 for 50Ω coaxial cable

and a inductive reactance of 50Ω is conventionally written as:

$$75 + j50$$

For our consideration of impedance 'j' can simply be regarded as a convention for reactance. The ' +j' indicates inductive reactance and a '−j' indicates capacitive reactance. When the antenna is at its resonant frequency the +j and −j parts are equal and opposite so only the resistive part remains.

Impedance can be represented using a chart with Cartesian co-ordinates as shown in Fig 2.3.

This method of plotting and recording the impedance characteristics of antennas is rather like a map's Mercator projection, with the 'latitude' and 'longitude' of R and jX respectively plotted to define an impedance 'location'. Resonance, where the inductive and capacitive reactances in a tuned circuit or antenna element are equal and opposite, exists only on the zero reactance vertical line.

Before we can make full use of an impedance chart we need an instrument for determining a position on it. A professional impedance bridge is shown in Fig 2.4. As you can see, there are two calibrated controls, one for R and the other for

j. Information from the calibrated dials on the instrument can be used to establish the impedance position on the chart.

There is another method of describing impedance. If you refer to Fig 2.5 you can see that impedance is the vector sum of resistance and reactance. Impedance can therefore be described by a scalar (magnitude described by length) quantity and an angle, which gives a polar co-ordinate. This should not be

Fig 2.4. General Radio 1606 RF impedance bridge. The indicated reactance value is valid for 1MHz and must be divided by frequency to get the true reactance. Inductive or capacitive reactance is established with the use of the switch located between the two dials

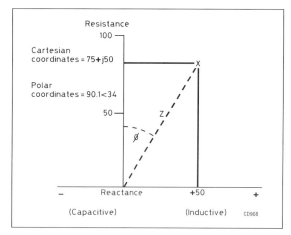

Fig 2.5. Impedance derived from resistance and reactance, plotted on *Cartesian co-ordinates.* The dotted lines show *polar co-ordinates*

difficult to visualise. Using our map analogy again the familiar great circle map gives a position in length (distance) and angle (beam heading).

An instrument for measuring impedance to give polar co-ordinates is the vector impedance meter [Note 1] – see Fig 2.6. The instrument is being used to measure the impedance of a tuned circuit in terms of magnitude and phase angle, which can if necessary be converted to the more familiar Cartesian co-ordinates using a calculator – see Appendix 4.

These instruments are expensive but it is not difficult to build simple instruments to measure impedance. Methods of constructing RF impedance bridges are described later in this chapter.

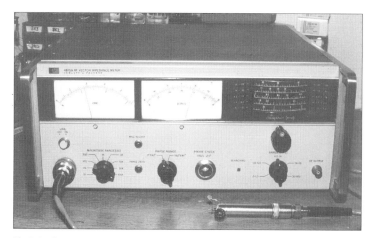

Fig 2.6. The Hewlett-Packard HP4085A vector impedance meter. The meter on the left reads magnitude and one on the left reads phase angle. The measurement frequency is read off from the dial on the right

REASONS FOR MEASURING ANTENNA IMPEDANCE

The impedance of the low-radiation-resistance point at which the antenna is normally fed is known as the *feed impedance*, or simply the *antenna's imped-ance*. The ability to measure this parameter is very important in antenna design. For example, the tra-ditional method of measuring antenna bandwidth uses the SWR-frequency curve. By plotting the im-pedance/frequency characteristic, more information can be obtained regarding the effectiveness of the matching system; ie the impedance curve can be fitted more effectively within a given SWR contour.

In addition to showing how impedance can be plotted, the chart in Fig 2.4 illustrates the limita-tions of SWR as a means of determining the charac-teristics of the feedpoint of an antenna. The two circles shown in Fig 2.4 are circles of constant SWR, one for 2:1 and the other for 1.5:1. Using our map analogy they can be regarded as SWR contours. When you measure SWR to try to find out what is going on at the antenna you are measuring the ef-fect of the antenna having a different value of im-pedance to that of the transmission line connected to it. However, an impedance of 100 + j0 would give the same SWR as an impedance of 25 + j0. You will see that there are a large number of im-pedance values that can give an SWR of 2:1. If you measure an SWR value of 2:1 then all you know is that you are somewhere on the 2:1 circle. This ex-plains why an SWR meter is not necessarily the best instrument for adjusting an antenna with a match-ing network such as a gamma match.

If you make several impedance measurements of an antenna over a range of frequencies they can be used to produce an impedance *signature* of the antenna. Fig 2.7 shows two of these signatures, which were obtained when evaluating the double toroid antenna [1].

The dotted line shows that the re-sistance is around 8Ω at resonance, and explains why no amount of an-tenna pruning would bring the SWR value to usable proportions. With a suitable matching circuit, the imped-ance is very close to 50Ω at resonance as shown with the dashed line.

(Resonance is where the inductive and capacitive reactances in a tuned circuit or antenna element are equal

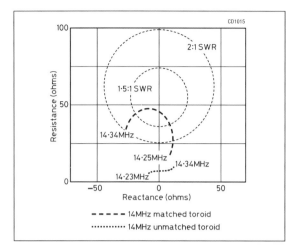

Fig 2.7. Impedance signatures of a double toroid antenna

and opposite, and this condition exists only on the zero reactance vertical line of Figs 2.4 and 2.7.)

There are other reasons for measuring antenna impedance:

- Adjustment of an antenna matching system, such as a gamma match, is much easier if the impedance is known because the appropriate direction of correction can be made. Using an SWR meter can be frustrating because the direction of correction is not known and can only be achieved using a hit-and-miss approach.
- Impedance measurements can be used to measure antenna radiation resistance. This information is useful in determining how an antenna is to be constructed. For example, if the radiation resistance is very low, then the current in the antenna element will be high and it should be constructed using low-resistance material (tubing rather than wire) if losses are to be minimised.
- Any calculations involving the use a Smith chart require an impedance figure as a basis for using the chart. The Smith chart is described later in this chapter.

Antenna impedance measurements can normally only be done via a length of transmission line. However, the actual antenna impedance will rarely be the same as the measured impedance because of the impedance transformation except when the line is an exact multiple of $\lambda/2$.

There are two ways to find out what the real antenna impedance is:

- Measure the electrical length of the feeder and use a transmission line calculator, such as the

Smith chart, to find the antenna impedance. It isn't difficult and the method is described on p25.
- Measure the impedance of the antenna using $\lambda/2$, or a multiple of $\lambda/2$, of coaxial cable. I use this method quite frequently but it does have a couple of disadvantages. Because the cable is resonant it can result in antenna currents on the outer conductor of the cable, which can give inconsistent impedance measurement results. These currents can be minimised using a current balun.

If you make several impedance measurements over a range of frequencies, remember that the cable is $\lambda/2$ on one frequency only.

It is obvious that it is important to know the electrical length of the feeder whichever method you use. Several methods of measuring feeder electrical length are described in this book:

- Using a GDO is described in Chapter 3.
- Using the Smith chart later in this chapter.
- Chapter 6 – 'Coaxial Cable'.

IMPEDANCE MEASURING TECHNIQUES

Impedance measuring techniques have been classified into two groups by Bert Weller, WD8KBW [2]. These are *null methods* and *deflection methods*.

Null methods usually employ balanced bridges where the unknown impedance is matched to a calibrated adjustable standard impedance and the match indicated by a null on a meter or a noise null in a receiver. An example of a balanced bridge is shown in Fig 2.8.

Balanced bridge methods have some advantages – they can be made direct reading, so that no calculations are required; and the accuracy of the measurement is independent of the calibration of the null meter indicator. It has an upper frequency limit of between 30 and 50MHz, depending on the bridge construction.

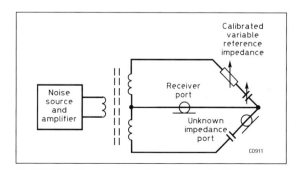

Fig 2.8. RF bridge using an adjustable standard impedance

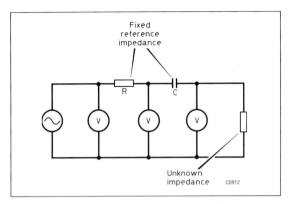

Fig 2.9. Basic three-meter RF bridge using a fixed standard reference

The disadvantage of the balanced bridge is that the relatively complex bridge network contains many stray impedances, both series and shunt, which may change with bridge adjustment or frequency or both. A second disadvantage is the need for a rather detailed calibration of the adjustable standard impedance. Nevertheless, the balanced bridge is the most popular method of impedance measurement found in amateur radio journals and handbooks [3, 4].

Deflection methods compare the unknown impedance with a fixed standard impedance, and the ratio is indicated by the reading (deflection) of a meter. Because the meter can only indicate a scalar relationship, the deflection methods have provisions for making more than one comparison so that the resistive and reactive parts of the unknown can be determined.

Typically three readings are required (see Fig 2.9) and are the source of one name for the technique – *the three-meter method.*

The fixed standard is usually one leg of a half-bridge, and the simpler circuit and absence of an adjustable reference impedance reduces the stray impedances. This makes for greater accuracy and the ability to operate at higher frequencies; I have constructed one of these that gives good results at 146MHz.

The disadvantage of the method is that the accuracy of measurement is dependent on the accuracy of the voltage measurements. In addition they are not direct reading like balanced bridges: some calculation is required to reduce the raw measurements to impedance values. It is probably for this reason that the deflection method of measuring impedance has not been popular in the past although the ability to computerise the method may change this.

During the course of making experiments with antennas the following represents two of the most common situations where impedance measurements are required:

- When adjusting the matching between the feeder and the antenna. In this case accuracy is not important and the objective is to adjust the matching system for a resistive reading of 50Ω and zero reactance if 50Ω coaxial cable feeder is being used.
- To plot the impedance over a range of frequencies to obtain an antenna characteristic. In this case many measurements are required, together with the greatest accuracy possible.

I use a noise bridge for antenna adjustments and a three-meter impedance-measuring bridge for impedance characteristic plotting. The reason for using a specific instrument for a specific task is because the noise bridge is more convenient and the three-meter bridge is more accurate.

THE NOISE BRIDGE

The noise bridge uses the null method already described. Wide-band RF noise is used as a source and a receiver is used as frequency-selective null detector. Noise bridges don't have a reputation for accuracy but they are small and convenient to use. The accuracy and the depth of the null depends mostly on the layout of the bridge network and the care taken in balancing out the bridge.

The description of a noise bridge that follows is by Derek Pearson, G3ZOM, who has made a kit available – see Appendix 2. The front panel is illustrated in Fig 2.10, and the circuit diagram is shown in Fig 2.11.

It can be used to measure impedance in terms of series resistance and reactance, within the frequency limits 1 to 30MHz. The useful range is approximately 0 to 200Ω. The reactance range is dependent on frequency and the capacitance swing of the variable capacitor used in the variable arm of the bridge. As a rough guide, using the suggested 250pF variable:

At 1MHz: 5000Ω capacitive to 1200Ω inductive
At 30MHz: 170Ω capacitive to 40Ω inductive

Balancing the bridge

The bridge has to be balanced to obtain a reasonable calibration over the intended range. Connect a suitable receiver to the detector socket and a non-reactive (carbon or metal film) across the UNKNOWN socket. The resistor leads must be kept as short as

Fig 2.10. The G3ZOM noise bridge, front panel. The reactance (X) scale is calibrated in ohms, X_C (negative) or X_L (positive), at 1MHz. It is necessary to divide by frequency to get the true reactance reading. The UNKNOWN or ANTENNA socket is to the left and the connection to the receiver is top right

possible to reduce the unwanted reactance to a minimum (important at the high-frequency end of the range). Set RV1 to maximum resistance and CV1 to maximum capacitance (fully meshed). Tune the receiver to around 14MHz and switch the noise bridge on. A loud 'rushing' noise should be heard from the receiver and the S-meter (if fitted) should show a good signal strength.

By listening to the noise level, and observing the S-meter (if fitted), adjust CV1 to obtain a decrease in volume (a null). Then adjust RV1 for a deeper null. Repeat these two adjustments until the deepest null has been reached. Temporarily mark the null positions of RV1 200Ω and CV1 to zero.

Set the receiver within the 1 to 2MHz range and repeat the nulling procedure. This time the null will be much sharper so careful adjustment is needed. The positions of RV1 and CV1 should be the same or close to those obtained previously. If not, the wiring around the bridge components is probably too long. Short wiring lengths are essential.

Repeat the procedure again with the receiver set to around 30MHz. This time the null will be much wider. The position of RV1 should again be close to that obtained previously, but it will probably be

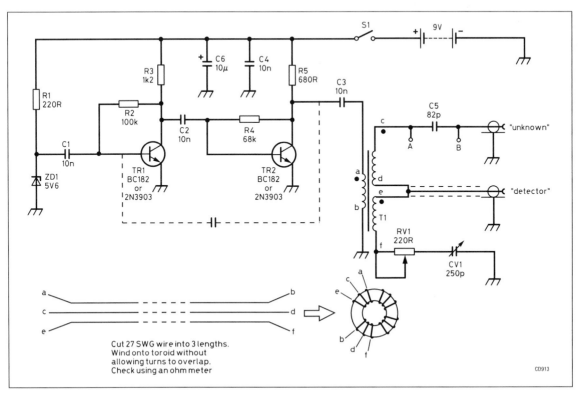

Fig 2.11. Circuit diagram of the G3ZOM noise bridge. The circuit can be modified by connecting a capacitor as shown in the dotted lines. This causes the amplifier to work as a multivibrator and tone modulates the noise source [5]

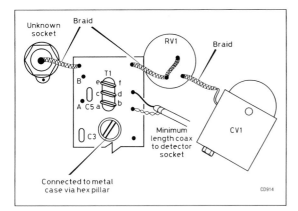

Fig 2.12. Layout of bridge components

found that the position of CV1 is somewhat different to before. If this is the case, the situation can be remedied by adding a small-value balancing capacitor between pin A and chassis in Fig 2.12.

Both the value and the position of this balancing capacitor will need to be determined by trial and error. Try, say, 10pF to pin A and repeat the nulling procedure at 2 and 30MHz. If the situation is worse than before, try a 10pF capacitor between the chassis and RV1 (where it connects to T1). One or the other position will result in an improvement which is worth the effort to obtain reliable measurements. Even greater accuracy can be obtained by adding compensating inductance to the bridge but this has not been found necessary to date.

The instrument shown in Fig 2.10 has a better than 50dB null at 10MHz. Additional reading on the subject to be found in reference [6].

Calibration

Calibration can now be carried out. Tune the receiver to around 14MHz.

Resistance scale

Connect suitable resistors, one at a time across the UNKNOWN socket, nulling the bridge and marking the resistance values of the test resistors on the RV1 scale. CV1 should remain at its zero position. The resistance scale should be fairly linear, allowing simple interpolation of unmarked values.

Reactance scale

Connect a 51Ω resistor across the UNKNOWN socket, using short leads. Null the bridge and mark the position CV1 as zero '0'.

Leave the 51Ω resistor in place and connect a

selection of capacitors across C5 (use terminals A and B), nulling the bridge each time and marking the reactance scale with the capacitance value. This part of the scale represents series inductance (positive reactance or X_L.

With the 51Ω resistor still in place connect a series of capacitors across CV1, again nulling and marking as before. This part of the scale represents series capacitance (negative reactance, or X_C). Note that the scale will only be linear if a linear capacitance law variable is used for CV1.

Reactance scale calibration – capacitance or ohms?

At this stage the reactance scale is temporarily calibrated in capacitance. Most published designs leave the reactance scale calibrated this way and use either a graph or a formula to make the conversion to the required reactance value in positive or negative j ohms (see Fig 2.3). The reactance scale of the professional bridge (see Fig 2.4) is calibrated in reactance at 1MHz and the only conversion required is to divide the measured value by frequency. You can use either method of calibration, using the conversion graph or formula in Appendix 4.

Using the noise bridge

This bridge, in common with all other impedance measurement bridges, measures the impedance presented to the UNKNOWN socket. This may not be the same as the antenna impedance because of the impedance transformation effect of the coaxial cable connecting the antenna to the bridge; this aspect is discussed later in this chapter – see 'Smith chart'. Also see Chapter 6 – 'Coaxial cable'.

RV1 and CV1 are then varied alternately to obtain the best null. The equivalent series resistance is obtained directly from the RV1 scale.

Impedance at the UNKNOWN socket is measured by connecting the noise bridge as shown in Fig 2.13. The receiver or transceiver is tuned to the measurement frequency and the R and X_C controls adjusted for minimum noise. These controls interact and the sharpest dip must be found by trial and error. Antenna impedance measurements can be accomplished in one of two ways:

1. At the transmitter end of the feeder (Fig 2.13(a)). By using a multiple of $\lambda/2$ at the frequency of measurement, the antenna feed impedance is reflected back to the transmitter end of the feeder. Obtaining such a length of feeder is described later in this chapter and also in Chapter 3. The

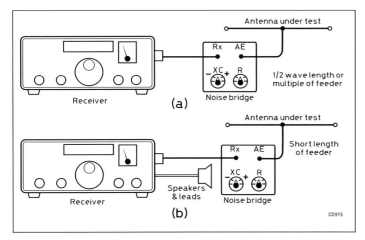

Fig 2.13. Noise bridge and receiver connections for antenna impedance measurements

disadvantage of this method is that the antenna matching network (eg gamma match) is at the antenna, remote from the impedance measurement, making the method rather cumbersome.

2. At the antenna end of the feeder (Fig 2.13(b)). The adjustment, and the measurement of the results of the adjustment, is far more convenient. However, the method is limited to situations where there is access to the antenna *in situ.* A further disadvantage is that the noise null detector, the receiver, also has to be close at hand, which may be rather inconvenient 20m up a mast or on the roof of a house. The problem can be overcome by leaving the receiver in the shack. A small speaker or a pair of headphones can be connected to the output of the receiver via another feeder or a couple of wires from the rotator cable. The feeder length is immaterial.

Make sure that the receiver/headphone arrangement is earthed to prevent an electric shock hazard.

I use a lightweight foldover mast for experimental antenna work, and here the method of measuring antenna impedance is as described in (1) above but with a small difference. The transceiver is located next to the antenna mast and connected to the antenna via a multiple of $\lambda/2$ of feeder. The use of a current choke (see Chapter 6) is recommended when using a multiple of $\lambda/2$ length of feeder.

The antenna is folded over to allow access to the matching device, which is then adjusted. The antenna is then raised to its full height and the impedance is then measured.

The noise bridge is the most convenient method for adjusting the antenna to the feeder. To illustrate its simplicity in use, the steps required to adjust a gamma match using this technique will be given. The method assumes the feeder impedance to be 50Ω, the driven element to be near to resonance and the gamma match component dimensions and capacitor value to be appropriate for the frequency in question.

1. Connect the noise bridge as shown in Fig 2.13(a).
2. Measure the impedance. If the reactance is not zero adjust the gamma capacitor until the measured reactance is zero.
3. If the resistance is greater than 50Ω, shorten the gamma rod. Repeat step 2.
4. If the resistance is lower than 50Ω, lengthen the gamma rod. Repeat step 2.

THE THREE-METER IMPEDANCE MEASURING METHOD (3-M Z BRIDGE)

I have used this method of measuring impedance for the last 20 years and became interested in the technique after reading an article on the subject in *QST* [7]. Although it is a simple instrument to construct it will produce results comparable to laboratory instruments if good basic constructional and operational practices are followed.

As stated in the introduction, this method compares the unknown impedance with a fixed standard impedance, and the ratio is indicated by three voltmeter readings. In this variation of the method, five readings are made. One of the additional readings allows in-place calibration of the reference capacitor and the second permits several solutions for the unknown impedance, so giving an indication of the random errors that may be present in the data.

The fixed standard impedance comprises a resistor and capacitor – see Fig 2.14. An RF excitation voltage, at the measurement frequency, is applied to Z via R and C. The voltages across R and C are measured together with the input voltage E_a, the voltage across Z and the voltage across Z, plus C. The excitation level is adjusted until $E_r = 5V$ then all the other voltages are then measured.

The RF voltages are measured using diode probes, selected by a switch. These probes measure peak volts and require a high-impedance voltmeter – a

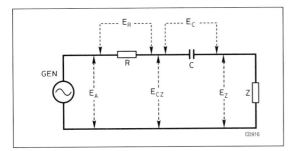

Fig 2.14. Block diagram of 3-M Z bridge showing the voltage measurement points

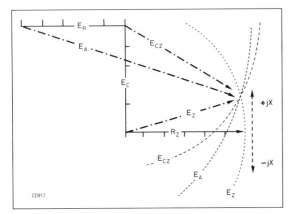

Fig 2.15. Method of determining impedance from measured voltages – see Fig 2.14

digital voltmeter is ideal. Impedance values are derived from the voltage data by calculation but this may be simplified in one of two ways:

- By using a graphic method shown in Fig 2.15. The voltage readings obtained from the instrument are plotted on graph paper using a pair of compasses and a ruler. The complex impedance is identified as the point where a set of three arcs intersect.
- By using a computer with a suitable program. See Appendix 3 for the program listings [8, 9].

The full circuit is shown in Fig 2.16. For greatest accuracy the value of R and the value of C need to be appropriate to the range of impedance and frequency respectively of the measurements being made. For example, most measurements are made using 50Ω impedance coaxial cable on one or more of the amateur bands. R can therefore have a resistance of 50Ω and C a reactance of 50Ω. In practice a reactance value for C of between 25Ω and

100Ω will give reasonable results although highest accuracy will result if the reactance of C is near to 50Ω. To obtain the most accurate results the reference capacitor value should be appropriate to the measurement frequency.

The original article suggested a reactance value of between 25 and 50Ω for reference reactance C. Although values of up to 100Ω still gave reasonable results the capacitor value should be changed for different bands, as shown in Fig 2.16, to obtain the greatest accuracy.

Replacing the reference capacitor at each measured frequency band is, to say the least, inconvenient. A method recommended by John Bazley, G3HCT, overcomes this problem [10]. He used a plug-in reference capacitor utilising PCB connector strip. It might also be useful to make the reference resistor plug-in when measuring high or low impedances; in other words the reference component must be similar to the impedances being measured if greater accuracy is required.

The area around the unknown Z port is quite sensitive to component lead length. On the other hand, the reference capacitor lead adjacent to the reference resistor appears as a small component of negative capacitance and is accommodated within the voltage measurements. Nevertheless, component leads should be kept as short as possible.

A low-power transmitter with a variable power output can be used as an excitation source. It is very important that the harmonic output from the

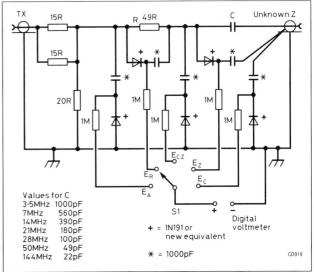

Fig 2.16. 3-M circuit diagram

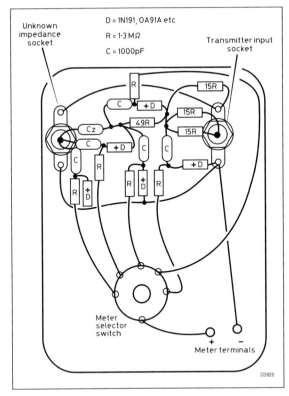

Fig 2.17. Component layout of a 3-M impedance measurement bridge

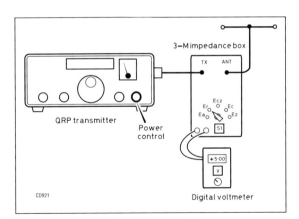

Fig 2.18. Three-meter test bridge and transmitter connections for antenna impedance measurements

excitation source is kept as low as possible; if your results are inconclusive this will probably be the cause.

An attenuator is used at the input so the transmitter is isolated from the variations of unknown impedance as the transmitter frequency is varied during a series of measurements. These attenuator resistors must be capable of dissipating the transmitter power without overheating, otherwise the voltage readings will drift during the measurement. A switched variable attenuator is also useful because of the variation in excitation level required when measuring a wide range of impedances.

Power stability of the excitation source is also important, ie that E_r remains constant while the other parameters are being measured.

Building the 3-M *Z* bridge

The circuit and the layout of the impedance-measuring bridge are shown in Figs 2.16 and 2.17 respectively. The unit is built in a die-cast aluminium box with the components mounted on the inside of the lid.

Because of the need to change the reference capacitance with each band, to give greatest accuracy, some thought should be given to making the replacement of this component fairly easy. If the bridge is to be used at VHF the reference capacitor should be soldered into place; the layout in Fig 2.17 worked at 145MHz.

Using the 3-M *Z* bridge

Connect the unknown impedance, excitation source and digital voltmeter to the three-meter test bridge as shown in Fig 2.18.

1. Set the switch to read E_r.
2. Set the transmitter to the lowest power level and switch on.
3. Increase the power until the voltmeter reads 5V; record this on a note pad as '50'.
4. Note the voltages at the other switch positions (12V being recorded as '120' and 6.3V as '63' etc); then check the stability of the transmitter power output by checking position E_r again. The readings should be repeated if the excitation level has drifted more than about 0.1V.

Graphic method of extracting impedance from data

All that is required is a sheet of linear graph paper, a pencil and a pair of compasses. The method is illustrated in Fig 2.19.

1. Draw a horizontal line on the graph paper whose length is equal to E_r.
2. Draw a vertical line down from the right-hand side of line E_r whose length is equal to E_c.
3. Place the point of the compasses on ① and draw

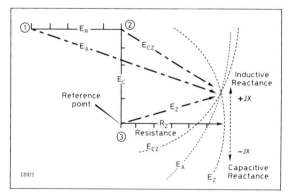

Fig 2.19. Method of extracting impedance from 3-M data using linear graph paper

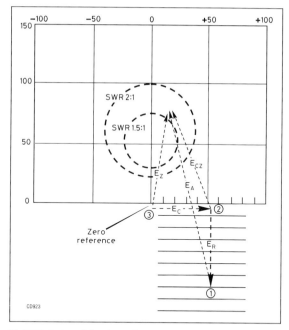

Fig 2.20. Determining impedance from 3-M data using special chart

an arc whose radius is equal to E_a. Repeat for ② and ③ for radius values E_{cz} and E_z respectively.

4. Mark the point at which the arcs intersect. An exact intersection of all three arcs is not always possible due to the errors in the data.

A horizontal line from the reference point to the arc intersection gives the resistive value of impedance. A vertical displacement up or down from the resistive line gives the value of the inductive or capacitive reactance respectively. If the arcs do not intersect, take the centre of the triangle formed by the non-intersecting arcs as the impedance point.

The special chart shown in Fig 2.20 can also be used for extracting impedance from 3-M data. A blank copy of this chart is given in Appendix 5 and may be photocopied. SWR circles (50Ω) have been added so that impedance measurements can be correlated with SWR.

1. Draw a horizontal line from 0 (zero reference) to the right, whose length equals E_c.
2. Draw a vertical line down, starting from the right end of line E_c, whose length equals E_r.
3. Draw arcs of E_z, E_{cz} and E_a as described for Fig 2.19.
4. Read off impedance from where arcs intersect.

Extracting impedance from 3-M data using a computer

The computer program listings are given in Appendix 3 for processing 3-M data using an IBM PC compatible computer. [Note 2]

The program ZCHECK is written in GW BASIC and is compatible with GW and QUICKBASIC. When it is run you will be prompted for items of data. (The exception is E_r (B) which the program assumes to be 50.) The program prints the solution as soon

as the last item of data is entered. In addition it will report errors, which will give an indication of data reliability.

Use E_a, E_{cz} and E_z from Fig 2.22 to test the program. This is actual data obtained by measuring a resistor with long leads and a resistor with a small capacitor in parallel.

The program will amend any data resulting in a small geometric non-intersection – see Fig 2.21. It will also inform you of any change in any item of data required to effect this intersection – see Fig 2.22. The program will make 10 attempts to correct a non-intersecting error. If the data cannot be corrected during these attempts the program will report this and not give a solution.

In Appendix 3 there is also a small program called ZSMALL for use with a BASIC programmable calculator. This listing is a derivative of program ZCALC. It has been designed specifically to fit into the 1k memory of the Casio PB110 or a similar pocket computer. It performs all the calculations but does not report errors or amend faulty data. It has been found very useful for field work with the 3-M instrument.

Examples of results obtained using computer programs

The results shown in Figs 2.24 and 2.25 were obtained using a graphics program and data stored in

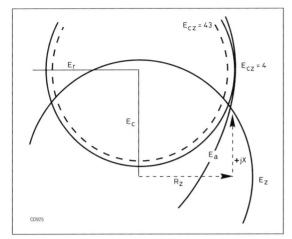

Fig 2.21. Graphic solution showing an error in E_{cz} (dotted) resulting in a non-intersection. An increase in E_{cz} (solid line) shows an intersection

```
     Ea   (A)  98
     Ecz  (C)  45
     Ec   (D)  50
     Ez   (E)  56
If there is more than one line of data below then the data has been corrected
Last line indicates corrected data used to determine impedance.

Ea (A)= 98 , Ecz (C)= 45 , Ec (D)= 50 , Ez (E)= 56
Ea (A)= 98 , Ecz (C)= 46 , Ec (D)= 50 , Ez (E)= 56
Ea (A)= 98 , Ecz (C)= 47 , Ec (D)= 50 , Ez (E)= 56
Ea (A)= 98 , Ecz (C)= 48 , Ec (D)= 50 , Ez (E)= 56


SOLUTION
   Resistance    46.4
   Reactance    + 38.3

   ERRORS
   R= (+/-)   1.6
   X= (+/-)  11.7


Goto Main Menu 1.  Repeat this program 2. ?
```

Fig 2.22. Printout of screen display showing corrections made by the program to create an intersection

Fig 2.23. General view of equipment used to make 3-M impedance measurements. Here a PB110 BASIC programmable calculator is used to extract impedance from the data.

a data file. This method is useful for producing impedance characteristic plots or signatures of an antenna or component over a range of frequencies.

The 3-M method is an accurate method for determining the electrical length of a transmission line: see Chapter 6 – 'Coaxial cable'.

Excitation level

It is not necessary to use 5V across the reference resistor for the 3-M method to work. Using some other, lesser, voltage would overcome the difficulty of adjusting the transmitter level to exactly 5V before measurements could commence. However, the graphic method and the computer programs derived from the graphic method are based on a reading of 5 (input as 50).

You can modify the program ZCALC (see Appendix 3) by changing the lines shown in the listing. If you do go this route for all the programs then you will have to modify TODISK, TABLE and GRAPHEGA with an additional matrix box to accommodate the E_R (B) variable.

You will also need an additional column in TABLE to record this value.

I have checked the system while at the same time reducing excitation voltage. It appeared to give good results but errors increased sharply if any one of the measured voltages fell below 1V. This level may depend on the type of diode being used but ZCALC will give a good indication of the errors.

3-M hardware design improvements

This instrument appears to give very good results when built with standard components and is accurate enough for most antenna adjustment purposes. However, WD8KBW suggests the following if greater accuracy is required:

• Position the power attenuator remotely from the test bridge. This reduces the chance of coupling between the high

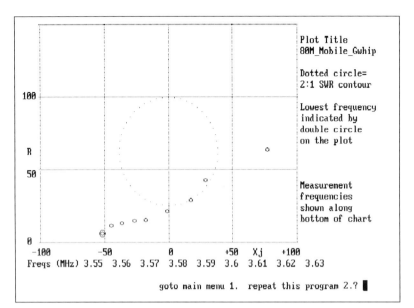

Fig 2.24. Measurements on a short 80m G-whip, illustrating why the best SWR obtainable was 2:1. Note that the measurements at 3550 and 3620kHz are slightly out of line with the other data on the graph and show probable errors

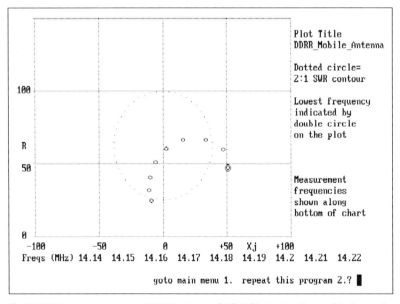

Fig 2.25. Measurements on a DDRR antenna [11]. It illustrates the rapid change in impedance with frequency (narrow bandwidth). It also shows the low-frequency side of resonance exhibits inductive reactance rather than capacitive reactance, compared with other antennas

voltages and currents in the attenuator and the voltmeters.

• Provide shielding between the voltmeter circuits and the RF line.

• Calibrate the voltmeter diode probes on an AC voltage (between 5 and 10V); they should read within 2% of each other.

• Calibrate the reference impedance using a good-quality ohmmeter.

Automating the 3-M method

It is should be possible to automate the process of creating impedance characteristic signatures over a range of frequencies using a computer. This could be achieved using an analogue/digital converter to allow the computer to read the data directly. Switching of the diode voltmeters and frequency control of the excitation source could also be controlled by the computer.

This would reduce errors due to power drift because all parameters would be measured very quickly. At the same time it would remove human error introduced when the data is transferred from the voltmeter to the computer manually.

CHECKING THE CALIBRATION OF RF BRIDGES
Calibration using dummy loads

Calibration of the noise bridge was described on p14. The 3-M bridge is self-calibrating but it is important to have some idea of the accuracy of any bridge that you are using.

A set of accurate dummy loads can be used for checking the calibration. A minimum of three loads is required. Assuming a 50Ω system, one is required for 50Ω and the other two should be 25Ω and 100Ω respectively. These loads should have minimum lead inductance so they should be constructed with the leads as short

Table 2.1. The effect of lead length on termination measurements							
INPUT PARAMETERS				RESULTS		+/- ERRORS	
Ea	Ecz	Ec	Ez	RES	jX	RES	jX
124	81	45	68	66.3	+0.4	3.1	6.2
128	80	46	70	71.5	+8.6	3.3	9.1
129	84	45	67	67.9	-5.8	3	5.7

as possible. I make these loads from four small ¼W resistors in parallel, built into a PL-259 plug.

WD8KBW noted [12] that carbon composition resistors are often recommended for RF service, but such resistors are not stable. Metal film or carbon film make a better choice for standards. They are more stable than carbon composition resistors and are available with tighter tolerances. Most resistors have a series inductance and a shunt capacitance such that the reactive effects cancel up to frequencies of about 100MHz for resistances of about 100Ω. Lower resistance values show series inductance and higher values show shunt capacitance.

I made a series of measurements, using an HP4085A vector impedance meter, which rather confirmed the above generalisation regarding resistors at RF. A 20Ω carbon film resistor (5% tolerance) measured 20.5 + j0.5 at 3MHz, which moved to 20.5 + j18.4 at 70MHz. A similar resistor of 180Ω showed no change in reactance as the frequency was moved up to 80MHz. This implies that a dummy load should be constructed from higher-value resistors in parallel.

Table 2.1 shows the measured impedances, using a 3-M impedance bridge, of a metal film resistor, soldered directly to the base of the UNKNOWN impedance socket with the following variations:

- Total lead length of 10mm (½in).
- Total lead length of 50mm (2in).
- Total lead length of 10mm, plus a small parallel capacitor.

These dummy loads can also be used for calibrating SWR meters. This is discussed at the end of this chapter.

Calibration check using coaxial cable and a dummy load

The main difficulty with checking the calibration of an RF bridge is verifying the reactance scale.

A novel approach, first described by W N Carron [14], uses a length of coaxial cable with a resistive load twice or half the characteristic impedance of the

coaxial cable. Even without knowing the electrical length of the test cable, some idea of the accuracy of the measurements will be apparent by any deviation from the 2:1 SWR contour when the results are plotted on an impedance diagram. The ideal results, obtained by calculation, are shown in Fig 2.26.

I checked my 3-M impedance bridge using a 3.8m (12ft 5in) length of RG213/U cable terminated with a 100Ω resistor. There is nothing significant about the coaxial cable length – I just happened to have a piece that long. The data from the first test were not as good as hoped for and are shown in Fig 2.27.

Some tests were then done to find the reason for these errors; they appeared to have two main causes:

1. Harmonic content in the excitation source.
2. Value of reference component inappropriate for the value being measured.

Further measurements were made at the frequencies where the errors were greatest and a filter was used to reduce any harmonic content that may be present; the value of the fixed reference capacitor was altered for each band. Previously it was thought that replacing the capacitor for every frequency band was unnecessary. 2000pF was used for 160m, 560pF for bands 80 to 30m and 200pF for bands 20 to 10m, rather than the values shown in Fig 2.16. Both these measures improved the accuracy. The data are shown plotted in Fig 2.28.

ADMITTANCE

As you know, the method of calculating the total value of several resistors in series is to add their individual values. The simplest way of calculating resistors in parallel is to add their reciprocals; the answer is also a reciprocal and has to be converted back to R to be in a form with which we are more familiar.

$$\frac{1}{R_1} + \frac{1}{R_2} + \frac{1}{R_3} = \frac{1}{R}$$

The reciprocal of R is conductance (symbol G) and you could work in conductances if you were dealing with calculations involving lots of parallel circuits.

The reciprocal (or the dual, see Chapter 1) of

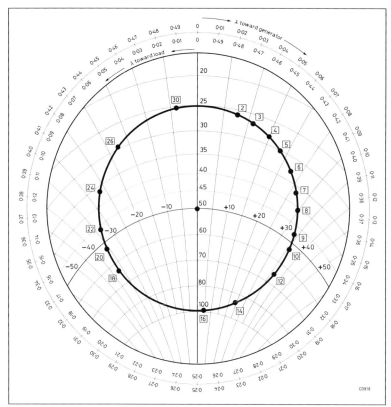

Fig 2.26. Results of an ideal impedance plot of a 25Ω resistor made via a length of coaxial cable. This impedance map is on a Smith chart and is described in the text

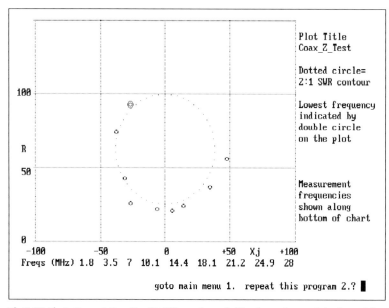

Fig 2.27. First attempt. Results of 3-M impedance bridge impedance plot using a 3.8m (12ft 5in) of RG213/U terminated with a 100Ω resistor

impedance is admittance (symbol *Y*).

The reciprocal of reactance is susceptance (symbol *B*). Conductances and susceptances in parallel-connected circuits can be added in the same way that resistances and reactances can be added in series circuits. The unit of conductance, susceptance and admittance used to be the mho but is now the siemen (S).

The reason for describing admittance is that it is important to know just what it is that your RF bridge is measuring. If the bridge is an admittance bridge then the result, like the calculation of parallel resistors described above, will need to be converted into the more familiar ohmic impedance.

You can find instruments at rallies and flea markets for measuring admittance, which should not be rejected because the units are unfamiliar. An example of a commercial admittance bridge is shown in Fig 2.29.

A very interesting RF bridge was described by G0RUN in *Radio Communication* [14]. This instrument is an admittance bridge circuit, which allows one side of both the capacitor and the variable resistor in the bridge to be earthed. Good ergonomics in the external layout of controls were sacrificed in order to get the best possible internal layout and the greatest accuracy.

You can use a normalised Smith chart calculator (see p23) to convert admittance to impedance.

THE SMITH CHART

The Smith chart was invented by Phillip H Smith and described as a transmission-line calculator [15]. One version of the chart is shown in Fig 2.26. Compared to

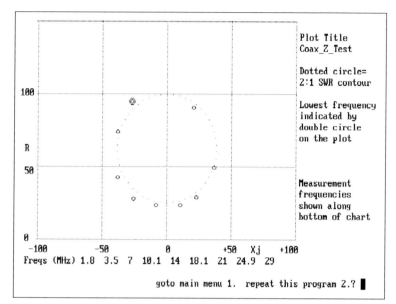

Fig 2.28. Second attempt. Results of 3-M impedance bridge impedance measurements after identifying some of the causes of error

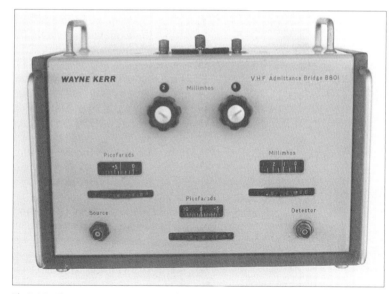

Fig 2.29. The Wayne-Kerr VHF admittance bridge type B108. The conductance is read from the two centre-top and right-hand calibrated controls (calibrated in millimhos). Susceptance is derived from the bottom centre and right controls calibrated in plus or minus picofarads; susceptance is calculated from the measured value and the measurement frequency

all the other impedance maps we have encountered in this chapter, it can be considered simply as a different projection, just as maps have different ones such as the Mercator projection or the great circle projection. The most obvious difference with the

Smith chart is that all the co-ordinate lines are sections of a circle instead of being straight. The Smith chart, by convention, has the resistance scale decreasing towards the top. With this projection the SWR circles are concentric, centred on the 50Ω point, which is known as the *prime centre* – see Fig 2.30.

One of the advantages of the Smith impedance map projection is that it can be used for calculating impedance transforms over a length of coaxial feeder. Because the reflected impedance varies along the feeder it follows that you need to know the electrical length of your coaxial feeder to the antenna. You can then calculate the antenna impedance from the impedance measured at the shack end of the coaxial feeder using one of the impedance bridges already described.

An impedance transformation using the Smith chart is illustrated in Fig 2.31. An additional scale is added around the circumference, calibrated in electrical wavelength (λ). Halfway round the chart equals 0.25 or λ/4, while a full rotation equals 0.5 or λ/2.

Two lengths of 50Ω coaxial feeder are shown superimposed around the circumference of a Smith chart in Fig 2.31; one length λ/4 long and the other 3λ/8). Both lengths are connected to a load having an impedance of 25 + j0. The λ/4 length of line (0.25) gives a measured impedance of 100 + j0 at the other end while the 3λ/8 section (0.375) gives an impedance of 40 + j30. It can also be seen from Fig 2.31 that a λ/2 length of coaxial cable would transform the impedance back to 25 + j0.

A practical Smith chart calculator

You can make a Smith chart calculator using the charts in Appendix 5. One chart has a restricted

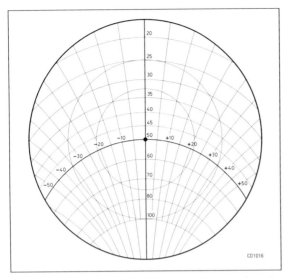

Fig 2.30. A restricted-range Smith chart. Note that the 1.5:1 and 2:1 SWR circles are concentric around the prime centre

impedance range but is easier to use in reasonably well-matched systems. It is used where the impedance excursions are limited and do not cause an SWR much greater than 2.5:1. The other is the standard chart which covers impedances from (theoretically) zero to infinity.

For this exercise we will make an impedance calculator using the restricted range chart – see Fig A5.3 in Appendix 5. Make a photocopy of the chart, enlarging it to bring it to a usable size. The chart is then glued to a circular sheet of stiff cardboard or thin aluminium. A small hole is drilled in the chart and backing material at the 50 + j0 point.

From a piece of very thin Perspex, transparent plastic or celluloid, cut a circle the same size as the chart to make an overlay. A hole is then drilled exactly at the overlay centre. Identifying the centre point should be no problem if a pair of compasses are used to mark the overlay before cutting.

Make a cursor by drawing a line along the radius of the overlay, using a fine-tipped marker pen. Cover the line with a strip of Sellotape™ or similar to prevent the line rubbing out. Trim off the excess tape.

Fix the transparent overlay to the chart with a nut and bolt with the tape covered line against the chart. Adjust the nut and bolt so that the overlay can be easily rotated, as shown in Fig 2.32.

The uses to which this calculator can be put are numerous and the description of its use will be restricted here to three examples.

Measuring coaxial cable electrical length

Earlier in this chapter it was explained why it is important, when making antenna measurements, to know the electrical length of

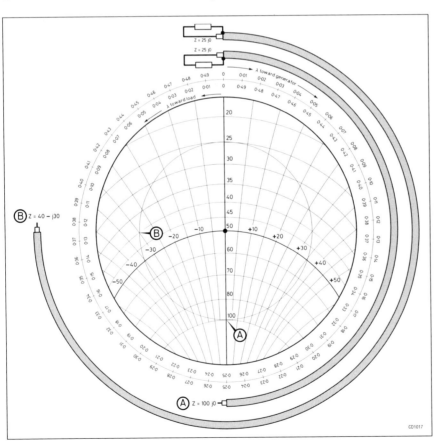

Fig 2.31. Smith chart, with transmission line electrical length scale, superimposed on two lengths of coaxial cable

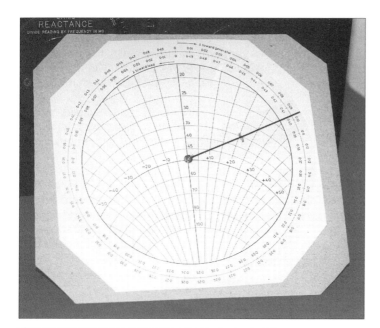

Fig 2.32. General construction of the Smith chart calculator

transmission line between the antenna and the point of measurement.

You can find the electrical length of coaxial cable by physically measuring its length and multiplying it by the cable velocity factor, or by using a dip meter as described in Chapter 3.

A more accurate method is to measure the electrical length directly using an RF impedance measuring instrument and the Smith chart. It also assumes that the transmission line losses are low; in practice this means that the procedure will only work with relatively short lengths of fairly good quality coaxial cable. This is described in Chapter 6 – 'Coaxial cable'.

1. Terminate the load (antenna) end of the cable with a 22Ω resistor.
2. Measure the impedance at the other end of the feeder.
3. Move the cursor so that it intersects the measured impedance point. The cursor will now point to the electrical wavelength of the feeder marked on the outer scale entitled 'wavelengths towards generator'.

The cable may be several half-wavelengths and part of a half-wavelength long. The Smith chart will only register the part of a half-wavelength, which is all we are interested in regarding the impedance transform effect.

Calculating antenna impedance from measured impedance

This is a method of calculating antenna impedance from a measured impedance value, using coaxial cable whose electrical length has already been determined.

1. Connect the cable to the antenna.
2. Measure the impedance at the other end of the cable.
3. Move the cursor over the measured impedance point and mark the point on the overlay with a wax pencil.
4. Follow the cursor radially outwards to the scale entitled 'wavelengths towards load'. Write this number down.
5. Add the length of cable in wavelengths to this number.
6. If the number is larger than 0.5, subtract 0.5.
7. Rotate the overlay until the cursor points to this number on the 'wavelengths towards load' scale.
8. The antenna impedance will be found on the chart directly under the wax pencil mark.

Example

1–4. The measured impedance is 35 + j20Ω and the cursor points to 0.407 on the 'wavelengths towards load' scale.
5. The cable electrical length was measured as 0.13λ. Then 0.407 + 0.13 = 0.537λ.
6. Off scale – too big! Subtract 0.5λ = 0.037λ.
7. Rotate the overlay until the cursor points to 0.037 on the 'wavelengths towards load' scale.
8. The antenna impedance is shown as 28 – j8Ω under the cursor at the same radius as the measured impedance.

Measurement of SWR

Calculation of SWR is very simple using the Smith chart. The result is useful for correlating impedance measurements with SWR measurements. To measure SWR:

1. Move the cursor over the measured impedance point.
2. Mark the point on the overlay with a wax pencil.
3. Move the cursor to the zero point on the outside scales.

4. The SWR can be read off as 50 divided by the mark on the cursor. The impedance measured in the example above gives a reading of 27 + j0. Now 50 divided by 27 equals 1.85; the SWR in this case is 1.85:1.

You can of course calibrate the cursor in SWR. Just place the cursor in the vertical zero position and place marks on the cursor at the 33.3, 25 and 20 resistance points to give SWR marks at 1.5:1, 2:1 and 2.5:1 respectively.

The normalised Smith chart

Most Smith charts are normalised so that they can be used at any impedance and not restricted to 50Ω, as are the ones so far described. This is achieved by assigning 1 to the prime centre; 0.5 on the chart then corresponds to 25Ω and 2 corresponds to 100Ω in a 50Ω system. The normalised chart can be used to convert impedance to admittance and vice versa. You can make a normalised Smith chart calculator from a chart in Appendix 5. Make a cursor by drawing a line along the diameter of the overlay, using a fine tipped marker pen. Cover the line with a strip of Sellotape to prevent the line rubbing out. Trim off the excess tape.

To convert admittance to impedance:

1. Choose a normalising admittance corresponding to the prime centre of the chart. This is usually 20mS (= 50Ω).
2. Convert the impedance to normalised admittance by dividing each component of the admittance value by the normalised admittance (20mS in this case).
3. Move the cursor over the measured admittance point.
4. Mark the point on the overlay with a wax pencil.
5. Move the cursor 180° so that the unmarked section of the cursor lies over the measured admittance point.
6. The mark on the cursor from step 3 gives the normalised impedance reading.
7. Convert to actual impedance ohms by multiplying by the reciprocal of the normalised admittance ($^1/_{20}$ mS = 50Ω in this case).

Example

In this example 16 – j13.6mS is to be converted to impedance using a 20mS normalised chart.

1. Normalise admittance:

$$\frac{16 - j13.6}{20} = 0.8 - j0.68$$

2. Move the cursor over the measured admittance point.
3. Mark the point on the overlay with a wax pencil.
4. Move the cursor 180° so that the unmarked section of the cursor lies over the measured admittance point.
5. The mark on the cursor from step 3 gives the normalised impedance 0.72 + j0.6.
6. Convert to actual impedance by multiplying by $^1/_{20}$ mS (50Ω) as:

$$(0.72 + j0.6) \times 50 = 36 + j30\Omega$$

The accuracy obtained using this simplified calculator is not high but is sufficient for most purposes. If you want greater accuracy then use the formula in Appendix 4. You can then use the Smith chart calculator to check the calculations.

MicroSmith

The most common use of the Smith chart is in the design of impedance-matching networks. Although such networks are beyond the scope of this book they are relevant to antenna system design. I have recently found that the easiest way to design them (as opposed to the empirical methods I used to employ) is to use a computer and the MicroSmith computer program. MicroSmith is a Smith chart simulation program that performs such calculations quickly and easily with the aid of an IBM PC compatible computer.

Wes Howard, W7ZOI, the author of this program, originally wrote it for his personal use in professional applications and still uses it extensively. The program has been modified for use by the engineering student and radio amateur.

It has been written so that frequent reference to the manual is unnecessary. A dynamic tutorial exercise comes with the program; an example of one of the exercises is shown in Fig 2.33.

An example of how MicroSmith can be used to solve a multiband antenna problem is shown in Fig 2.34. It shows the effect of adding capacitors to the feeder of a G5RV-type antenna to reduce the SWR [19].

The availability of MicroSmith is given in Appendix 2.

THE STANDING WAVE RATIO (SWR) METER

The standing wave ratio (SWR) meter is probably the best known of all antenna instruments around today. It is usually used to indicate the degree of mismatch between the feed impedance of the

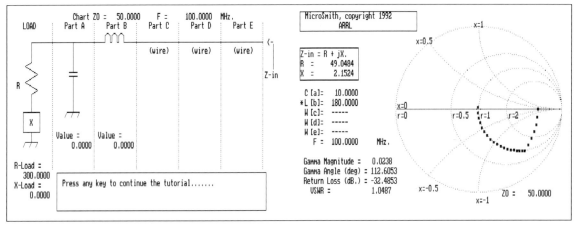

Fig 2.33. Two tutorial displays illustrating the results of matching with an L-network. Left: the matching network. Right: the Smith chart calculations used to show how the network converts the load impedance to the feed impedance

antenna and the characteristic impedance of the transmission line, and achieves this by measuring the ratio of the forward (incident) travelling wave compared with any reverse (reflected) wave caused by reflection due to mismatch. The basis of the SWR meter is a directional coupler that can sense either the forward or reverse waves. However, if a dummy load is connected directly to the antenna socket of an SWR meter it will indicate 'SWR' even though there is no transmission line present. The reason for this is that the SWR meter measures current and voltage relationships from which SWR is assumed. The meter detects reflected waves because their voltages and currents are out of phase.

The ability to measure SWR has assumed greater prominence since the advent of the solid-state untuned RF power amplifier with its fixed output impedance. SWR meters are cheap and easy to obtain, due mainly to the low-cost CB equipment on the market. Additionally, everyone who is associated with, or interested in, amateur radio possesses an SWR meter and knows how to use it.

Because it can remain connected into the transmission line while the station is in operation the antenna system can be constantly monitored, and the presence of any fault that may occur on the antenna system will be detected.

The SWR meter can be used as a relative power meter. In this case the forward meter is set to a predetermined value, which is then monitored to ensure the level remains constant. This is a valuable asset when using the transmitter as an RF source for impedance measurements using the three-meter method – see 'Measurement of field strength' (Chapter 4), and 'Plotting polar diagrams and measuring antenna gain' (Chapter 5).

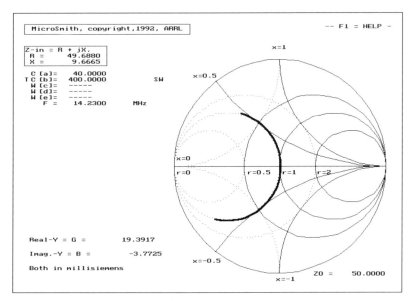

Fig 2.34. Screen shot of the main screen of MicroSmith, showing the variation in impedance caused by altering the value of C2 in the toroid matching network – see Fig 7.18

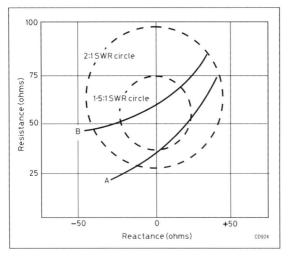

Fig 2.35. This impedance chart shows two SWR values, one at 1.5:1 and the other at 2:1. Curve A indicates the lowest SWR when the reactance is not zero while B shows lowest SWR at resonance

The SWR meter is unable to determine the nature of the impedance causing the mismatch. This can best be illustrated by the impedance chart in Fig 2.35. This shows two SWR values, one at 1.5:1 and the other at 2:1. It can be seen that the diameter of the circle is proportional to the standing wave ratio. On the Smith chart the SWR circles are concentric.

This SWR value can be caused by any number of impedance values on the circle. The SWR meter does not therefore measure antenna feed impedance although the latter affects the SWR value. Neither does lowest SWR necessarily indicate resonance. Resonance occurs when the reactance is zero as shown in Fig 2.35, which shows two antenna frequency/impedance characteristic curves. Curve A indicates the lowest SWR when the reactance is not zero while B shows lowest SWR at resonance. See also Fig 2.7 and accompanying text.

Additionally, SWR readings can be downright misleading. For example, if the transmission line becomes lossy, eg due to moisture, then the reflected wave will be attenuated and the SWR ratio will improve, even though the antenna system efficiency has deteriorated.

ANTENNA ANALYSERS

There are now RF measuring instruments known as *antenna analysers*. They comprise wide-range tuneable low-power RF generators, usually with a digital frequency readout; the SWR is measured with an internal sensor. Some instruments also have the ability to measure resistance or impedance at resonance.

This instrument is referred to as an *active standing wave ratio meter* by Gerd Janzen, DF6SJ. Gerd has devoted a book [16] to a whole range of RF measurements to which one of these instruments can be used.

The idea of a comprehensive antenna measuring instrument all in one box, battery powered for portability, is very attractive. Unfortunately there seems to be very little published regarding its construction. The only one I know of, to date, is the 'comprehensive antenna analyser' by WM6T [17]. This instrument is based on the Motorola MC1648 IC which provides a low-distortion, AGC-controlled signal in the range 1.6 to 30MHz in order to measure SWR. It also measures impedance using a series differential bridge.

The two main suppliers of commercial antenna analysers at the time of writing are MFJ and Autek. The signal level required to measure SWR is very small; I measured the signal on an MFJ unit and it was just a little over 3mW – obviously better than tuning up an antenna using a transmitter.

The following is a brief specification of these instruments from the manufacturers' literature.

Autek RF-1 antenna analyser

• A stable oscillator covering 1.2 to 35MHz in five overlapping bands with fine tuning capable of being set to 10kHz at 28MHz with the digital counter
• SWR measured relative to 50Ω
• RF impedance (at resonance) measured in ohms (0 to 2000Ω)
• Capacitance measured in picofarads (0 to 9999)
• Inductance measured in microhenrys (4 to 300)
• Battery powered (life approximately 12 hours) with 'auto off'
• All measurements displayed digitally by an LCD

An example of how this instrument can be used to measure coaxial cable impedance is taken from the instruction book.

"If you think the cable is 50Ω connect a non-inductive 50Ω resistor at the end of the cable. Slowly sweep the frequency in the 'Z' mode. If the cable is 50Ω the 'Z' will change very little. If the cable is, for example, 75Ω the 'Z' would swing cyclically with frequency. The object is to find a resistor at the end of the cable that gives a 'flat' 'Z' with frequency change. This measurement procedure will also work with 300 to 600Ω lines."

This instrument is very small, which makes it very useful for field work.

MFJ-249/259 HF/VHF SWR analysers

The MFJ-249 has just one meter and the MFJ-259 has an additional meter for reading the resistive component of the impedance.

- A signal source from 1.8MHz to 170MHz in six overlapping bands
- Frequency display on an eight-digit liquid crystal display
- Measures an antenna's SWR at a specified frequency
- SWR displayed on analogue meter
- It also incorporates a frequency counter from 10Hz to 170MHz

The MFJ instruments also provide an external input socket to use the unit as a frequency counter. The counter is more than adequate for the amateur test bench. Its frequency range is from about 10Hz to well over 200MHz with a sensitivity of 200mV in the HF range.

A very interesting application for the MFJ-249/249, by AF6S [18], is to turn the unit into a wide-range dip meter using a simple add-on probe. After experimenting with a range of inductor probes on the SO-239 socket of the MFJ-249, AF6S devised a single probe which can be used to provide accurate and clear dip measurements over the whole range of the instrument.

I copied the design of the simple add-on probe as described by AF6S. It was tested with a 'standard' 7MHz tuned circuit made from a 5μH coil and 100pF capacitor and it was able to detect it at a distance of about 30mm (see Chapter 3 regarding GDO sensitivity). MFJ now provide two probes to cover the range.

I found that these instruments are particularly useful when experimenting with antennas. The results of these tests were good and correlated well with conventional SWR meter readings. This instrument is particularly useful for evaluating new designs, especially where resonances of early prototypes fall outside the band. It was used for setting up a 20m mobile model of the toroid antenna described in Chapter 7.

The MFJ-248 is shown being used to evaluate a VHF version of the toroid antenna in Fig 2.36. The left-hand SWR meter shows the lowest reading at resonance to be around 1.6:1, caused by a resistance (at resonance) of 26Ω. Using this instrument it is easy to adjust the capacitor matching network

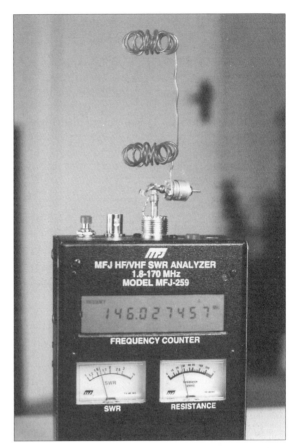

Fig 2.36. The MFJ-248 is shown being used to evaluate a VHF version of the toroid antenna

(shown at the base of the antenna) to achieve a feed impedance of 50Ω.

The only problem with these instruments is their inability to operate in the presence of a strong RF field. SWR readings on the antennas at the RSGB HQ gave very poor results because of the proximity of Brookmans Park radio station and the local 50MHz beacon.

NOTES

[1] Vector impedance bridge, from the collection of HP test equipment of Allen Grey, G8LCO.
[2] Disk of software sold with the *ARRL Antenna Compendium Vol 4*.

REFERENCES

[1] 'Evaluation of the G2AJV toroidal antenna', Peter Dodd, G3LDO, *Radio Communication* August 1994.

[2] 'Variations on the three-meter method of measuring impedance', A E Weller, WD8KBW, unpublished article.

[3] 'A noise bridge for 1.8 through 30MHz', *The ARRL Antenna Handbook*, 1988 edn, p27-15.

[4] 'The RF noise bridge', *Radio Handbook*, 21st edn, W I Orr, W6SAI.

[5] 'Tone modulated HF impedance bridge', E Chicken, G3BIK, *Radio Communication* June/July 1994.

[6] 'Improving and using RX noise bridges', *QST* August 1989.

[7] 'Measurement of R + Jx', W8CGD, *QST* June 1966.

[8] 'Measurement of antenna impedance', Dodd and Lloyd, *QEX* November 1987.

[9] 'Technical Correspondence', *QEX* May 1988.

[10] 'Measurement of antenna resistance and reactance', John Bazley, G3HCT, *Radio Communication* June 1987.

[11] 'The mobile roofrack antenna', P Dodd, G3LDO, *QST* November 1988.

[12] 'Resistors at HF', A E Weller, WD8KBW, private correspondence.

[13] 'The hybrid junction admittance bridge', W N Carron, *Antenna Compendium*, Vol 3, ARRL, 1992.

[14] 'An RF admittance bridge for 2 to 30MHz', Jack Gentle, G0RVN, *Radio Communication* July 1965.

[15] 'Smith radio transmission-line calculator', Phillip H Smith, *Electronics*, January 1939.

[16] *RF Measurements with An Active Standing Wave Ratio Meter*, Gerd Janzen, DF6SJ, DARC Verlag GmbH, Baunatal. ISBN 3-88692-023.

[17] 'A comprehensive antenna analyser', Aubra E Tilley, WM6T, *QEX* August 1994.

[18] 'An accurate dip meter using the MFJ-249 SWR analyzer', David M Barton, AF6S, *QST* November 1993.

[19] 'Optimising the multiband wire antenna', Tony Preedy, A45ZZ, *Radio Communication* November 1995.

3 Measurement of resonance

MOST radio amateurs are aware that antenna elements, coaxial cable (or any transmission line), or any lengths of metal that make up the antenna system, have to have a property called *resonance*.

From Chapter 1 capacitance is defined as the ratio of potential energy to stored charge; and inductance can be defined as the ratio of kinetic energy (current) to stored flux (because inductance stores kinetic energy in the form of a magnetic field). Both capacitors and inductors exhibit reactance (X), measured in ohms, that involves both stored energy and angular velocity.

When an inductor and capacitor are connected together, in series or parallel, they form a tuned circuit with a natural resonant frequency. This resonance occurs where the energy stored in each of the reactive components is equal; oscillating from the inductor to the capacitor and back at a frequency determined by their respective values.

At resonance the reactances comprising the tuned circuit are equal, the positive and negative reactances cancel, and only the resistive component remains. The phase angle between current and voltage is zero and power is dissipated by the resistive component of the circuit.

A tuned circuit comprising a capacitor and an inductor is said to have *lumped constants*. An antenna element also has a resonant frequency but in this case the inductance and capacitance are distributed along the conductor and it is said to be a *linear* or *distributed* circuit. The frequency in this case is determined by the length or wavelength of the conductor. Wavelength is related to frequency and the velocity of light (and radio waves) as:

$$\lambda = \frac{299,793,077}{f}$$

where λ is the wavelength in metres and f is the frequency in hertz. 299,793,077 is the velocity of light in free space, in metres per second (300×10^6 is accurate enough for most antenna calculations).

Because RF energy oscillates twice along the conductor in one cycle the shortest conductor to resonate at a given frequency is a half-wavelength ($\lambda/2$). This oscillating RF energy is carried throughout the region of space surrounding the antenna element with the conductor itself only guiding the wave that carries the energy. If the element is constructed of plastic insulated wire then a small part of the region of space comprises material where the velocity of light is lower than that shown in the formula above. The result is that a given length of plastic-covered wire has a lower resonant frequency compared with the same length of bare copper wire. You can check this by measuring the resonance of two identical lengths of copper wire, one covered with plastic insulation and the other without.

The main characteristic of resonance of a conductor is that it can absorb and radiate RF power at that resonant frequency.

Lengths of wire and tubing that make up antenna systems and supports, and transmission lines from the transmitter to the antenna, all have an electrical resonance at some frequency. The house electrical wiring and the tubing that make up a central heating system, and even the metal frame of a greenhouse, also have resonances.

The effect of these resonances of nearby conducting objects on an antenna radiation pattern can sometimes be quite dramatic. This is because a re-radiated signal from a nearby object can enhance or degrade the total signal in a particular direction. Indeed, the operation of the parasitic-beam antenna depends on it.

The strength of a radiated field from an antenna is related to the amount of current flowing in the antenna element. A metal object located within the electromagnetic field will tend to absorb and re-radiate some of this energy. When the resonant frequency of the metal object is not the same as the excitation field the induced current and voltage are out of phase and very little power is absorbed. When the metal object is at resonance more power is absorbed. The absorption wavemeter or diode field-strength meter, comprising a calibrated tuned circuit with a diode RF voltmeter to indicate relative field strength, uses this principle.

The amplitude and the phase of a re-radiated electromagnetic wave will depend on the distance between the antenna and the metal object but the closeness to resonance of the latter also has an effect. From this it can be seen that the effect of metal objects close in both distance and resonant frequency to the antenna is difficult to predict.

The antenna feeder is also resonant at some frequency. A resonant feeder can re-radiate the signal and distort the antenna pattern just as a nearby metal object can. These 'antenna currents' on the transmission line can be avoided if a way of measuring feeder resonance is known.

On the face of it, a resonant length does appear to be the most suitable for an antenna – the voltage and current are in phase so all we have to do is to find a point to connect the coaxial cable so that all the power is transferred to the antenna. Only when the voltage and current are in phase can power be efficiently transferred to the antenna.

This chapter will describe methods of measuring the resonant frequencies of antenna elements, co-axial cable and tuned circuits. Also described is a method of measuring inductance or capacitance in a tuned circuit.

To measure resonance of an element we need to feed RF energy into it. One method of achieving this is to use a dip oscillator.

THE DIP OSCILLATOR (GDO)

The most useful attribute of the dip oscillator is that a direct connection with the tuned circuit being measured is unnecessary. The instrument is more commonly known as a *GDO* from the time when it was a 'grid dip oscillator'. Although this instrument now uses a bipolar transistor or an FET as the active element of the oscillator it will be referred to throughout this chapter as a 'GDO' because this is the abbreviation it is mostly known by.

RF power from a calibrated tuneable oscillator is absorbed by a resonant circuit when it and the oscillator are tuned to the same frequency. Some indication of oscillator energy loss is required and there are several ways this can be achieved:

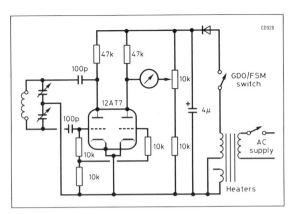

Fig 3.1. My original home-constructed GDO with the 12AT7 double triode

- By measuring the level of base, gate or grid voltage, which is proportional to the peak-to-peak level of the oscillator waveform. The early vacuum tube or valve instruments used this method by measuring the grid current; and were known as *grid dip oscillators*.

- By measuring the DC current through the active element (ie FET) of the oscillator, which in some circuits, is roughly proportional to the peak-to peak level of the oscillator waveform.

- By using a diode to measure the peak-to-peak oscillator voltage. This method is the most popular with solid-state designs. Early designs suffered from the disadvantage that if the oscillator waveform amplitude fell below the conduction level of the diode all indication disappeared. Later designs use Schottky barrier diodes or detector bias so that this problem is minimised.

All the older-type grid dip meters seem to work well and possess adequate sensitivity. I have an old Q-Max GDO-1A GDO that operates very well right up into the VHF band, yet the circuit is very primitive. It comprises a 12AT7 double triode, one half used as an oscillator and the other half as a half-wave rectifier for the HT supply, which in these days of semiconductors is an unbelievable 300V!

I also have an old home-made instrument (see Fig 3.1) which has the best sensitivity of all the GDOs I have tried. This is probably because it employs the brute-force technique of the Q-Max GDO described above and uses a 12AT7 double triode, with the second triode being used as a meter amplifier to increase the indication of resonance. In this instance resonance is indicated by an increase in meter reading because of inversion in the amplifier.

Although the GDOs already described possess the necessary sensitivity they suffer from the disadvantage of requiring a mains AC supply. If such an instrument is used for antenna measurements then a long extension cable is required which, in addition to the hazards of mains AC supply leads in a possibly damp environment, can be dangerous if you are tangled up in antenna elements while balanced on the top of a step-ladder.

The obvious answer is to use a GDO employing a transistor or FET and to run the instrument from a battery. However, the performance of some designs, including some commercial ones, has in the past been disappointing. You can check the performance of a GDO as described below. A good GDO should possess the following features:

- Good sensitivity. Some indication of sensitivity can be checked by squeezing the coil of the GDO between the thumb and forefinger and noting the meter deflection; this should dip to at least 50% of the maximum reading. The GDO should also be capable of measuring resonance of a high-capacitance tuned circuit at a distance of 60 to 70mm (2–3in). I use a parallel-tuned circuit, comprising a 5mH inductor with a 100pF capacitance, as a standard – see Fig 3.9.
- Large frequency dial with smooth reduction gear tuning. The GDO could have a frequency counter instead of the dial but this would increase the complexity of the instrument. Provision for connection of the GDO to a frequency counter is probably a better arrangement.
- Meter large enough to see the dip clearly. An audio indication of a dip is also useful.
- Be self-contained with no power leads.

THE G3WPO FET GDO

The most comprehensive GDO that I have seen so far which meets the above specifications was designed by A T Bailey, G3WPO [5, 6]; the circuit is shown in Fig 3.2. The G3WPO oscillator is a push-pull Kaliatron circuit covering 0.8 to 215MHz in six ranges.

This circuit offers the most consistent output and wide range, without resorting to tapped coils, feedback arrangements or similar complications.

To obtain consistent results over a wide range of frequencies the gain on different bands is set by external fixed resistors mounted within the coil former, and these set the oscillator gate 2 voltage. C1 is a Japanese polyvaricon dual-gang 260 + 260pF variable capacitor.

The RF from the oscillator is detected by D2/D3, which are Schottky barrier diodes biased into conduction by a stable voltage (adjustable by preset resistor RV1).

Because of its relative complexity this GDO is not a quick evening project, as most of my test equipment tends to be, and I doubt if it would have built it if a kit had not been available (see Appendix 3). In operation this GDO was the best of the solid-state designs tried, particularly at VHF. This is probably because the circuit is based on a VHF design [6]. The only complaint about this instrument is an ergonomic one. The frequency readout dial is located on the opposite side to the coil, making it difficult to maintain coupling of the coil to the antenna element and read the tiny frequency dial at the same time. However, if this instrument is used with a frequency counter then the above-mentioned limitation is circumvented.

A SIMPLE DIP OSCILLATOR

The best of the simple solid-state GDOs so far discovered were two very similar designs published in the 'Technical Correspondence' column of QST [3, 4]. The circuit of my variation of these two designs, plus improvements incorporated by G3ZOM, is shown in Fig 3.3.

This circuit does not measure gate current directly; instead it measures the total current through the FET. This is large compared with that flowing in a base or gate of a solid-state oscillator. However, the variation of current through resonance is only a small part of the total current through the FET. The dip is enhanced by offsetting the meter reading using a potentiometer in a bleeder network. This is set so that the meter reads about 75% FSD when the instrument is not coupled to a load.

This design does not perform very well on the VHF bands with the circuit values shown and the dip tends to reverse if the coupling is too tight. This suggests that reducing the 100pF capacitors in the tuned circuit to a smaller value would improve the performance at VHF. This instrument met all the criteria of a good GDO, described earlier, on all the HF and lower VHF bands.

The simple GDO shown in Fig 3.3 is easy to construct and, provided the necessary components are available, can be constructed in an evening.

This is not a complete description of how to make the instrument, but rather a few notes to emphasise the important aspects of construction.

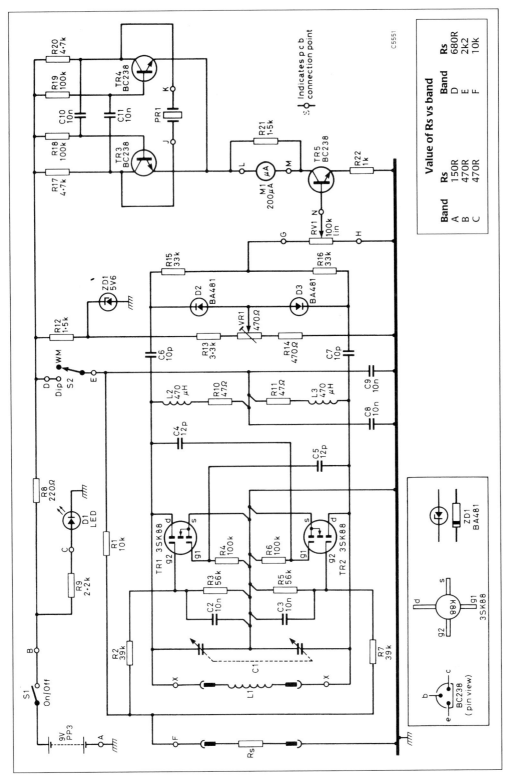

Fig 3.2. The G3WPO FET GDO

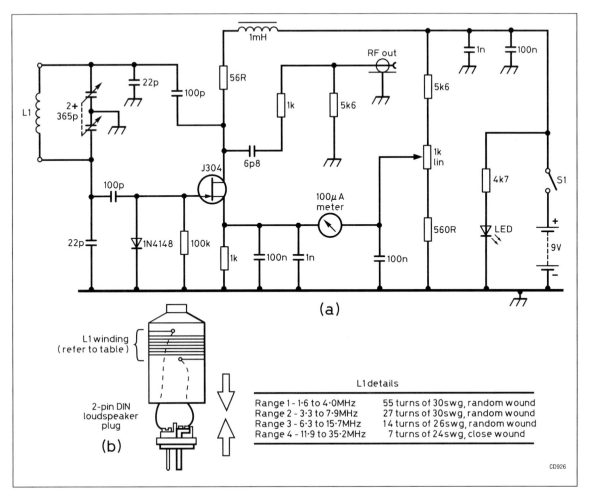

Fig 3.3. (a) Circuit of an FET GDO based on two designs featured in *QST* 'Technical Correspondence' and subsequently modified by G3ZOM. (b) Details of coil construction

The most important part of a dip oscillator is the tuning capacitor and frequency read-out dial. Sometimes a whole assembly can be obtained from an old transistor radio. The coil socket should be located as close to the tuning capacitor as possible so that the coil leads can be kept short. The rest of the circuit can be wired around these main components. Choose a coil plug and socket arrangement that is practical. All the circuits so far discussed use two-pin coil plugs and sockets. This means that simple arrangements using crystal holders or phono plugs and sockets can be used. The arrangement shown in Fig 3.3 uses two-pin DIN loudspeaker plugs for the coils.

A frequency counter is the most convenient instrument for calibrating the dial although a receiver can also be used for this purpose. If you have a frequency counter then it can be used in conjunction with an uncalibrated GDO. A frequency counter is a worthwhile investment and has many other uses in home construction projects. Try to obtain one with a liquid crystal display; LEDs are difficult to read in bright sunlight.

The set-up shown in Fig 3.4 shows a GDO being used to measure the frequency of a tuned circuit, with a link-coupled frequency counter used to measure the frequency. The circuit in Fig 3.3 has an output for a frequency counter so the link coupling is not necessary.

Flea markets and rallies are a useful source of material for making GDOs. I located a Japanese LDM-810 dipper whose Nuvistor triode had 'died'. The

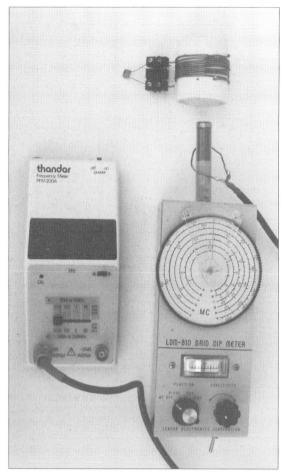

Fig 3.4. Set-up for measuring resonance of a tuned circuit. A link coupled frequency counter is used to give a more accurate measurement of frequency

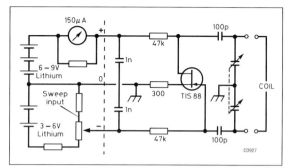

Fig 3.5. The VHF/UHF dipper by SM6MOM/W6

Although this method loses some of the dip enhancement caused by offsetting the meter it has the advantage of giving the meter an improved GDO/FSM function. To use the instrument as a FSM the negative bias is increased so that the circuit stops oscillating. According to SM6MOM/W6 it is in a near-oscillating state. This arrangement is claimed to give more sensitivity when used as a FSM.

MEASUREMENT OF ANTENNA ELEMENT RESONANCE

Antenna elements are measured by coupling the coil to the current point of the element and varying the frequency of the GDO until a dip in the meter is seen. Measuring the resonance of wire elements should not provide too many difficulties provided a sensitive instrument is used.

If your GDO lacks sensitivity, additional coupling to the element can be achieved by forming a small loop in the wire element and taping it – see Fig 3.6. All GDOs that I have tested will couple into an element modified in this way. If the element being measured is connected to a length of unterminated coaxial cable then the measured resonance will include this length of cable. If you want to measure a driven element resonance, disconnect the coaxial feeder and short the feedpoint, where appropriate.

The G3LDO antenna element resonance measuring kit

Coupling to tubular elements is more difficult because the coupling between a small-diameter coil and a long wire or tubular element is very loose. If a dip cannot be obtained in the normal way then a different type of coil may be required to improve coupling. I tried using a GDO with a large-diameter one-loop coil with a flat side as proposed by G6XN [8].

chassis, calibrated tuning mechanism and coils made it a suitable candidate for an experimental solid-state GDO – see Fig 3.4.

A VHF/UHF GDO

A variation of the circuit in Fig 3.3 has been described by SM6MOM/W6 [7] and is shown in Fig 3.5. It measures the current through the FET, which is set by varying the bias on its gate. The circuit will work up to 450MHz but it is important that the decoupling capacitors on the supply side of the 47kΩ resistors are efficient (ie have the lowest inductance) at these frequencies. Surface-mount capacitors soldered directly to a piece of sheet copper that is also soldered to the centre divider/ground of the variable capacitor are recommended.

Fig 3.6. A wire element can be looped into a single-turn coil for increased coupling to the GDO

Fig 3.7. The coat-hanger type coil will even enable the GDO to be coupled into a metal ladder. A 3.7m (12ft) section of a ladder had a resonant frequency of 35.7MHz

This method really does work. My home-brew/ LM810 GDO uses an FT283 crystal socket for the coils. The coil was replaced by a wire coat-hanger (the diameter of the wire fitted the coil socket). With this modification the increase in coupling was dramatic and it was possible to measure the resonant frequency of any bit of antenna junk lying around the garden, provided it was within the frequency range of the coat-hanger coil.

The calibration of the coat-hanger coil was somewhat arbitrary but this did not matter because the GDO was being used in conjunction with a portable frequency counter.

Although the coat-hanger shaped coil worked very well on the high HF and lower VHF bands a coil design for the lower frequencies posed a problem – how to wind a multi-turn coil on a large-diameter former. Various formers ranging from large-diameter plastic tube to plastic flowerpots were tried.

All these coil formers gave good results, with the larger-diameter coils giving the best coupling to antenna elements. However, they all suffered from the practical mechanical problem of how to support

the large-diameter coil, the GDO and make the measurement at the same time.

The final design was so simple that I wondered why I didn't think of it in the first place. The coil is wound on a short board, 100mm (4in) wide and 10mm thick – see Fig 3.8. (These dimensions are not critical.)

The size of this coil was a somewhat arbitrary; seven turns, which tuned from 8 to 18MHz, covered the 14MHz band which was of interest at the time. An additional single-turn loop is used to couple the frequency counter to the GDO coil.

The coupling of this pick-up coil to the main winding can be adjusted with respect to the main winding until just enough energy is available to operate the frequency counter.

The board provides a platform for the GDO, frequency counter and even a note pad. The flat-sided coil couples into any antenna element, with the board providing a stable point to rest the measuring kit against the element while measurements are being made.

Fig 3.8. The G3LDO Mk 4 antenna element resonance measuring kit

USING THE GDO TO MEASURE TRANSMISSION LINE RESONANCES

It is very useful to be able to measure the resonant length of a length of coaxial cable. Sometimes we wish to avoid resonances in lengths of transmission line to reduce the effects of antenna currents on the line. On the other hand, we need resonant lengths to make a coaxial balun or a phasing network for a directional array or for a circularly polarised Yagi.

One method of measuring transmission line resonances, using a GDO, is described below. Other methods are described in Chapter 6 – 'Coaxial cable'.

Fig 3.9. Method of coupling GDO to feeder for measuring electrical length

A GDO can be used for measuring these transmission line electrical lengths. A coaxial transmission line is a linear circuit with a well-defined series of harmonic responses based on the lowest harmonic frequency. These resonances can be measured by shorting one end of the feeder and fitting a small wire loop to the other end so that the GDO can be coupled to it. I use a PL259 socket with a coupling loop soldered to it which plugs into the connector at the end of the feeder – see Fig 3.9.

If the length of the feeder is not known (perhaps part of an installation that has been in place for some time) then look for a series of resonances using the higher-frequency coils of the GDO. The frequency difference between these resonances is the lowest resonant frequency of the feeder.

For example: on the coaxial cable from the shack to the three-element 10m beam on the roof the following resonances in megahertz were measured:

$$47.24 \quad 35.4 \quad 23.7$$

The differences between these figures are 11.84 and 11.7. The GDO coil covering the appropriate range was then plugged in and the lowest resonant frequency at 11.76MHz was measured. This is the *electrical*, not the physical, length and it is the electrical length that is important. If you are curious as to the total physical length of feeder, use the formula below:

$$\text{Length (m)} = \frac{150 \text{ TLVF}}{\text{LRF}}$$

$$\text{Length (ft)} = \frac{487.5 \text{ TLVF}}{\text{LRF}}$$

where TLVF is the transmission line velocity factor

and LRF is the lowest resonant frequency. This is not the most accurate method of measuring resonance because the loop necessary for coupling to the GDO will give a slightly lower resonant frequency than indicated. However, the SWR method shown in Chapter 6 requires a T-section coaxial coupler, which also slightly adds to the length of the cable under test.

MEASUREMENT OF INDUCTANCE AND CAPACITANCE USING A GDO

A GDO can be used to measure the inductance of a coil or the value of variable capacitor or trimmer.

Make an inductance standard of 5µH. It should resonate at 7.1MHz in parallel with a 100pF capacitor. My inductance standard comprises 10 turns of 22 SWG (21 AWG) enamelled copper wire wound on a short length of 1.5in (40mm) diameter plastic waste pipe – see Fig 3.10.

Extra wire length should be allowed to make a half-winding each end of the coil, built into the inside of the pipe. These windings can be adjusted to aid or oppose the general winding pattern, thereby

Fig 3.10. Construction of standard inductance with a half-winding each end of the coil for tuning

allowing a degree of adjustment to set the inductance standard to the correct value. The wire ends are terminated in a screw terminal block to enable the capacitors for testing to be connected conveniently.

To measure inductance, connect a 100pF capacitor across the coil and measure the resonant frequency. Use the chart in Fig 3.11 to determine the coil inductance.

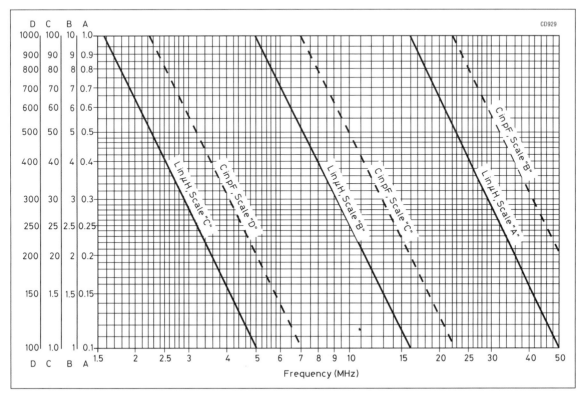

Fig 3.11. Chart for determining unknown values of L and C in the range 0.1 to 100µH and 2 to 1000pF, using standards 100pF and 5µH (from the *ARRL Radio Amateur's Handbook*)

To check the maximum value of a variable capacitor or trimmer, ensure it is fully meshed and note the resonant frequency, then read the capacitance value on the chart in Fig 3.11.

To measure the minimum capacitance of a variable capacitor, connect a small fixed capacitor, of say 30pF, in parallel with the unit under test. Measure the frequency and look up the capacitance on the chart, then subtract the value of the fixed capacitance. This procedure is used because it is not possible to measure a dip if the tuned circuit capacitance is very small.

REFERENCES

[1] *ARRL Radio Amateur's Handbook*, 1978 edn, ARRL.

[2] 'Technical Correspondence', Peter Lumb, G3IRM, *QST* June 1972.

[3] 'Technical Correspondence', W1CER, *QST* November 1971.

[4] 'A FET dip oscillator for 1.6–215MHz with tone dip feature', A L Bailey, G3WPO, *Radio Communication* November 1981.

[5] 'The G3WPO FET dip oscillator Mk 2', A L Bailey, G3WPO, *Radio Communication* April 1987.

[6] *VHF/UHF Manual*, 4th edn, G R Jessop, G6JP, RSGB, 1984, p11.47.

[7] 'A grid-dip meter for VHF and UHF', Carl G Lodström, SM6MOM/W6, *VHF Communications* February 1995.

[8] *HF Antennas for All Locations*, 2nd edn, Les Moxon, G6XN, RSGB, 1994.

4 Measurement of field strength

THIS chapter gives a brief description of the characteristics of electromagnetic waves and details the construction and use of instruments for measuring them. Although reasons for field-strength measurements appear in this chapter their uses in measuring antenna performance are described in Chapter 5.

TEM WAVES, FIELD ZONES AND POLARISATION

An electromagnetic wave comprises electric (E) and magnetic (H) components perpendicular to each other. If the x co-ordinate is taken along the line in the direction of wave travel, then the E and H field vectors lie entirely in the yz plane. The wavefront is a plane surface normal to the direction of propagation and is called a *transverse electromagnetic wave* (TEM).

It can best be envisaged as the surface of a rapidly inflating balloon, otherwise known as a *wavefront*. However, a small area of this expanding surface can be regarded as a plane at a distance from the source. A TEM wave in which the electric and magnetic vectors, while varying in magnitude and sign, remain along the same axis in space is said to be *polarised*, the plane of polarisation (by convention) being that contained in the electric vector, ie the xy plane in Fig 4.1.

Two antennas must be co-polarised (polarised in the same direction) in order to communicate; totally cross-polarised antennas theoretically cannot communicate. Polarisation is important on paths that don't alter the transmitted polarisation (a line-of-sight VHF/UHF or microwave link, for example). It is also important when making antenna measurements on an antenna range.

For the purposes of examining signal strengths the areas around an antenna are classified as the *near* or *induction* field, and the *far* or *radiation* field.

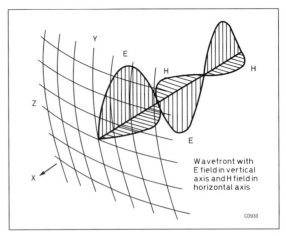

Fig 4.1. Conceptual diagram of transverse electromagnetic wave

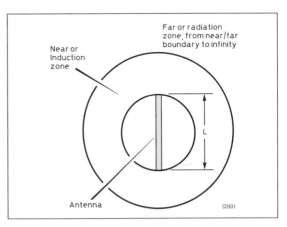

Fig 4.2. Near and far fields of an antenna

The approximate near/far field boundary is defined as:

$$R = 2L^2/\text{wavelength}$$

where L is the length of the antenna as illustrated in Fig 4.2.

Table 4.1. Voltage, current field strengths and power density compared

Volts/metre	Amps/metre	Watts/square metre
100	0.265	26.5
10	0.0265	0.265
1	2.65×10^{-3}	2.65×10^{-3}
0.1	2.65×10^{-4}	2.65×10^{-5}
0.01	2.65×10^{-5}	2.65×10^{-7}

This subject is discussed in more detail in reference [1].

ELECTRIC FIELD-STRENGTH MEASUREMENTS

Electric field-strength measurements using a field-strength meter (FSM) are useful to:

1. Make comparative measurements of various antennas to assess relative gain.
2. Plot a polar diagram to record antenna directivity.
3. Enable a transmitter antenna to be tuned for maximum efficiency or gain.
4. Align a VHF radio or TV antenna to obtain the greatest signal strength from a transmitter.

From the practical point of view of measuring field intensities, antenna gain and directivity measurements should only be made in the far field. In this field the strength of the electric E field, measured in volts per metre, is 377 times the strength of the magnetic H field, measured in amperes per metre – see Table 4.1. This ratio is determined by the impedance of free space (377Ω) and remains constant from the near/far field boundary to infinity, ie the far field.

Units of field strength of an RF field

If we were to use an antenna that transmitted electromagnetic waves equally in all directions it would cause an expanding spherical wavefront, a section of which is shown in Fig 4.1. (An antenna that can transmit equally in all directions is called *isotropic* and is only possible in theory – see Chapter 5).

By the time the wavefront has expanded to a radius of 1km the radiated power would have been spread over an area of 12,566,371m². A 1m² section of this 1km radius expanding electromagnetic balloon (see Fig 4.3) would have a power flux density of approximately 1µW/m², assuming a radiated power of 12.5W EIRP (effective isotropic radiated power).

At 2km the 1µW is spread over 4m² so the power flux density is now down to 0.25µW/m². We can

therefore see that the E and H fields decrease at a rate inversely proportional to the square of the distance and this effect is true at any frequency.

A receiver antenna placed in this electromagnetic field will have a small amount of RF voltage induced into it – see Fig 4.4. An antenna being used for receive has a *capture area*, which depends to some degree on its size. Because the length of a half-wave (λ/2) dipole is proportional to wavelength (and inversely proportional to frequency) the capture area of such a dipole varies with frequency as shown in Fig 4.5. A receiver antenna with a capture area of 1m² will capture 1µW of RF energy in a field with 1µW/m² power flux density.

The unit of power flow density is watts per square metre. As previously stated, the impedance of free space is 377Ω, and hence the power density can be expressed as a field strength, either in volts per metre or amps per metre using Ohm's Law:

$$P = V \times I = V^2 / R$$

Thus:

$$\text{Field strength (V / m)} = \sqrt{\text{Power flux density} \times 377}$$

Similarly the relationship between the voltage components of the field is given by:

$$\text{Volts/metre} = 377 \times \text{amperes/metre}$$

This relationship is shown in Table 4.1.

In measuring field strength, the field is usually sampled by a dipole antenna. A λ/2 dipole will produce an open-circuit voltage at its terminals equal to the field strength in volts per metre multiplied by the wavelength in metres and divided by π. For example, at 70MHz a 1V/m electric field will produce a terminal voltage of 1.36V.

It is important to understand the comparative magnitudes of signal strength. Consider the following examples:

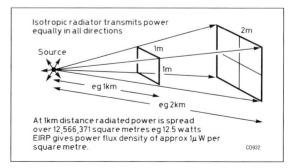

Isotropic radiator transmits power equally in all directions

Source

eg 1km

eg 2km

2m

1m

1m

At 1km distance radiated power is spread over 12,566,371 square metres eg 12.5 watts EIRP gives power flux density of approx 1µW per square metre.

CD932

Fig 4.3. Diagram showing the inverse square law of electromagnetic radiation

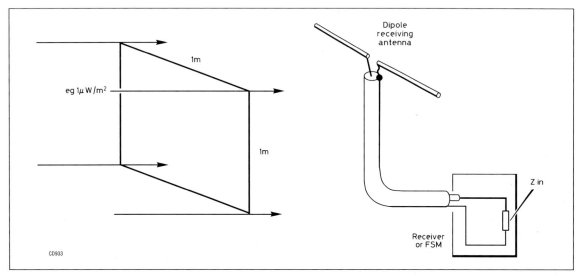

Fig 4.4. Receiving antenna in an electromagnetic field with a flux of 1μW/m²

- If a simple diode FSM is to be used, what is the signal level required to obtain a full range of readings?
- Will an amplifier be necessary to enable a diode

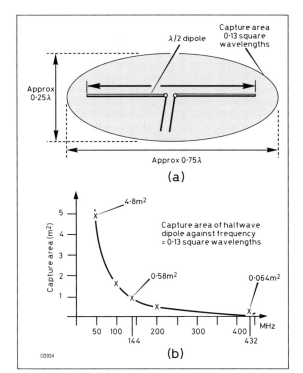

Fig 4.5. Capture area of a dipole receiving antenna. (a) The approximate capture area of a dipole. (b) The capture area of a dipole relative to frequency

FSM to be calibrated using a signal generator having a maximum output of 2mV at 75Ω?
- If an antenna polar diagram is to be plotted, what will be the range of signal levels that will need to be measured?
- If a communication receiver is used as a FSM, how much attenuation will be needed?

Commercial calibrated signal-strength meters are available on the surplus market although they are not plentiful. They nearly always comprise an intrinsically sensitive instrument with a linear scale. A built in switched attenuator is required to cover the range of signal strengths that may be encountered. Each range usually covers around 14dB.

The signal levels encountered when making field-strength measurements will depend on circumstances. For instance, signal strengths in the millivolt range will occur when tuning an antenna for maximum efficiency using a transmitter as an excitation source. On the other hand, if only a low-power transmitter or signal-strength meter is available then the signal strengths could be in the microvolt range. See Fig 4.6.

GENERATING A CALIBRATION SIGNAL

The most practical way of measuring field strength is to construct a field-strength meter and to use a signal generator to calibrate both its frequency and sensitivity. A simple field-strength meter is easy to construct. An instrument for generating a radio frequency signal is of course the signal generator, and

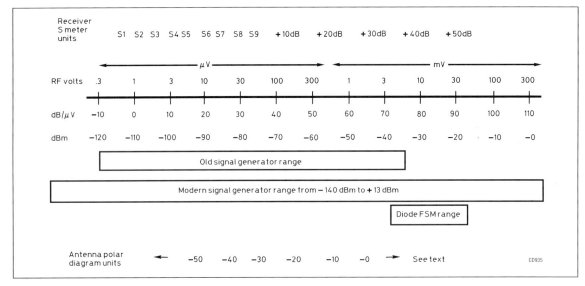

Receiver S meter units	S1	S2	S3	S4	S5	S6	S7	S8	S9	+10dB	+20dB	+30dB	+40dB	+50dB
	◄——————————— µV ———————————►									◄——————————— mV ———————————►				
RF volts	.3	1	3	10	30	100	300	1	3	10	30	100	300	
dB/µV	−10	0	10	20	30	40	50	60	70	80	90	100	110	
dBm	−120	−110	−100	−90	−80	−70	−60	−50	−40	−30	−20	−10	−0	

Old signal generator range

Modern signal generator range from − 140 dBm to + 13 dBm

Diode FSM range

| Antenna polar diagram units | ◄— | −50 | −40 | −30 | −20 | −10 | −0 | —► | See text |

CD935

Fig 4.6. Units of signal strength, approximate comparisons

you will see the units of signal strength marked on the attenuator for calibration of field-strength meters.

At this stage it is suggested that you beg, borrow or buy a signal generator. Not only can this useful item of equipment enable you to calibrate FSMs, it is good for checking RF amplifier gain and attenuator loss. Other uses, outside the scope of this book, include lining up receivers and transmitter driver stages. A signal generator is a worthwhile investment. Older instruments are relatively cheap and plentiful, although in many cases rather large and heavy!

When you buy a signal generator ensure that it has either a calibrated attenuator (usually in decibels per microvolt) or an RF level setting control with a meter to indicate the level of output (usually in microvolts and millivolts). Modern (expensive) signal generators use the dBm scale, ie decibels with reference to 1mW at 50Ω.

I make most of my measurements at VHF in the course of VHF modelling of HF antennas and use a Marconi Instruments VHF Test Set TF 982A of the early 'fifties vintage – see Fig 4.7. It has an RF output of up to 2mV in four ranges. In addition it has a high output range (variable level but uncalibrated), useful for exciting an antenna for field-strength measurements.

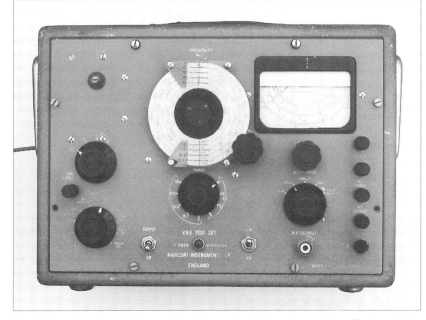

Fig 4.7. Example of an older type of signal generator that can be used to calibrate an FSM

CONSTRUCTING A FIELD-STRENGTH METER

The diode field-strength meter

The FSM circuit most often described in literature for antenna adjustment is the simple diode FSM [2, 3]. It has the virtue of simplicity but lacks sensitivity for some applications. All my early experiments and measurements of polar diagrams of VHF models were made using this type of meter employing a germanium point-contact diode. The circuit is shown in Fig 4.8.

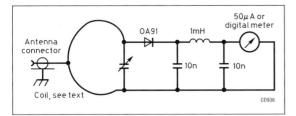

Fig 4.8. VHF diode field-strength meter

This instrument appears so simple as to make construction notes seem superfluous but the following points are worthy of note.

The coil comprises just over one turn of 18 SWG wire. The variable capacitor value is not critical – my Mk 1 FSM used an air-spaced variable, of unknown capacitance, from an old transistor radio. The antenna is tapped one third of a turn from the bottom of the coil and the diode one third of a turn from the top.

The size and shape of the enclosure are unimportant but should be made of metal to prevent RF energy from entering the tuned circuit by any path other than the pick-up antenna. The instrument can be calibrated using a GDO or signal generator.

The meter should have the highest sensitivity possible. Because the FSM is used for either adjusting an antenna for maximum performance or for polar diagram plotting it is preferable to mount the meter separate from the detector.

The filtering shown in the meter leads was found to be adequate. Originally filtering in both leads was used but in practice it does not seem to be necessary.

Although the point-contact germanium diode gives good linearity (provided the load resistance is high enough) it does not appear on the list of diodes in all manufacturers' catalogues these days. For this reason the properties of other diodes were investigated. Some basic information regarding diodes is covered in Chapter 1 because the diode

is fundamental to the measurement of RF in all measuring equipment. In this chapter the discussion of diodes is restricted to their application in field-strength meters.

Three different types of diode were tried in the VHF field-strength meter: germanium, silicon (signal types) and Schottky barrier (the latter also sometimes known as *hot carrier diodes*).

The characteristics of the circuit in Fig 4.8, using a germanium diode and a silicon diode, are illustrated in Fig 4.9.

The Schottky barrier signal diode BAT85 will only operate in this circuit if the diode is tapped well down the coil near to the 50Ω antenna tap. This may be due to the relative high capacitance of the BAT85. Some experimenting with the position of this tapping point can be carried out to obtain the highest sensitivity.

Fig 4.9 shows two sets of characteristics of the diode FSM; the first set using a 50µA (600mV) analogue meter, the second using a digital voltmeter as the field-strength indicator. The digital voltmeter is preferred for two reasons:

- The higher input impedance of the meter resulted in a more linear and sensitive instrument for the reasons explained under 'Diodes' in Chapter 1. Additionally the input impedance is the same for

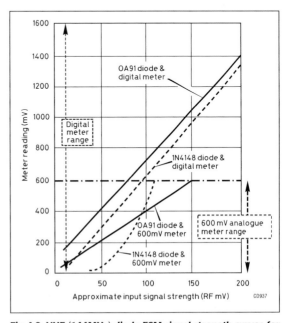

Fig 4.9. VHF (144MHz) diode FSM signal strength curves for germanium and silicon diodes

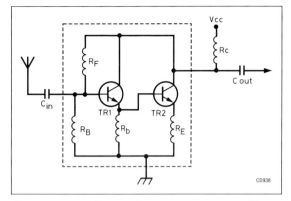

Fig 4.10. Internal diagram of a MAR-type MMIC amplifier

all DVM ranges, so that the characteristics of the diode are not changed if the range is changed.
- The observable resolution and range of the digital voltmeter is greater than the analogue type, making it easier to record the test results. It also gives the FSM greater dynamic range. An autoranging digital voltmeter might be useful in this application.

The characteristics of a diode FSM using a BAT85 diode are similar to one using a germanium diode FSM as shown in Fig 4.9.

Increasing the sensitivity of a FSM using an RF amplifier

The problem with the simple diode field-strength meter is its lack of sensitivity, which is in the tens of millivolts range – see Fig 4.6. The obvious way to move the sensitivity of the FSM into the microvolt range is to use an RF amplifier.

The easiest way of obtaining RF gain is to use a MMIC (monolithic microwave integrated circuit). A MMIC is a multi-stage bipolar RF amplifier housed in a small transistor-like package. It gives a broad frequency response from DC to over 1GHz, has a 50Ω input and output without matching networks and has good stability. These qualities make it an excellent candidate for increasing the sensitivity of a diode (or any other) FSM. They are now widely available – see Appendix 3.

Although the internal circuit of a MMIC looks deceptively simple (a simple two-stage bipolar DC-coupled amplifier – see Fig 4.10), the secret of the performance of this device is in the precise nature of the manufacturing process.

To hold the operating current constant over a wide temperature range requires an external biasing

resistor. This resistor should be a standard carbon-composition type, which has a positive temperature coefficient. This complements the negative coefficient of the chip resistors inside the MMIC. Because the MMIC is DC coupled, external DC blocking capacitors are required to keep the bias voltages off the signal paths. A circuit of the MMIC and the external components required is shown in Fig 4.11.

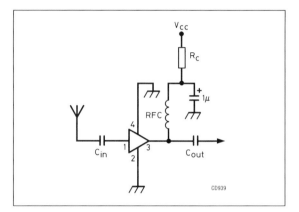

Fig 4.11. Pin-out and biasing arrangements for an MMIC amplifier

MMICs give a lot of gain at very high frequencies. This requires a large and solid ground plane to keep the return paths as short as possible. To obtain the greatest gain from these devices requires microstrip construction. Fig 4.12 shows the construction of an RF amplifier using such techniques.

For HF and VHF a simpler technique can be used. It comprises a brass sheet ground plane, bolted to the inside of a small aluminium box, and is described in the ARRL *Microwave Handbook* – see Fig 4.13. It allows the MMIC common leads to be soldered directly to the ground plane.

THE G4VSO SENSITIVE HF FIELD-STRENGTH METER

The non-linearity disadvantage of diodes and the general low sensitivity of diode FSMs can be overcome by using this circuit by G4VSO – see Fig 4.14. It was designed to overcome the sensitivity problem encountered when making adjustments to an HF antenna when using a low-power transmitter as the excitation source.

It uses a simple RF amplifier to raise the signal level before detection and an amplifier to drive the meter. This second amplifier also increases the value

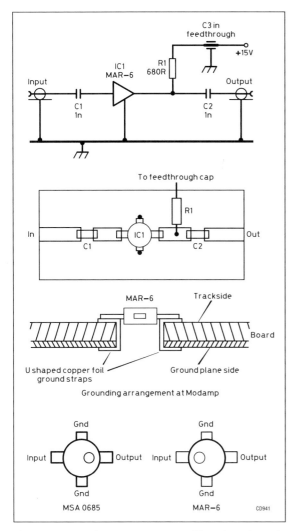

Fig 4.12. Construction of a MMIC RF amplifier using microstrip techniques

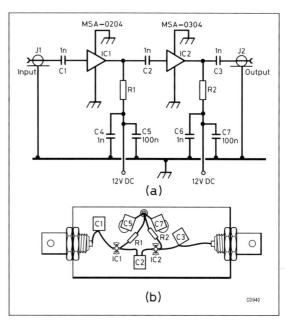

Fig 4.13. A MMIC HF and VHF RF amplifier constructed on a brass sheet ground plane. The circuit is shown in (a) and the component layout in (b)

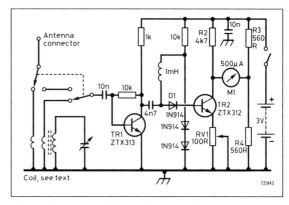

Fig 4.14. G4VSO sensitive HF field-strength meter

of the diode load resistance, thereby improving linearity. RV1 has two functions:

- It biases diode D1 into conduction to avoid the non-linear portion.
- Nulls the bridge RV1, TR2, R2, R3, and R4 so that M1 reads zero under no-signal conditions.

The tuned circuit inductor comprises 20 turns on a T50-6 with two turns input/output, tuned with a 10–450pF capacitor.

Typical calibration graphs, measured on the prototype for 1, 10 and 30MHz, are given in Fig 4.15. The RF amplifier gain decreases considerably at higher frequencies.

REQUIREMENTS OF AN FSM FOR MEASURING ANTENNA DIRECTIVITY

Field-strength meter requirements for plotting polar diagrams are often different to those for straightforward antenna adjustments. The range between the minimum and maximum values that may be recorded when making polar diagram plots can be greater than 50dB. For this reason linear scales might be inappropriate.

A good-quality communications receiver with a well-calibrated S-meter can be considered to be a field-strength meter. This instrument would have a

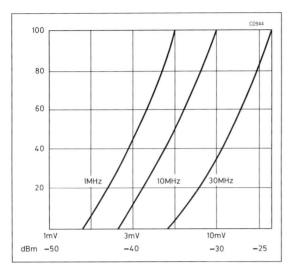

Fig 4.15. Typical calibration graphs for G4VSO field-strength meter

dynamic range of over 80dB and uses a logarithmic scale – see Fig 4.6.

Non-linear amplification

In Figs 5.4, 5.5 and 5.6 of Chapter 5 it can be seen that an antenna polar diagram can be plotted on a linear or log scale, and there is even the ARRL log scale, which is a compromise between the linear and log scales. The text also describes the advantages and disadvantages of these scales. Up until now only FSMs that give an output that has an approximate linear relationship between the signal at the input and the DC voltage output have been considered. If an output that has any other relationship between the input and the output is required then we need non-linear amplification.

Even an approximation of these functions may be more realistic than a linear plot shown in Fig 5.4. A polar diagram plotted using a function that approximates a logarithmic or the ARRL log-periodic scale allows real antenna models to be compared directly with computer models, which are normally plotted on a log or log-periodic scale.

The following is a discussion of methods and circuits that may be used to obtain non-linear amplification.

Linear FSM with amplitude shaper

One such circuit is the diode function generator. It can be used to produce a function whose slope decreases with amplitude; this is ideal for our purpose. This circuit does require a signal of a few volts

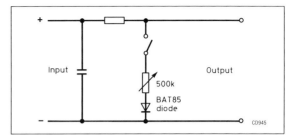

Fig 4.16. A simple amplitude-shaping circuit

at a relatively low impedance so it is not suitable for use with the diode FSM.

The simplest amplitude signal-conditioning circuit so far devised is shown in Fig 4.16. It comprises simply a BAT85 Schottky diode in series with a variable resistor. This has been used with limited success with the output from a commercial heterodyne voltmeter, which gives a linear output.

The effects of this single-stage shaper on the polar diagram of a two-element beam can be seen with the shaper switched out (Fig 4.17(a)) and switched in (Fig 4.17(b)). A more satisfactory shaper would probably require two or three stages to obtain the right shape. The effect of compressing the main lobe and increasing the signal level so that the rear lobes are visible can be seen quite clearly.

The output normally drives a meter. When I use this FSM to produce polar diagrams I disconnect the meter and replace it with a resistor. The voltage across this resistor is then measured on a digital voltmeter for manual plotting or input to a computer for automatic plotting (this technique is described in Chapter 5).

Non-linear amplifier

Use a basic operational amplifier with a non-linear element in the feedback path. A diode could be used. This device has a square-law relationship between current and voltage and it can be difficult to obtain good results.

A design for an FSM with a logarithmic response appeared in the ARRL *Radio Amateurs' Handbook*, 1973 edition [4]. It is reproduced here in Fig 4.18, with circuit description notes, because it does not appear in any subsequent versions of the handbook. The input tuned switched coils, L1 and L2, are resonated to the required frequency by C1. The original coil data quoted 44 turns on No 24 enamelled wire on a T-68-2 core for L1, tapped four turns from ground. L2 was 15 turns of No 24 enamelled wire on a T-68-2 core, with L3 comprising of two turns

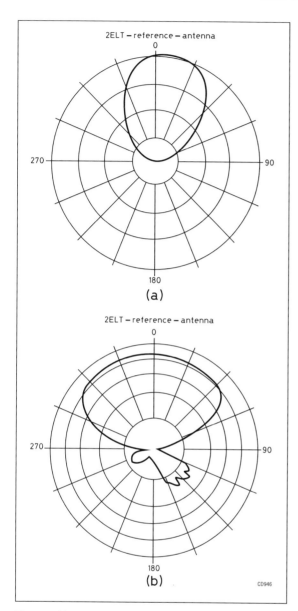

Fig 4.17. (a) VHF two-element beam polar diagram, plotted using FSM with linear output. (b) Plotted with the main lobe compressed using the circuit in Fig 4.16

wound on top of L2. Forward bias is applied to D1 via a 1MΩ resistor to improve linearity at low signal input levels. Two operational amplifiers produce a voltage at pin 10 of IC1b proportional to the logarithm (thus decibels) of the input voltage. Two scale ranges are available: 20dB and 40dB.

Accuracy is within 1dB. About 1mV of signal is necessary to provide a meaningful movement of M1.

The output voltage from IC1b is displayed by meter M1.

With no signal applied, a small amount of quiescent current will appear on M1. R1 is a DC offset control and is mounted on the rear of the panel. It permits some variation of the absolute readings by shifting the DC levels at the output of IC1b and may be used to set the meter to some convenient reference mark. The combined values of R2a and R2b should be 8kΩ. R2a is a trim pot to allow proper adjustment to exactly that value. R3a and R3b serve a similar purpose and should be set for a total resistance of 16kΩ.

The disadvantage of this design of FSM is that all the gain in the instrument occurs after the diode. Readings made at low levels are not as accurate as those made in the upper portion of the scale.

An ordinary transistor connected as a diode can be used as a feedback element (see Fig 4.19) to give a logarithmic characteristic over a nine-decant range. A second transistor of a complementary pair can be used to prevent the circuit going out of control if the input polarity reverses.

Software function

The linear output of an FSM can be used to plot polar diagrams automatically using a computer – see Chapter 5. A software function can be introduced to modify the amplitude response of the data when it is input to the program. An example of this is shown in the polar diagram plotting software listed in Appendix 3.

MODIFYING A BROADCAST RECEIVER FOR USE AS AN FSM

I made a useful FSM for the 2m band from a broadcast tuner/amplifier. It can be converted into a FSM with approximate log-type characteristics by using the AGC voltage as an indication of signal strength. The best tuner to use for this purpose is one of the earlier designs that uses air-spaced capacitors and unscreened tuning coils. The model that came to hand was a Teleton and the front-end of the receiver is shown in Fig 4.20.

The oscillator frequency of the unmodified receiver tuned the range approximately 100 to 200MHz, which indicated the oscillator was tuned high of the input signal. It was possible to move the oscillator to the low side of the 2m band (tuning the range 134 to 137MHz approximately) by stretching the coil and adjusting the trimmer on the oscillator section of the ganged tuning capacitor. This

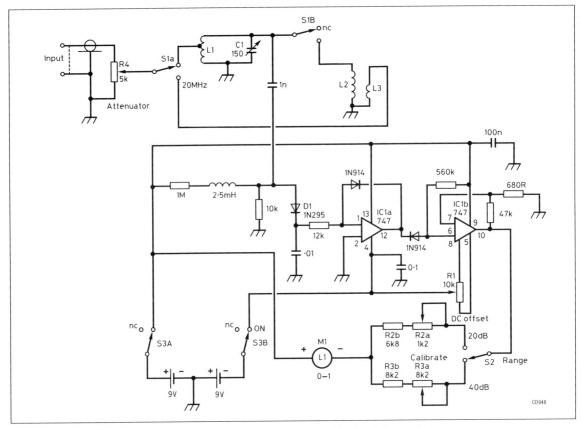

Fig 4.18. Calibrated FSM with log characteristics (ARRL *Radio Amateur's Handbook,* 55th edn)

arrangement was not satisfactory so half a turn from the oscillator coil was also removed to make tuning easier.

Approximately half a turn was removed from the antenna and mixer input stages. Using the signal generator the receiver was aligned by compressing or stretching these coils and fine tuned using the capacitor trimmers.

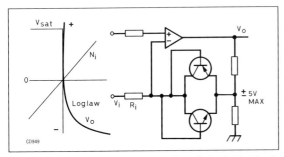

Fig 4.19. An operational amplifier using diodes in the feedback path to obtain logarithmic characteristics

The signal-strength DC voltage can be found by looking for diodes located part of the way down the IF stage. The Teleton receiver had two diodes; one gave a positive voltage and the other a negative one that varied with signal strength. The measured DC voltage produced by the diodes went up to 3V, with an increase in input voltage, before gain compression set in. The output of this receiver was used in conjunction with an A/D converter to produce many of the computer-derived polar diagrams shown in Chapter 5.

USING A COMMUNICATIONS RECEIVER AS A FIELD-STRENGTH METER

A communications receiver with an S-meter can be used as an FSM. It has high sensitivity and a logarithmic (decibel) response. In practice a receiver requires the RF gain to be turned to maximum for the S-meter to function correctly. Under these circumstances a receiver is very sensitive and an attenuator is necessary. This is connected into the

Fig 4.20. Teleton broadcast tuner/amplifier using air-spaced capacitors and unscreened tuning coils. The oscillator coil can be seen near the top of the photo next to the tuning capacitor; the antenna coil is near to the front panel at the bottom

Fig 4.21(a). Commercial switched attenuator with nine pi-network attenuators to give a maximum of 102dB attenuation in 1dB steps. Note that careful screening is required to achieve this range of attenuation

feeder between the pick-up antenna and the receiver antenna socket.

You can use the switched attenuator shown in Fig 4.21 or the potentiometer-variable attenuator used in Fig 4.22. Methods of using a receiver and attenuator for measuring comparative and absolute antenna gain are described in Chapter 5.

If you use the receiver or a transceiver as an FSM you must not transmit or you will burn out a low-power attenuator. Use the transceiver with the microphone disconnected.

Low-power switched attenuator

The switched attenuator described below is designed specially for performing gain measurements using a receiver or an uncalibrated field-strength meter. It comprises eight pi-network attenuators to give a maximum of 81dB attenuation in 1dB steps – see Fig 4.6.

This attenuator is based on designs in the ARRL *Radio Amateurs' Handbook* [2] and the RSGB *VHF/UHF Manual* [3]. These designs use small DPDT slide switches. When the attenuator

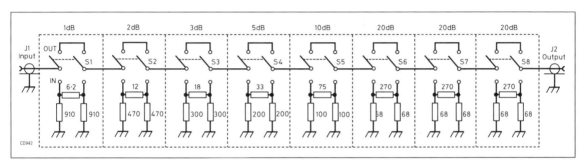

Fig 4.21(b). Switched attenuator with eight pi-network attenuators to give a maximum of 81dB attenuation in 1dB steps

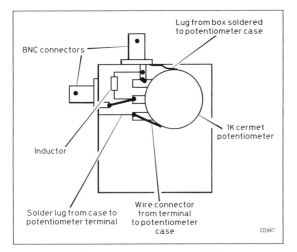

Lug from box soldered to potentiometer case

BNC connectors

1K cermet potentiometer

Inductor

Solder lug from case to potentiometer terminal

Wire connector from terminal to potentiometer case

CD947

Fig 4.22. Variable attenuator constructed from a cermet potentiometer

is used for gain measurements these switches are in constant use so the design illustrated in Fig 4.21(b) uses DPDT toggle switches with a long-life wiping action.

The attenuator can be built into a die-cast box with screens between the switched sections, or a complete enclosure can be constructed from double-sided printed circuit board. The layout should be similar to Fig 4.21(a). Interconnecting wires should be kept as short as possible.

Using a potentiometer as an attenuator

If the attenuator calibration requirement is not critical a carbon, or better still a cermet, potentiometer will make a useful variable signal-strength attenuator. Two or more potentiometers can be cascaded for higher attenuation but they will have to be constructed in a sealed, shielded box. The design shown in Fig 4.22 can be roughly calibrated for HF or the low VHF bands.

MAGNETIC FIELD-STRENGTH MEASUREMENTS

The magnetic FSM detects the magnetic component of the electromagnetic field rather than the electric field.

In the near field the relationship between the E and H fields with distance is complex and depends on the impedance of the source of radiation. The magnetic component from a dipole decreases rapidly up to a distance slightly less than $\lambda/6$ where the E and H fields have the equal intensity, so

magnetic field measurements are made close to the antenna element.

Magnetic field-strength measurements can be used to give some indication of RF current in a conductor. RF current could be measured by means of a 'hot wire' RF ammeter in series with the wire. This is impractical because it is necessary to break the conductor to insert the ammeter (very impractical with metal tube) and the resistance of the ammeter itself can affect the current being measured. Because the magnetic field close to a conductor is proportional to the current flowing in the conductor the instrument can be used to measure current.

The ability to measure the magnetic field of an electromagnetic wave is useful for the following reasons:

1. To check antenna currents in antenna elements and measure their distribution to check feed symmetry etc.
2. To assess the efficiency of a radiator or ground radial system. Low current in a radial, compared to a known good reference radial, indicates an inefficient radial.
3. To detect the presence of antenna currents in the coaxial feeder.
4. To detect induced currents in conductors not intended to be part of the antenna system, such as guy wires, masts and towers.
5. To ascertain the possible disturbance of the antenna performance by checking for RF currents in metal objects that make up the surrounding environment, such as water and gas pipes, drainage pipes, house electrical wiring and telephone wires.

Two types of RF current detectors will be described, one that is tuned to measure RF current a short distance from the conductor and then an aperiodic clamp-on current meter.

Tuneable current meter

A tuneable current meter is sensitive and can measure current some distance from the conductor. The following design for a tuned current meter was first described in *QST* [6, 7].

It was constructed using a variable capacitor, ferrite rod, diode, capacitor and resistor found in an old transistor radio.

The circuit is illustrated in Fig 4.23. Although the circuit calls for a 50μA meter, a 500μA one was used because it was available from one of my many junk boxes.

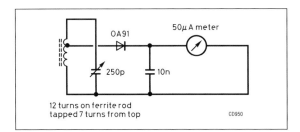

Fig 4.23. Circuit diagram of tuneable magnetic FSM

The coil is wound on a ferrite rod, and in this case comprised 12 turns with a tapping at the fifth turn to the diode. The coil inductance will depend on the type of ferrite used. My instrument covers from 5 to 18MHz using a 250pF variable capacitor.

According to the original article [7] the ferrite should have a μ (relative permeability) of about 40 for frequencies up to 50MHz although an ex-transistor radio ferrite rod appears to work well at 20MHz.

The component layout is shown in Fig 4.24. The instrument is built into an aluminium box. Any non-ferrous metal is suitable provided it shields the detector circuit from the electric field of the electromagnetic wave and does not impede the magnetic component of the wave.

A slot is cut across the top with a hacksaw and filed smooth with a thin file. This slot is needed to prevent the box acting as a shorted turn.

As was stated earlier in this chapter, the magnetic component of a TEM wave decreases very rapidly with distance from the conductor.

A method of maintaining the distance between the instrument and the conductor is required to ensure that measurements can be repeated consistently. This was achieved by glueing two clothes pegs on to the rear of the instrument which can then be clipped on to a wire or small-diameter conductor. The instrument can be suspended on larger conductors by using plastic strips. These are looped around the conductor and clipped together with the clothes pegs.

CLAMP-ON MAGNETIC CURRENT MEASUREMENT

RF current can be measured using a clamp-on transformer. The requirements for such an instrument to measure absolute RF current of 1A FSD given below are by Dennis Walker, G3OLM [8].

A measuring system for measuring current should present a low resistance so as to ensure minimum disturbance to the circuit conditions. 'Low resistance' is of course a relative term and in the context of measuring current on antenna wires and transmission lines it is the effective characteristic impedance which determines what is an acceptable value. This characteristic impedance will normally lie in the range 50 to 1000Ω. As long as the current measuring system has an input resistance of not more than 0.5Ω there should be little problem in disturbing the conditions by introducing the system.

With the wide availability of small ferrite rings it is possible to take a small current sample in a precise proportion. Rectifying the sample and applying the output to a moving-coil meter provides a predictable and reliable method of current indication which will tolerate large overloads, is linear scaled and will respond quickly. Let's design a system to

Fig 4.24. Tuneable magnetic FSM: external (left) and internal (right) views

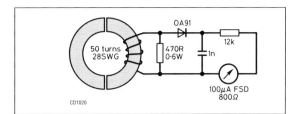

Fig 4.25. Circuit of an RF clamp-on current meter with an FSD of 1A

provide a full-scale indication of 1A when using a 100µA moving-coil meter.

The essential property of a current transformer is that the ampere turns on the primary are precisely balanced by the ampere turns on the secondary so that with a single turn on the primary side and 50 turns on the secondary we can expect precisely 20mA to be available to circulate in the secondary for each amp of primary current. In dealing with toroid ring cores a 'turn' simply means a pass through the central hole – it does not need to be complete.

The other necessary condition is that the secondary load must be low enough to allow the current to circulate, otherwise we do not have a current transformer! A value of 470Ω is suitable as this will reflect into the primary an equivalent resistance of 470/2500 or 0.18Ω which is low enough to meet the conditions outlined above. (Resistance is transformed according to the square of the turns ratio.)

Now with 20mA circulating in 470Ω we will have 9.4V RMS available for rectification, corresponding to 13.2V peak. We can expect to lose approximately 0.5V at the detector diode, leaving a DC voltage of 12.7V to drive the moving-coil meter. To obtain full-scale deflection of 100µA with 12.7V requires a total resistance of 12.7kΩ. The meter itself will contribute about 800Ω so an ordinary 12kΩ resistor will fit the bill with negligible error. As a result the effective resistance of the detector circuit will be much greater than the 470Ω so there will be negligible error due to loading here. A circuit of the current meter is shown in Fig 4.25.

On the subject of suitable cores for this application, the magnetic requirements are quite undemanding and almost any small ring of ½in to 1in diameter will be found suitable as long as it is intended for RF usage.

This arrangement is particularly useful when combined with a monimatch SWR meter; you can even use the same meter movement for both SWR and current with a little ingenuity. This enables you to determine the RF power output directly if there is a

good SWR. It is also possible to employ the current meter to calibrate the SWR indications to extend the power or current measurements well outside the range of the basic current meter!

A SENSITIVE ANTENNA RADIAL EFFICIENCY CHECKER

This device is a clamp-on current sensor designed to check the efficiency of antenna radials and was designed by J B Smith, VK9NS [10]. The instrument is constructed from two pieces of aluminium held together with a couple of smaller plastic clothes pegs. A snap-on ferrite core choke is used for the core.

It operates by comparing the measured current in a suspect radial wire with the current in a known good one. When transmitted power is fed to the antenna the total current in the antenna system is shared with all the radials. When the antenna radial current is being measured the antenna has to be energised for the duration of the check. It is desirable that this is done with low power and it follows that an instrument for checking radials must be sensitive. It must also have a sensitivity control so that the current can be set for maximum on the known good radial. The circuit for the radial checker is shown in Fig 4.26.

The gauge of the aluminium used for the arms of the peg must be at least 2mm (0.125in). Cut-out holes are required for the VU meter back, ferrite cores and the sensitivity potentiometer. The construction is illustrated in Fig 4.27.

The springs of the pegs should set the tension and should not be modified by any flexibility of the aluminium. Two plastic pegs give sufficient tension but you could try three. The prototype used ferrite from a clamp-on RF choke (Cirkit UF4 or similar). This is not critical – see the G3OLM current meter design.

The hole in the split U-core ferrite snap-on choke assembly assembled in the intended fashion is too large. The requirement is a maximum of around 10mm (0.4in) to take the centre of normal coaxial

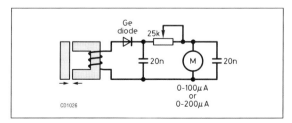

Fig 4.26. Circuit of the clamp-on radial checker

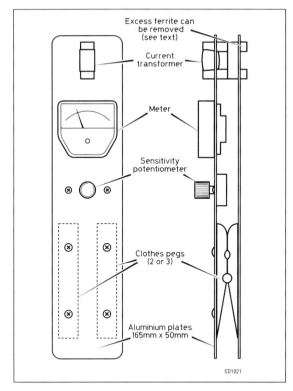

Fig 4.27. Mechanical layout of the clamp-on radial checker

cable with dielectric. By turning the bottom half U-core top to bottom, the resultant hole is perfect. The resultant flat surface also allows the two legs of the top U-core to sit flush and tight.

The inside clearance of the arms has to be larger than the depth of the meter used. This depth is dictated by the height of the small plastic pegs used which is about 11 to 12mm (0.6in) and is more than sufficient.

Place the two arms together and make the rectangular cut out for the top and bottom cores – the fit should be reasonably tight. On the top arm, file the long edges with a half-round file to make sure the coil winding has clearance and is not touching the metal.

When closed the jaw end of the arms should be parallel, thus ensuring the accurate mating of the top and bottom ferrite surfaces. To achieve this the bottom ferrite has its top flat face about 2 to 3mm (0.125in) above the inside surface of the bottom arm. Make sure it is square and level, glue in place with Araldite™ or similar and allow to set.

Set the two small pegs flat on the base and allow suitable clearance for the meter and the sensitivity

potentiometer. Glue with Araldite and allow to set. Attach the top plate onto the pegs using four small self-tappers. (It makes sense to be able to take the thing apart.) Now open and set the 'jaw' to about 2 to 3mm (0.125in) more than the parallel position. (Put the shank of a suitable drill in the jaws of the small pegs to achieve this.)

Construct the current transformer by winding 12 to 14 turns of 22 SWG enamelled copper wire on the top core. Wrap a layer of tape over the core before winding the coil – the edges of the ferrite are very sharp. Wrap tape over the finished coil, make sure the tails are clear and so on.

Place the top U-section of ferrite (with coil) through its cut-out and let it 'sit' on the top of the ferrite core below. A couple of elastic bands were used to keep everything in place and yet be able to move the top core slightly. Make sure the coil and wire tails underneath are clear of the metal arm and make sure there are no spaces for the Araldite to drip though. (A thin piece of paper between the faces will avoid disaster.) Araldite the top core in place and let it set. Later, the coil can be given a thick protective coat of Araldite on top. When the Araldite has set do the same to the underside.

When the drill shank and the elastic bands are removed the 2 to 3mm (0.125in) which has been set will now ensure good facing of the ferrite faces under the pressure of the peg springs.

The device can be split again and the meter, potentiometer, diode (use a germanium type) and the couple of capacitors can all be assembled and wired. Re-assembly should be easy by now.

Removal of the surplus legs of that bottom up-turned half-core should be tackled with care. (Hint: carefully use a fine grindstone wheel.)

This model is repeatable with the minimum of work. Not shown in the illustrations is a plastic wire guide at the jaws (fitted since the photos were taken). A couple of pieces of plastic either side with a 12.5mm (0.5in) hole (split of course) and held in place with Araldite.

COMMERCIAL FIELD-STRENGTH METERS

This is a description of some instruments that are specifically designed as field-strength meters or can be used as such.

The instrument in Fig 4.28 is a Sadelta FSM type TC-40 and as you can see is labelled 'Field Strength Meter'. It is designed for aligning domestic TV and FM radio antennas. This is an old instrument which covers the old VHF television bands. It also covers

Fig 4.28. Sadelta FSM type TC-40 designed for aligning domestic TV and FM radio antennas

Fig 4.29. Radio Interference Measuring Set 0.15–30MHz, Model No: RMSI

It has been found to be particularly useful for measuring the performance of HF antennas. It just shows that an FSM designed for one purpose can used for another. It has a very large meter whose scale can be read from 100m away using binoculars. The signal-strength attenuators on the front of the instrument are calibrated in decibels. A combination of the four switches allows levels of between 0 and 90dB to be set.

The bad news is that it was built in the days when portability had a different meaning and it is also guaranteed to flatten a fully charged car battery in a relatively short space of time.

By far the most useful piece of equipment that I have acquired so far is an instrument called a *heterodyne voltmeter* – see Fig 4.30.

This description gave little clue as to what its original use was. It was found that it could be used as an FSM with a continuous frequency coverage of from 100kHz to 230MHz in four ranges. It can measure signal strength in the region of 5µV to 50mV and has a switched selectivity of 2kHz or 200kHz.

It also has a loudspeaker monitor and internal chargeable batteries that can be charged with an internal mains charger. This has turned out to be a superb FSM and is used for the bulk of my antenna experiment measurements. I have found a further use for this instrument: as a noise level detector when using the antenna receiver noise bridge.

the 50, 70 and 144MHz bands and I have found it very useful for adjusting my 145MHz model antennas.

It is a superheterodyne receiver with good sensitivity to allow it to be used in areas of weak signal strength. To enable it to be used over a wide range of signal levels it has a range of attenuators. These are calibrated so that the FSD of the signal level meter can be selected as follows: 100µV, 300µV, 1mV, 3mV, 10mV and 30mV.

Using more familiar units, it will measure signal from about S2 or 3 to S9 + 50dB.

The instrument shown in Fig 4.29 is described as a 'Radio Interference Measuring Set 0.15–30MHz, Model No: RMSI.'

I have no information it but it is obvious from its construction that it is some type of specialised FSM for investigating the source and signal strength of unwelcome radio signals.

REFERENCES

[1] *The Handbook of Antenna Design*, Vols 1 and 2, Chapter 8.

[2] 'Field strength measurements 1.6–300MHz', *ARRL Radio Amateur's Handbook*, 1973 edn.

Fig 4.30. Heterodyne voltmeter wide range field-strength meter

[3] *VHF/UHF Manual*, 4th edn, G R Jessop, G6JP, RSGB, 1984.

[4] 'Calibrated log field-strength meter', *ARRL Radio Amateur's Handbook,* 1973 edn.

[5] 'Radiation patterns for antennas on different grid coordinate systems', *ARRL Antenna Handbook*, 1988 edn.

[6] 'An RF current probe', *ARRL Antenna Book*, 1988 edn, pp27-29 and 30.

[7] 'The Hampmeter', K2CU and W2OCM, *QST* October 1963.

[8] 'Current transformers and RF measurement', Dennis Walker, G3OLM, 'Technical Update', *Radio Communication* November 1995.

[9] 'The JS Snap RF current probe', J B Smith, VK9NS, *Radio Communication* June 1995.

5 Measuring antenna performance

THIS chapter describes how to assess antenna performance by measuring comparative gain, absolute gain and directivity using test equipment already described in Chapter 4.

You might question why such measurements are necessary. After all, the antenna computer modelling programs, described in Chapter 8, are very good – so why make measurements on a real antenna with all its uncertainties?

There are several reasons. With some geometries, such as the HF double-D (see Chapter 7), altering the antenna configuration is not easy with the computer model. Information may be obtained on a the eventual shape more quickly using a VHF model.

With very complex geometries, such as the toroid antenna (see Chapter 7), computer modelling is cumbersome and requires vast amounts of computer time and power.

Although computers are now relatively cheap and powerful, a complex model requires a lot of setting up. All wires have to be described as a straight line so the simple helix antenna, shown in Chapter 8, needs to be broken down into hundreds of wires to describe its structure. Information on this type of antenna may be obtained much more quickly using a VHF model.

Even with an antenna that can be modelled easily using a computer there has to be a transition from virtual reality to reality. The antenna has to be physically constructed and its performance checked to complete the study. You can't work much DX using a mathematical model.

Most of this chapter is devoted to measuring VHF beam antenna parameters, where the size of antenna and antenna range can be kept down to manageable proportions. HF antenna designs can be investigated by scaling them at VHF.

Methods for assessing the performance of full-size HF antennas are also discussed.

BASIC CONSIDERATIONS
Radiation patterns and antenna gain

The performance of an antenna can be measured by energising it with a known level of RF power and then performing a number of field-strength measurements. These measurements are made at a constant distance in the far field (see Chapter 4) at different angles relative to the antenna under test (AUT). A large number of these measurements would produce a three-dimensional polar diagram or space pattern.

The antenna performance is then determined by comparing it with some reference antenna. However, radiation from a practical antenna never has the same intensity in all directions. For this reason a hypothetical point source antenna which radiates equally in all directions has been devised– this is known as an *isotropic radiator*. Because the field strength is the same in all directions it follows that the three-dimensional polar diagram or space pattern of an isotropic radiator is a sphere.

This is illustrated in Fig 5.1(a). Radiation from an isotropic source located at the centre of a sphere will give uniform illumination to the inside of the sphere.

The isotropic radiator is used with antenna mathematical modelling – see Chapter 8. Such a radiator is a theoretical concept. In practice a single $\lambda/2$ dipole is used because it is the simplest practical form of radiator, and is generally accepted as a basis for comparison. The radiation pattern of a dipole is not uniform (see Fig 5.1(b)) and has a power gain of 2.15dBi. Gain measurement figures, using the dipole radiator as a reference, are symbolised 'dBd'.

The far-field pattern of an antenna is one of its most important characteristics. The complete field pattern is a three-dimensional or space pattern and its complete description requires field-intensity measurements in all directions – see Fig 5.2.

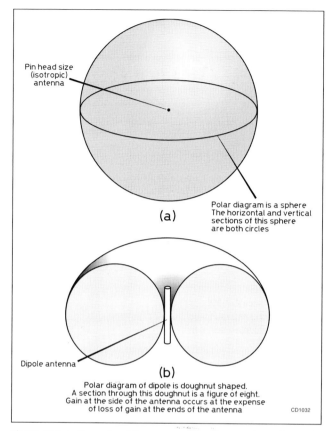

(a)

Pin head size (isotropic) antenna

Polar diagram is a sphere The horizontal and vertical sections of this sphere are both circles

Dipole antenna

(b)

Polar diagram of dipole is doughnut shaped. A section through this doughnut is a figure of eight. Gain at the side of the antenna occurs at the expense of loss of gain at the ends of the antenna

CD1032

Fig 5.1. Three-dimensional free-space polar diagrams for an isotropic radiator (a) and a dipole (b)

In practice a full three-dimensional description is usually unnecessary and one or more sections through the three-dimensional space pattern will provide enough information. A useful analogy is the contour line of equal height on a map of a hill, which shows the general shape of the latter.

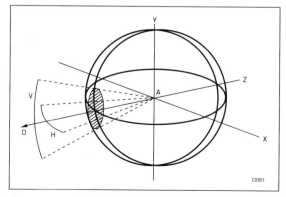

Fig 5.2. Radiation from an antenna

In the case of a polar diagram the contour line is one of equal signal strength but, like a map contour line, the shape can change depending where the section through the three-dimensional polar diagram is made. In practice two sets of measurements, one through the vertical and the other through the horizontal axis, are usually made (see Fig 5.2). These diagrams are drawn in space, away from any obstacle that could effect the diagram with reflections. Such diagrams are called *free-space* diagrams and, like the isotropic antenna, are theoretical and only used in antenna mathematical models.

Gain and directivity

The *gain* of an antenna in a given direction is the ratio of the radiation intensity in that direction to the maximum radiation intensity from a lossless reference antenna absorbing the same power. A $\lambda/2$ dipole is often used as the reference, in which case the gain is often quoted in dBd, ie decibels relative to a perfect $\lambda/2$ dipole.

Absolute gain is the ratio of the radiation intensity in a given direction relative to that which could be obtained if the power accepted by the antenna was radiated equally in all directions, ie isotropically – see Fig 5.1(a). While an isotropic antenna cannot be constructed, the concept provides a useful absolute reference, and antenna gain quoted in professional literature is usually expressed in dBi (decibels relative to an isotropic radiator). See Fig 5.3 and the antenna computer modelling described in Chapter 8.

The property of an antenna to radiate more strongly in some directions than others is called its *directivity*. If practical antennas were lossless, the isotropic gain would be equal to the directivity. In the real world, losses ensure that gain is always less than directivity. While it is perfectly possible for the two antennas to have the same directivity, the lossier of the two will have less gain.

POLAR DIAGRAM PLOTTING SCALES

The range of intensities measured in plotting these diagrams can exceed 50dB (see Fig 4.6 in Chapter 4).

The effect of measuring polar diagrams of a dipole and an array comprising four 19-element Yagis on a linear scale is shown in Fig 5.4. The linear

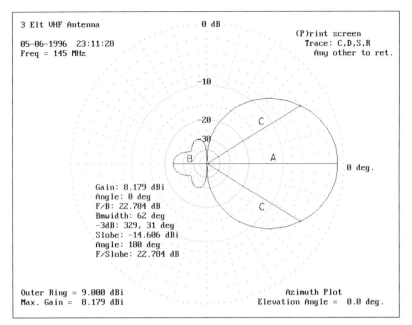

Fig 5.3. Polar diagram showing directivity (A), gain, front-to-back ratio (A/B) and 3dB down power beamwidth (C). A description of this display is given in Chapter 8

plot can only show features from maximum signal strength down about 15 to 20dB or so. This gives a very optimistic picture of directivity and suppresses the back lobes.

If, on the other hand, either of these antennas were connected to a receiver, and a plot were to be made using the receiver S-meter readings, then the plots would probably look more like those shown in Fig 5.5.

Each of these plots have strengths and weaknesses. The linear scale has the advantage of being very sensitive in to changes in level in the region of maximum signal strength and is useful for making gain comparisons between different antennas. A polar diagram plotted on a logarithmic (linear decibel) grid, on the other hand, displays a signal level range of at least 80dB. This grid gives a much more accurate picture of how the antenna will perform when connected to the station receiver, and explains why the directivity of a given antenna is often not as good as its published polar diagram might suggest.

The log-periodic polar plot

The ARRL has devised a polar diagram having a log-periodic grid – see Fig 5.6.

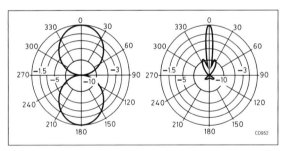

Fig 5.4. Antenna polar diagram using a linear voltage plot (*ARRL Antenna Book*)

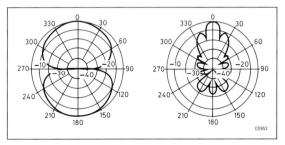

Fig 5.5. Antenna polar diagram using a linear-log plot (*ARRL Antenna Book*)

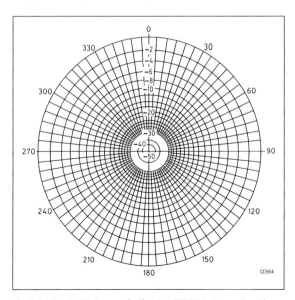

Fig 5.6. The ARRL log-periodic plot (*ARRL Antenna Book*)

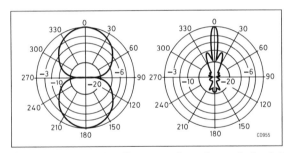

Fig 5.7. Antenna polar diagrams using a log-periodic plot (ARRL Antenna Book)

Instead of the graduations varying linearly with the log of the field intensity, as shown in Fig 5.5, they vary periodically. The constant of this periodicity is 0.89 for 2dB intervals. This represents a compromise between the extremes of linear and linear decibel grids so far described. It possesses good sensitivity to small changes in maximum signal while at the same time is able to display the minor lobes. Examples of polar diagrams, using this scale, of the same antennas plotted in Figs 5.4 and 5.5 are shown in Fig 5.7.

The effect of ground

The ground under the antenna acts as a reflector. Electromagnetic waves from the antenna radiate in all directions and some of these waves are reflected by the ground. If the reflected wave is in phase, or partially in phase, with a direct wave it enhances radiation and increases gain at a particular angle. Other combinations of reflected and direct waves, whose phases tend to cancel, reduce gain at other angles.

In Fig 5.8 waves A and C enhance gain while B and C tend to cancel and reduce the gain. This is the cause of the familiar vertical or elevation antenna patterns. This aspect is most important and has implications viewing any horizontal polar diagram

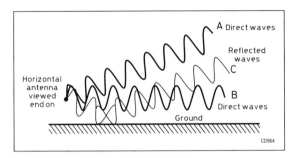

Fig 5.8. Diagram illustrating the effect of ground reflection on directly radiated waves

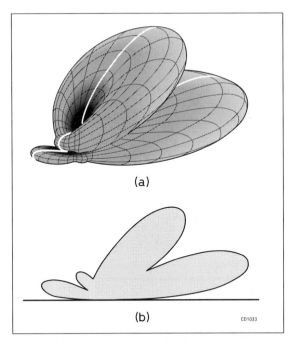

(a)

(b)

Fig 5.9. (a) Three-dimensional polar diagram of a three-element beam showing a vertical or elevation section. (b) Radiation pattern measured through this section

of a practical antenna. It is also important that ground effects are taken into consideration when setting up equipment on an antenna range.

Consider the three-dimensional polar diagram of a three-element beam in Fig 5.9(a). If we take a vertical cross-section of this diagram, it produces the elevation diagram shown in Fig 5.9(b), but where do we draw a section to make the horizontal diagram?

We can't draw it through the true horizontal because of the effect of ground. What we do in practice is to plot the horizontal diagram at a given angle of radiation. This section is therefore a cone (see Fig 5.10).

It is important to consider the height above ground because of the ground effect. If the antenna is over half a wavelength ($\lambda/2$) high, several lobes and nulls can be produced and it might be difficult to set the antenna under test and the measured antenna for optimum measurement. If the height of the antenna under test is set at $\lambda/2$ then there will only be one major vertical lobe, making it easier to set up the antenna range.

It is important that all the antennas are tested at the same height and frequency if the comparisons are to have any meaning – see Fig 5.11.

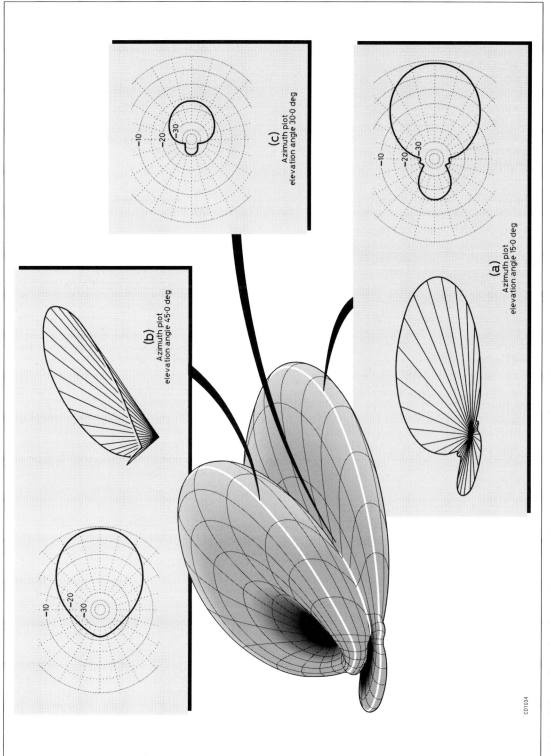

(c)
Azimuth plot
elevation angle 30·0 deg

(b)
Azimuth plot
elevation angle 45·0 deg

(a)
Azimuth plot
elevation angle 15·0 deg

CD1034

Fig 5.10. (a) Three-dimensional polar diagram of a three-element beam showing a horizontal conical section at the angle of maximum radiation. (b) Diagram at the angle of maximum radiation. (c) Diagram at an angle other than that of maximum radiation

SCALE MODELLING OF HF ANTENNAS

In the VHF scale model, wavelengths, capacitances and inductances are reduced in proportion to the linear dimensions while gains, impedances, dielectric constants and permeabilities are unchanged. Conductivity is the exception and increases in inverse proportion to the scale factor.

In practice little is lost in scaling antennas of copper tube or wire. Poor conductors like real earth are very difficult to scale. It is more practicable to ensure the earth conductivity is the best the test range will allow. In practice this can be achieved by maintaining the ground of the test range in a moist condition during spells of dry weather.

In choosing a scale the size of the test site must be taken into consideration. In amateur practice we are limited to the 145MHz band or the 432MHz band. On the 50MHz band the test site is too big to perform measurements in an average-size garden. In the following modelling descriptions the 145MHz band has been used because of the availability of test equipment for it.

THE VHF ANTENNA TEST RANGE

An antenna test range should comprise a wide open space

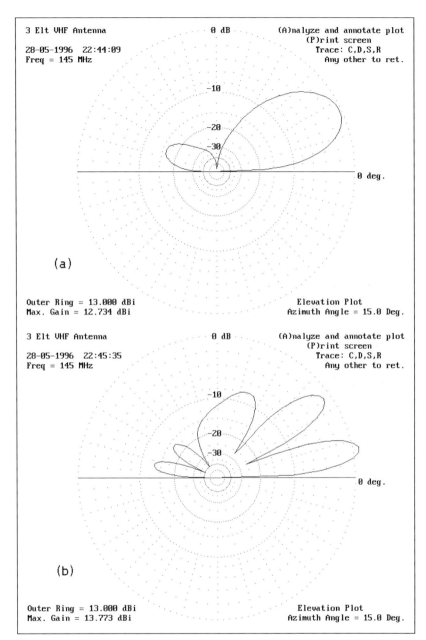

Fig 5.11. Calculated elevation pattern of a three-element 145MHz Yagi at (a) 0.5λ high and (b) 1.25λ high

with no nearby objects likely to cause distortion of the electromagnetic field. In practice this is not so easy because the test range will probably be a back garden. Nevertheless good results can be obtained if some precautions are taken.

Preliminary tests of an antenna range can be achieved by radiating an electromagnetic field from a dipole antenna and transmitter in the centre of the range. A magnetic detector is then used to locate any areas of re-radiation caused by hidden metallic objects. The range can be further checked by making a polar diagram of a dipole, using a diode FSM, described later in this chapter, with the source antenna at different heights and distances (details on how to do this are described later). If the plots show fairly symmetrical patterns then the test range should be free from unseen and unknown electromagnetic obstructions.

If the first set of dipole polar diagrams are asymmetrical, before suspecting the range check the antenna.

- Are the currents on the two halves of the dipole equal? Check that the elements are the correct length.
- Is the feeder resonant at the operating frequency? If so there could be antenna currents on the line, thereby distorting the pattern. Ensure the feeder is not resonant at the operating frequency.
- Is the feeder matched to the antenna?

Once you have a dipole that is symmetrical and correctly matched this is your standard for checking the gain of antennas as well as for checking the test range.

In some cases antennas can be tested indoors. I have used the living room of a house as a test range with surprisingly good results. Provided the range passes the tests mentioned above there seems no reason why this should not be done. I have also worked with the antenna indoors by a large window, with the source antenna in the garden in a tree. Indoor experimental work has the considerable advantage of not being limited by the weather. Even if the indoor range is less than perfect, a lot of preliminary work, such as construction, initial tune-up and matching, can be achieved.

On the other hand the plumbing and wiring in some houses has a very detrimental effect on antenna performance. See 'Adjusting full-sized HF beams' later in this chapter. One look at the mixture of steel, lead and copper pipes that constitute the plumbing in my present house and it is not difficult to see why antennas perform so badly in its vicinity.

The local park can be pressed into service as an antenna range if all else fails, the main disadvantage being that all test gear, antenna models have to be transported there. Additionally, only battery-operated test equipment can be used.

PRODUCING POLAR DIAGRAMS USING THE DIODE FSM

Test equipment

This is a description of how to make polar diagram measurements using the diode field-strength meter [1]. Because the diode FSM is rather insensitive (see

Chapter 4) a transmitter with an output of up to 10W is required.

The professionals measure antenna performance by exciting a source antenna which floods the antenna test area with RF. The AUT is coupled to the receiver or field-strength meter, which measures the field strength as the antenna is rotated.

Because of the reciprocity relation of an antenna (the transmitting and receiving directivity characteristics are broadly the same) it is not important which antenna is energised and which is used as the receiver antenna. When making measurements of amateur radio antennas I prefer to use the test equipment the other way around and energise the antenna under test (AUT), using a simple antenna for the receiver or field-strength meter. There are two reasons for this:

- The SWR of the AUT can be monitored. This ensures the antenna is matched to the feeder in the first place. Any subsequent change in SWR as the antenna is rotated could indicate coupling into nearby objects that may affect the results. Antenna comparisons are meaningless unless the SWR is better than 1.5:1.
- The SWR meter can be used as a sensitive indication of relative transmitter power output when the transmitter is being used to energise the AUT.

The source transmitter should also be stable and free of spurious outputs. It can be an amateur radio transceiver whose transmitter power output level can be controlled, such as the FDK Multi-700EX. On the other hand, any surplus commercial or military transmitter will do – the most important feature it should possess is that the RF power output should be variable. Most equipment of this nature does not have this facility so needs to be modified.

Fig 5.12 illustrates how this equipment is connected up.

To recap, the following items of test equipment are required for polar diagram measurements:

- Transmitter with variable power control.
- SWR meter, coaxial cable and connectors.
- AUT mast and rotator mechanism.
- Antenna to be tested.
- Diode field-strength meter with remote analogue or digital field-strength level indicator; see Chapter 4.
- Loop antenna for field-strength meter.
- Rectangular or square-section wooden mast with pulley and carriage for adjusting FSM height (this item only required if vertical patterns are required).

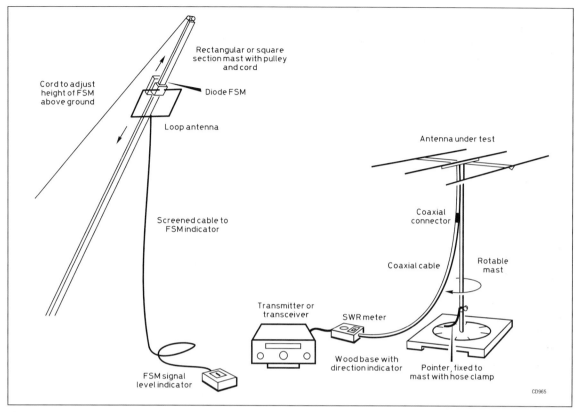

Fig 5.12. Antenna field-strength measurement test equipment

Antenna support and rotator

To obtain polar diagrams the AUT must be mounted on a rotatable support. The cheap TV rotator is convenient because it is remotely controlled and the experimenter need not go near the AUT when it is rotated to a new position. If a TV rotator is not available then a simple rotator can be constructed as shown in Fig 5.13.

It comprises a wooden base, painted white (or white plastic-covered wood) with a direction indicator drawn on it with a black felt-tip pen. A bolt is fixed to the centre of the indicator and the mast, and a length of copper or alloy tube slid over the bolt. An indicator pointer is fixed to the bottom of the mast with a hose clamp.

Antenna optimisation

It is important that all antennas being tested are fully optimised; it is no use comparing a fully optimised three-element quad with a badly tuned four-element Yagi. Optimisation includes adjusting for the best possible feeder to feed-point match possible.

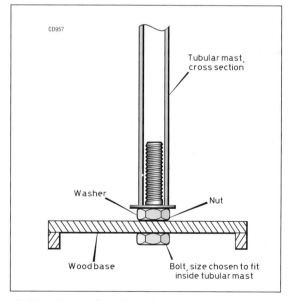

Fig 5.13. Construction of base, indicator and rotatable mast for obtaining polar diagram data (not to scale)

Polar diagram plotting procedure

Plotting polar diagrams involves recording lots of data. Keep all this data together in one notebook and label each test, together with any other relevant information. Leave room on the page for correction factors – this will be discussed later.

1. Position the diode FSM, with a suitable antenna, about eight or 10 paces from the AUT. The antenna can be a dipole or a quad loop; I prefer the latter because it is slightly less prone to ground effects. Position it at a point where the maximum signal strength is likely to occur at 0° on the rotator indicator. Place the FSM level indicator where it can be clearly seen from the operating position.

2. Set up the transmitter, feeder, SWR meter and the AUT. Switch on the transmitter. Set the power level to, say, 30% of maximum and check that the antenna matching is optimum (lowest SWR). Tune the diode FSM for maximum meter deflection or reading.

3. Fix the height of the FSM so that it is well inside the main vertical lobe of the AUT radiation pattern. Readjust the transmitter power if necessary.

4. Rotate the AUT for maximum signal strength on the FSM signal level indicator. Adjust the transmitter power level for about 75% of FSD if using an analogue meter, or for about 2V if using a digital meter.

5. Set the SWR meter to FORWARD reading and adjust the FORWARD level at a clearly defined resettable point (the meter scale on most SWR meters is red at levels greater than 3:1; this is a good point to set the RF power level).

6. Record the reading on the FSM level indicator and rotate the AUT in both directions to ensure the point of maximum gain is at 0°.

7. Rotate the antenna through 360° while watching the FSM signal level. In this way you can gain a mental picture of the AUT pattern. It is useful to make this preliminary check to ensure the antenna is working reasonably well before going through the routine of recording the data.

3 elt beam normalization factor 100/90 ≈ 1·11

AUT Heading	0	10	20	40	60	80	100	120	140	160	180
FSM Reading	90	88	80	60	42	25	10	8	15	17	19
FSM × Corr f	100	98	89	67	47	28	11	9	17	19	21

AUT Heading	200	220	240	260	280	300	320	340	360
FSM Reading	16	10	7	9	13	30	55	75	90
FSM × Corr f	18	11	8	10	14	33	61	83	100

Fig 5.14. Sample log page, showing how antenna signal strength data, with and without the correction factor, is recorded to produce normalised data

8. Set the AUT to 0° and record the level.
9. Switch off the transmitter. Rotate the AUT to a new heading.

I usually take a reading every 10° at the main lobe maximum to identify the point of maximum gain, otherwise readings every 20° may suffice. Additional readings can be made to identify the nulls. If you are using the simple antenna rotator, rotate the AUT to the new heading and move away from it before making any further measurement.

The transmitter is switched off and on between measurements because most transmitters are not continuously rated. Also, the channel should be monitored, and identification announcements made periodically.

Normalisation

The data obtained so far can be used to produce a polar diagram showing directivity on a linear voltage scale. This may be sufficient for your purpose.

However, the most common way of producing a polar diagram is to plot it so that it fills the whole of the plotting graph, a process known as *normalisation*. A correction factor is required to produce normalised data from the plotted results and is obtained by:

$$\text{Correction factor} = \frac{100}{\text{Maximum plotted value}}$$

Multiply each item of plotted data by the correction factor, as shown in the sample log page in Fig 5.14. A normalised polar diagram can then be plotted from these results. An example of normalised polar diagrams can be seen in Fig 5.3(a). The polar diagrams shown are plotted on log scales with the largest recorded signal strength assigned 0dB. All other signal values are therefore negative decibel figures. You can convert the linear voltage data to log values using the log chart in Appendix 4, or by using a calculator if you wish, but you will need an appropriate log scale on which to plot it. The 0dB figure of a log scale, or the 100% value of a linear voltage scale, needs to be assigned a reference point if comparative gain information is to be included in the polar diagram.

Dipole normalized from Max 55 to 40. Correction factor $\frac{40}{55} = .7272$

AUT Heading	0	10	20	40	60	80	100	120	140	160	180
Dipole Data	55	53	50	25	15	9	12	18	26	48	53
Dipole C fact:	40	38	36	18	11	6	9	13	19	35	38
AUT Data	98	96	89	68	50	33	18	16	23	25	27
AUT x C fact:	71	70	65	49	36	24	13	12	17	18	20

AUT & Dipole Heading	200	220	240	260	280	300	320	340	360
Dipole	50	44	26	18	8	19	25	46	55
Dipole x C fact:	36	32	19	13	6	14	18	33	40
AUT Data	24	18	15	17	21	38	63	83	98
AUT x C fact:	16	13	11	12	15	28	46	60	71

Fig 5.15. Sample log page, showing reference dipole and AUT data. All data are then normalised to dipole reference level of 40

Relative gain factors

A further set of tests is required to obtain relative gain information. Set up the test range using the AUT with the highest gain of the group tested.

Set the transmitter power to give near maximum FSD on an analogue meter or 2 to 3V on a digital meter. Rotate the AUT slightly clockwise and anticlockwise to ensure that the FSM is recording the lobe maximum. Record the signal level for that antenna.

Replace the antenna with a reference antenna (dipole) and repeat the measurement procedure. Repeat the measurement on any other antennas in the batch. It is important that each antenna tested is placed in the same position as the previous one(s).

Move the FSM and its antenna to a different position. Repeat the tests starting with the highest gain antenna as before, adjusting the transmitter output so that the signal levels are similar to those obtained in the first test.

These tests can be repeated as often as required – the greater the number of tests, the greater should be the accuracy. Obtain an average test value for each antenna by adding all the test figures of each antenna tested together and dividing by the number of tests performed.

These average data from the AUT and a reference dipole can be used to produce a gain figure for the AUT. For example, if the average maximum figure for the reference dipole were 35 and the AUT were 72,

$$N \text{ (dB)} = 20 \log_{10} V_1/V_2$$
$$N \text{ (dB)} = 20 \log_{10} 72/35$$
$$= 6.2\text{dBd}$$

This gain figure can then be added to the polar diagram.

Relative gain of the AUT and the reference dipole can be shown graphically. In this case the maximum recorded level for the dipole is adjusted to, say, 40%. The figure required to achieve this adjustment, the reference dipole correction factor, is then added to, or subtracted from the AUT data as shown in Fig 5.15. The AUT and the reference dipole data can then be plotted together to give a pictorial comparison, as shown in Fig 5.16.

Examples of tests on VHF models of HF antennas

The following are results obtained using the methods already described. All the antennas tested were VHF models of small HF beams. Construction of these models is described in Chapter 7.

All the data used to construct these polar diagrams were obtained using very simple equipment. The transmitter came from a club junk sale and the FSM was the simple diode model as described in Chapter 4.

Three-element beam

This antenna was used as the standard of comparison for the other antennas because more information existed for this type than any of the others. It was constructed to the design graphs from the *ARRL Antenna Handbook* [2].

This antenna was easy to adjust and to optimise,

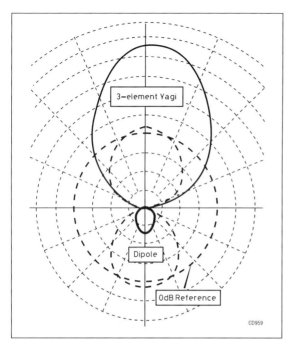

Fig 5.16. Three-element beam and dipole polar diagrams. Size of both diagrams adjusted so that dipole is set to a zero reference point

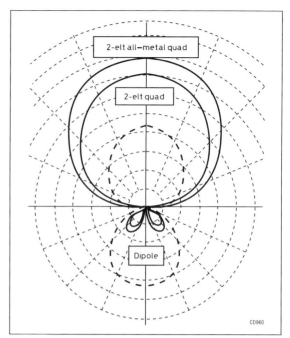

Fig 5.17. Reference dipole, standard quad and all-metal quad polar diagrams

and the adjustment of the gamma match was straightforward. The measured vertical and horizontal patterns, shown in Fig 5.16, were very similar to those given in the above book.

Quad

The elements of this model were constructed using 18 SWG stranded plastic-covered wire. The driven element was fed directly with coaxial cable and the reflector tuned with a stub. The driven element length and the reflector stub were adjusted for a compromise between front-to-back ratio and gain.

All-metal quad

The evolution of this all-metal version of the quad is described in more detail in Chapter 7. I was curious to know how it compared with more conventional types because the 14MHz version worked so well. Patterns for the standard quad and the all-metal quad are shown in Fig 5.17.

The bird-cage quad

This antenna, designed by G4ZU, is a quad with an X-type configuration; its construction is described in Chapter 7. It was tested, first with the parasitic element tuned as a reflector, then as a director. When

the parasitic element was tuned as a director the antenna exhibited a higher gain.

The driven element was gamma matched and the parasitic tuned for maximum front-to-back ratio. No amount of adjustment would reduce the two lobes radiated from the back and the polar diagram shown in Fig 5.18 was the best that could be attained.

ZL-Special

The ZL-Special is a two-element driven array with the driven element connected direct to the feeder and the reflector driven from this feedpoint via a two-wire transposed feedline. The element and spacing dimensions were obtained from a published HF design [3] and scaled to VHF. It was fed directly with 75Ω coaxial cable. On initial tests the SWR was found to exceed 3:1.

No improvement to either the high SWR or the gain could be achieved by experimenting with the lengths of the elements and phasing lines, although the horizontal pattern was good.

The ZL-Special antenna design is not as simple as it might first appear.

Mismatch losses

This VHF model of the ZL-Special exhibited good directivity but the measured gain was slightly less

This is particularly the case with calculated antenna gains. The MININEC derivative computer program (see Chapter 8) calculates antenna gains with *free-space* dBd (dipole in free space) as the reference, even when the antenna under test is calculated against ground.

All antennas have an interaction with ground, even a VHF antenna 10m high – see Fig 5.20. Unless you are designing antennas for aircraft or spacecraft it is important to consider ground effects at all times when measuring antenna gain.

Measurement of the vertical or elevation directive pattern is reasonably easy using the simple equipment already described.

The only additional item of equipment required is a rectangular or square-section wooden mast with pulley and carriage for adjusting the FSM height – see Fig 5.12. This allows the FSM and loop antenna to be moved up and down against calibration marks which coincide with vertical angles relative to the AUT. These calibration marks are dependent on the length of the range and the height of the AUT mast.

The lower half of the mast must be adjustable so that the lowest calibration point is at the same height as the AUT. If the AUT height is adjusted then the FSM mast height must also be adjusted.

The results shown in Fig 5.21 were obtained using a 6m length FSM mast located 6m away from the AUT and sloped 59° (measured from the horizontal)

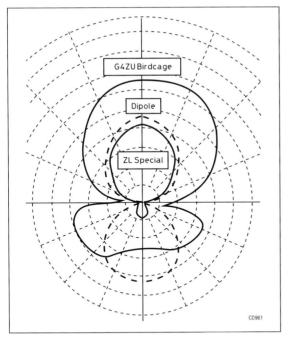

Fig 5.18. Polar diagrams of reference dipole, bird-cage quad and ZL-Special

than a dipole. The cause of this apparent loss was probably the mismatch which reduced the amount of power being fed to the antenna; the SWR relative power indicator will not give the correct relative level if the SWR is high when compared with a reference antenna whose SWR is low.

It is important that antennas or antenna models should be correctly matched to the feeder (SWR of 1.3:1 or less) if comparative gain measurements are to have any meaning.

Plotting vertical or elevation plane diagrams

The interaction between the antenna and ground has already been discussed. This interaction is complex, so to simplify matters when performing antenna mathematical models antenna gains are quoted as 'free space', that is with no ground present (see Fig 5.19).

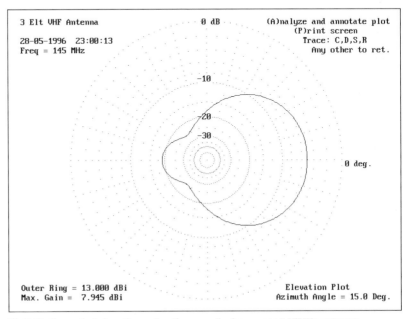

Fig 5.19. Computed elevation polar diagram of a free-space 145MHz antenna

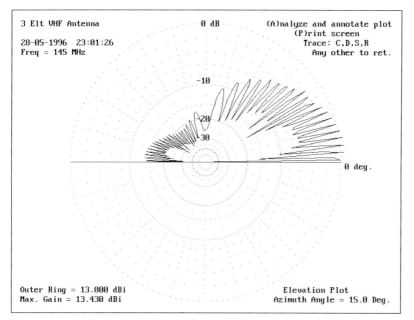

Fig 5.20. Computed elevation polar diagram of a 145MHz antenna 10m high

POLAR DIAGRAMS USING A SENSITIVE FSM

Test equipment

The commercial FSM gives more flexibility for producing polar diagrams. This is generally because it is sensitive and usually fitted with a switched, calibrated attenuator. Less power is required for the source and a signal generator can be used instead of a transmitter, provided it has a high enough output. The RF output of the signal generator is usually calibrated, so relative signal levels are easier to establish. Additionally, there is generally less restriction on frequency range compared with using a transmitter as the source.

A home-made FSM can be used provided it has all the features described above.

The FSM has a limitation – the meter. Generally this is an analogue meter and, because it is linear, it can only span a range of about 14dB. A large sensitivity range is normally accomplished by using several sensitivity ranges controlled by a switched attenuator. This switching is inconvenient for plotting polar diagrams manually and impossible if the polar diagram plotting is computerised. This is because of the need to keep switching sensitivity ranges as the polar diagram is plotted. Modern FSMs with digital signal readout and a good dynamic range overcome these problems to a certain extent.

A given sensitivity range can be extended by disconnecting the meter and replacing it with a resistor. The voltage across this resistor is then measured on a digital voltmeter. The range is not then limited by the meter but by the dynamic range of the FSM.

All AUTs should be tested with a transmitter to check that a low SWR exists before running the tests using the signal generator.

The procedure for plotting the polar diagrams is very similar to that for the diode FSM.

towards the AUT. The AUT mast should ideally, of course, be an arc with the AUT at the focus. This would, however, make the construction of such a mast unduly complicated. The distortion introduced by the straight FSM mast does not appear to invalidate the tests; the effects of AUT height above ground can be seen clearly seen in the diagram.

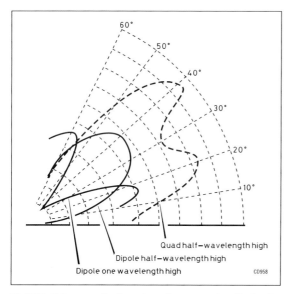

Fig 5.21. Reference dipole and quad, measured vertical polar diagrams

POLAR DIAGRAM PLOTTING USING A COMPUTER

Polar diagram plotting can be automated using a computer. This method takes much of the work out of plotting polar diagrams and speeds up the process considerably.

Storage of data and the application of functions for normalisation and conversion from linear to log scales etc are tasks amenable to computerisation. Additionally, very complex polar diagrams can be plotted that would otherwise be difficult using the manual method.

A method of converting the analogue data from the FSM to a digital form is required. A computer possessing a suitable built-in analogue-to-digital converter (ADC) is preferable, otherwise a special ADC has to be bought or constructed.

Suitable software is required. It should enable the computer to take the analogue data from the FSM and display it on the screen as an evolving polar diagram while the AUT is rotated.

Provision can be made for linking the computer to the rotator to supply heading information for the software. This can be done with a position digital encoder and input through the I/O port. Alternatively the system is simplified by having an adjustable polar plotting time which is set so that it is equal to the time taken for the rotator to make one complete revolution.

A minor disadvantage of this method is that the operator must ensure the rotator and plot routine commence simultaneously.

The layout and connections of the test equipment required to create polar diagrams using a computer are shown in Fig 5.22. The signal generator controls should also be accessible to the operator so that signal levels can be controlled easily.

The AUT antenna rotator control panel and computer keyboard should also be sited together because, if using the simplified method described above, they have to be operated together.

The FSM antenna, reference dipole and AUTs should be correctly matched to the feeder using a transmitter with an SWR bridge or an impedance meter. This is to minimise pick-up or radiation on the feeders.

Use of an IBM PC compatible computer

As was stated above, a computer with an ADC is required. All my early work was done using a BBC computer, which had the advantage of an ADC addressable in BBC BASIC. However, the software has been modified to run on the more widely used IBM PC compatible computer. A listing of the program is given in Appendix 3. It is also available on a disk [8].

Measuring equipment and the antenna test range

The following items are required to plot antenna polar diagrams using a computer. Details of the different items of equipment are described later.

- A field-strength meter (FSM) with remote analogue or digital field-strength level indicator. FSMs are discussed later in this chapter.
- Loop or dipole antenna for field-strength meter.
- Field-strength meter (FSM) or receiver with calibrated signal level indicator.
- Signal generator with calibrated variable RF output, or a transmitter with variable power output.
- Antenna under test (AUT).
- AUT rotator mechanism, mast and position indicator. The position indicator can be a piece of white cardboard held to the mast by a clip or clothes peg.
- SWR meter, coaxial cable and connectors.
- IBM PC-type computer.
- Analogue-to-digital converter (ADC)
- Digital voltmeter to monitor the signal level at the input to the ADC.
- Software to enable the data to be displayed as a polar diagram and to save and retrieve data from files.

The equipment is connected together as shown in Fig 5.22. The layout of my back garden antenna range is shown in Figs 5.23 and 5.24, while some of the antenna models are shown in Figs 5.24, 5.25 and 5.26.

MEASURING EQUIPMENT CONSIDERATIONS

Field-strength meters, signal generators and transmitters

When using a computer to plot the polar diagram, volts rather than millivolts are required to drive the ADC. The FSM should be able to provide a voltage range that is roughly equal to the input range of the ADC for greatest accuracy. If the input signal to the ADC only spans only from 0 to 2.5V on a 0 to 5V ADC converter, errors are effectively doubled.

If you use a simple diode FSM then a transmitter with a power output of up to 10W is required. This option has the advantage of simplicity. The transmitter should be stable and free of spurious outputs. The disadvantage of using this amount of power is that it can cause interference with other users. Frequent

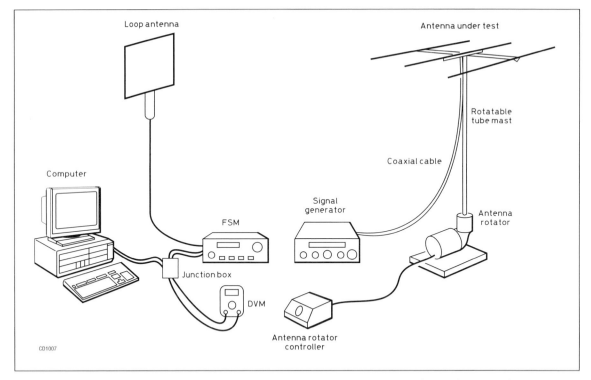

Fig 5.22. Equipment required to produce antenna polar diagrams using a computer. The AUT is energised by the signal generator. The computer takes analogue data from the FSM and displays it on the screen as an evolving polar diagram while the AUT is rotated

announcements stating your callsign are necessary to conform to the terms of the UK licence.

Use a modified receiver or commercial FSM, and use a signal generator to energise the AUT.

I use this approach mainly because I have found equipment that is suitable. Ex-military or commercial signal generators are easy to come by. They should have an output of about 100mV and the level should be calibrated, either on a meter on a dial. An alternative approach, which has not been tried, is to modulate the signal generator and measure the output of the audio system of the receiver to determine the signal level.

Fig 5.23. The computerised antenna range does not have to be expensive. The FSM is a converted FM broadcast receiver (left). The VHF signal generator was obtained at a flea market for around £15 ($23) and the old XT computer cost £50 ($75). The quad antenna under test can be seen in the background

may be necessary. This is connected into the feeder between the pickup antenna and the receiver antenna socket.

Using a switched attenuator has a further advantage. If you wish to make relative gain comparisons in decibels, the S-meter calibration is unimportant and is used only to set a reference level indicator. The relative decibel levels are then indicated by the switch settings on the attenuator. A suitable attenuator is described in the ARRL *Handbook* [5].

Analogue-to-digital converter (ADC)

A method of converting the analogue data from the FSM to a digital form is required. The IBM PC is not fitted with an ADC so some extra hardware is required. There are a whole range of ADCs that can be used. They can be constructed on an I/O board to plug into the expansion slot or input via the RS232 port or even the printer port. The one I have used is based on a simple, commercially available device called the Pico ADC-10, which plugs into the printer port. It has a range of 0 to 5V. Availability of this ADC and other information is given in Appendix 3.

AUT rotator

The AUT can be rotated by a TV antenna rotator but it does have a couple of disadvantages. The rate of rotation is rather low and it is not normally continuously rated, getting rather hot after a couple of measurements.

I use a motor and gear box originally used for some industrial application, which gives a rotation speed of about 15 seconds. It is convenient for the rotator to be able to rotate in either direction to prevent the feeder getting wrapped too tightly round the mast during successive measurements.

Fig 5.24. Three-element Yagi. The elements are constructed from 1.6mm hard-drawn copper wire fixed to a wooden boom with staples

Sensitive field-strength meters are not so plentiful but they can be obtained at radio rally flea markets; I have collected five over the years. A receiver is rather sensitive as a FSM and a switched attenuator

Software

A listing of the complete program is given in Appendix 3. The program performs the following tasks:

1. Displays a graticule with

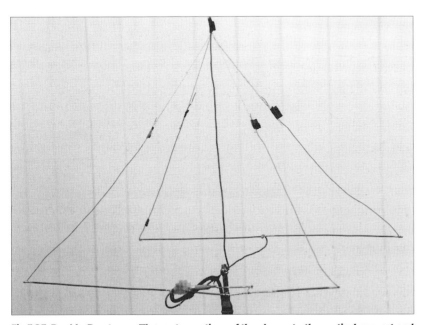

Fig 5.25. Double-D antenna. The centre sections of the elements, the vertical support and the boom are made from 1.6mm hard-drawn copper wire. The element ends are of thin multi-strand hook-up wire fixed to thin nylon cord supports with insulation tape

Fig 5.26. Quad antenna. The spreaders are of 10mm square wood and the elements are made from 1mm bare copper single-strand wire. The spreaders are connected to the 15mm copper tube boom using L-shaped metal fixings and hose clamps

heading information to provide a reference for the polar plot.

2. Samples analogue data from the FSM and plots it as a polar diagram over the graticule as the AUT is rotated.

3. Saves antenna data to a file and re-displays it when required.

In addition, provision is made for adjusting parameters, such as aligning the plotting time to the AUT rotation speed, and adjusting the sampled values for the required polar display.

The software is written in BASIC and is given as a listing; it will run in GW-BASIC and QUICK-BASIC. The program is menu driven and straightforward to use.

If you save the file using a suffix such as .DAT or .ANT then you will have to add it to the file name when you recall the file.

To keep the system as simple as possible there is no provision for the computer to read the AUT heading. Because there is such a range of IBM PC compatible computers, all operating at different speeds, the plotting time and the AUT rotation time must be adjusted so that they are identical. This adjustment is selected at the menu and has a default time of 30, which can be modified (line 1610).

A gain factor is used to modify the plot with reference to the graticule and is selected from within the program. If a scale factor is not entered then a default of 1.5 is assumed. This default can be modified at line 1200.

The plot scale can be modified to display data, previously stored on disk, as linear, log or ARRL log-periodic. The significance of these scales is described in Chapter 4.

The subroutine for acquiring the analogue data from the FSM, at line 630, will have to be modified if an ADC other than the ADC-10 is used.

The number of circles and spokes that make up the graticule can be altered (graticule subroutine at line 270).

The number of dots that make up the lines of the graticule can be changed. REM statements show where these changes can be made. The program will execute faster with a low number of dots. A higher number of dots will look better if the plot is printed.

The plotting points that make up the signal level line are made up of circles. The thickness of the line can be altered by changing the diameter of the circle, lines 1010 and 1410.

The display can be sent to the printer using the PRINT SCREEN key. Normally, this will only print ASCII characters but can be changed to print graphics by executing GRAPHICS.EXE before GWBASIC.EXE.

Measurement procedure

This measurement procedure assumes a signal generator and a sensitive FSM or receiver is being used.

1. Check that the AUT(s) are matched to the co-axial feeder using a transmitter and a SWR meter.

2. Connect the equipment as shown in Fig 5.22. The connection to the computer is made via the ADC (not shown). When making measurements in the 145MHz band I place the AUT just over 1m high. The measurement antenna is placed 4

or 5m high (12 to 15ft) high, and the two antennas are spaced about 12m (40ft) apart.

3. Place all the operating equipment, such as the
computer, the FSM output voltmeter, the FSM
frequency control and the AUT rotator so that
they can be operated or seen from an operating
position. The AUT mast and the position indicator must also be visible from the operating
position.

4. Point the AUT at the FSM antenna. Adjust the
signal generator and FSM to the measurement
frequency. Adjust the signal generator level and
the FSM attenuator or gain control so that the
output is appropriate to the ADC in use.

5. Rotate the antenna through 360° while watching the FSM signal level. In this way you can
gain a mental picture of the AUT pattern. It is
useful to make this preliminary check to ensure
the antenna is working reasonably well before
going through the routine of plotting the data.

6. Measure the AUT rotation time using a watch
with a seconds display. Select T at the menu and
adjust the plotting time. The program inserts a
signal so that a circle is plotted.

7. The program is written so that it starts at 90°
and rotates anti-clockwise. Set the AUT to so
that it is 90° to the FSM antenna. Set the indicator on the AUT mast so that it is pointing towards you.

8. Select option P at the menu. Start the AUT rotation and the software plotting simultaneously.

9. Check that the gain level is correct. If you are
making comparative plots of, say, a dipole and
a three-element beam then the gain should be
set so that the polar diagram of the antenna with
the greatest gain is contained within the
graticule.

10. When the polar plot is complete check that the
orientation is correct relative to the graticule. If
not, alter the position of the marker on the AUT
mast and repeat the plot.

11. When you are satisfied with the plot, the data
can stored on the disk by returning to the menu
and selecting option L.

Graticule/signal-strength calibration

The graticule on the display can be roughly calibrated so that the concentric circles represent relative field strength in decibels.

The AUT is pointed at the FSM antenna and the
program is started in the PLOT mode without turning the antenna. The attenuator control on the signal

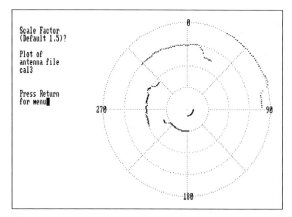

**Fig 5.27. Calibration plot. The small wobble in signal strength
is caused by the attenuator being adjusted to put the signal on
the circle**

generator is set to minimum and then increased
(decrease in signal) until the signal aligns with the
outer circle of the graticule. Repeat the measurements for the other circles, noting the difference in
decibels each time.

The program can be stopped while the attenuator
control is adjusted using the PAUSE key. Just press
RETURN to restart the program. An example of a
calibration plot is shown in Fig 5.27.

SOME RESULTS OF PLOTTING POLAR
DIAGRAMS WITH A COMPUTER

The following are some polar diagrams plotted using
an IBM PC compatible computer with the program in
Appendix 3. They are given to show the strengths
and limitations of the measurement process.

The polar diagrams shown in Figs 5.28 and 5.29
were plotted using a linear FSM (heterodyne voltmeter). The polar diagram in Fig 5.28 is shown plotted
on a linear scale. The polar diagram in Fig 5.29
shows the same antenna using a log scale; the
function is achieved in software. Note that the scale
factor, which is used to adjust the input data so that
the plot fills the graticule, has to be altered so that it
retains a reasonable size after the log conversion has
been applied. The disadvantage of using software to
extract a log plot is that the data, originally plotted
on a linear scale, does not have enough resolution to
give a good printout.

The polar diagrams shown in Figs 5.30 and 5.31
are of a three-element beam using the same FSM
and software as used to plot the dipole, shown
above. The ARRL log plot of a three-element beam
shown in Fig 5.32 was obtained using the modified

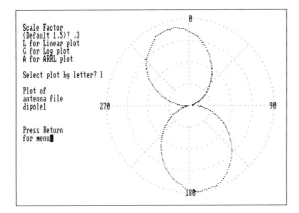

Fig 5.28. Linear plot of a dipole using a linear FSM

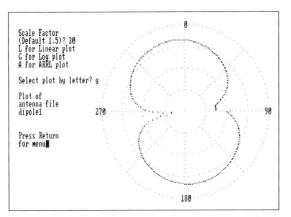

Fig 5.29. Log plot of dipole from data obtained using a linear FSM

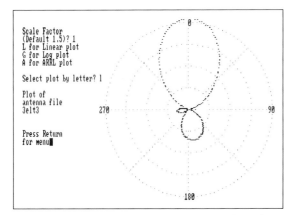

Fig 5.30. Linear plot of a three-element beam using a linear FSM. Spurious lobe caused by faulty construction and matching

VHF broadcast receiver described in Chapter 4 and no software function is necessary.

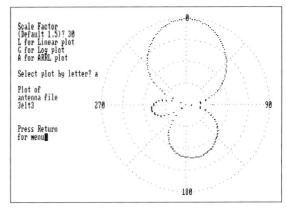

Fig 5.31. ARRL log plot of the three-element beam in Fig 5.30. Data was obtained using a linear FSM. This scale is useful for examining the spurious lobe

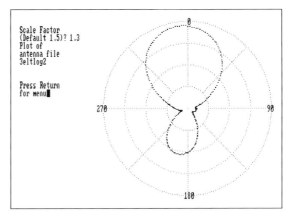

Fig 5.32. ARRL log plot of a three-element beam using the modified VHF broadcast receiver. The software has been modified so that no software function is requested or applied. Real antenna polar diagrams are never as perfect as predicted by software modelling programs shown in Chapter 8

The modified VHF broadcast receiver is now my preferred FSM for plotting polar diagrams. Because it has an approximate log function I have simplified the software by taking out the log type functions. This method produces superior data for the purposes of plotting polar diagrams. The polar diagram in Fig 5.33 is of the double-D compact antenna (see Chapter 7) and the plot shown in Fig 5.34 is that of the quad shown in Fig 5.26.

MEASUREMENT OF ABSOLUTE ANTENNA GAIN AT VHF

This method measures the gain of an antenna by comparing it with an antenna of known gain.

Because of the effects of ground, described early

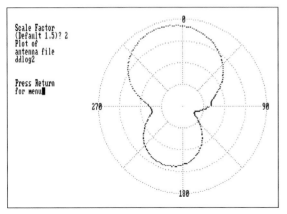

Fig 5.33. ARRL log plot of the double-D compact antenna, using the modified VHF broadcast receiver FSM

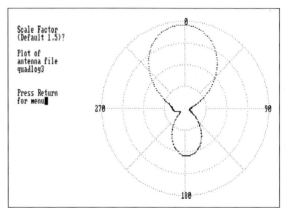

Fig 5.34. ARRL log plot of the quad antenna, using the modified VHF broadcast receiver FSM

in this chapter, any change in the position of any of the antennas used in the test can affect the recorded gain. This difficulty is overcome by making several gain measurements with the antennas in different positions, and taking the average of all these measurements. The measuring equipment is set up as illustrated in Fig 5.35.

Unlike all previous tests so far described, this test arrangement operates with the receiver connected to the AUT. The test range is flooded with a weak RF field provided by a source transmitter connected to

an antenna which is located a few wavelengths from the AUT.

The source, which should have a variable output, can be a low-power transmitter or a signal generator. This output should be monitored during the test to ensure that its level remains constant.

The receiver section of the test system uses an attenuator combined with a receiver, or transceiver, with an S-meter. A sensitive field-strength meter could also be used. The main advantage of this method is that the accuracy of measurements is not

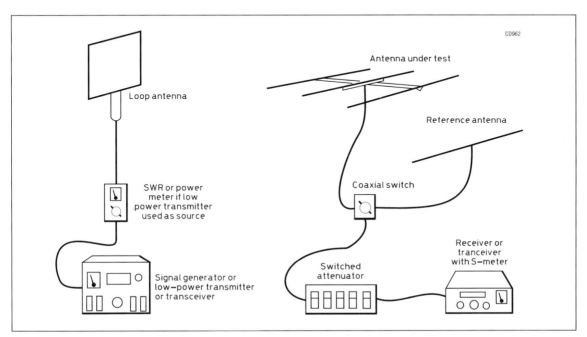

Fig 5.35. Equipment required to measure antenna gain using the receiver/attenuator method

restricted by the inevitable inaccuracy of the S-meter, which in this application is used only as a reference level indicator.

The accuracy of the measurements depends mainly on the accuracy and resolution of the attenuator – see Chapter 4.

In practice the method should give accuracies in the order of ± 1dBd. Remember that the gain figure produced by this method is gain relative to a reference dipole at the same height as the AUT, not relative to a dipole in free space, often used with antenna gain computer programs as described in Chapter 8.

Both the AUT and the reference dipole should be well matched to their feeder cables.

The S-meter on a receiver will only give the correct indication if the RF gain control is at maximum, so it is important that the source has a variable output so that the range of test parameters falls within the capabilities of the receiver test set-up.

1. Set up the source antenna in the clear at 8λ or more from the AUT. The source antenna should be positioned at angle of greatest signal strength of the AUT. In practical terms, at 145MHz this would require an AUT/source spacing of around 16m. The source antenna height should be 6m high assuming the AUT and reference antennas were 1λ high (2m).

2. The AUT and the reference antenna should be placed side-by-side at least 2λ apart. If they are too close they could have an unpredictable effect on each other's gain figures. With both antennas facing the source antenna the coupling between them should be minimal.

3. Switch to the reference antenna. Adjust the attenuator for an easily identifiable S-meter reading of around six to nine S-points.

4. Switch to the AUT and adjust its position for maximum signal. Adjust the attenuator for the same reading as obtained with the reference antenna. Record this attenuator reading. The difference between the two attenuator readings is the gain (or loss!) of the AUT relative to the reference antenna.

5. Repeat the process several times, with the reference and AUT antennas in slightly different positions.

6. Record all readings in your notebook. An average of six such readings should give a reasonable comparative gain figure. The feeders to the reference antenna and the AUT will also have losses, so they should be the same length.

Although the dipole is normally used as the reference antenna, other reference antennas may be more appropriate. A high-accuracy antenna standard has been developed by the National Bureau of Standards (NBS) in the USA.

PERFORMANCE ASSESSMENT OF FULL-SIZED HF ANTENNAS
Ground-wave tests with another station
The only way to obtain optimum performance from an HF antenna is to adjust it *in situ*, hence the emphasis on fitting it to a suitable mast – see Chapter 6.

One of the most frequently used and reliable methods of testing a rotatable HF beam antenna is with another station some distance away, say 2 to 3km (1 to 2 miles). Tests can be done at a closer range using low transmitter power or with an attenuator fitted into the antenna feeder of the receiver. As stated earlier, the receiver RF gain must be set at maximum for the S-meter to function correctly.

Tests can be conducted at greater distances, but it normally requires a higher-gain antenna at the opposite end of the link. Generally, at these greater distances, the S-meter readings are much lower but nevertheless provide valuable data if carried out at night when interference via ionospheric propagation is very low.

Tests can also be performed using a HF mobile station. The main advantage of using a mobile is that it can be sited at a distance that is more compatible with transmitter power and AUT gain. It is also easier to select a path free of power and telephone lines, which may disturb the radiation pattern.

Antenna testing using two stations has proved, over a period of many years, to be a reliable indication of the directivity of a HF beam antenna.

Tests on VHF models, and computed directivity patterns on computers, show that at different measurement angles the directivity remains fairly constant, although the gain at different measurement angles varies considerably.

Using a signal generator at close range
An indication of directivity can be obtained by using a modulated signal generator as a signal source. This is located at least 2λ away from the AUT. In practical terms, if the antenna is located on a mast at the bottom of the garden the signal generator can

be located inside the loft of the house in the apex of the roof. The AUT is connected to a receiver or transceiver with an S-meter which is viewed while rotating the antenna.

In this case a low-cost signal generator can be used because the signal level can be controlled by varying the length of the source antenna. If the AUT is located on, or close to the house, then this method may be impractical because of the problem of siting the signal generator.

Using a field-strength meter at close range

Directivity measurements using the signal generator method can be impractical if there are a lot of strong signals present. Under these circumstances it is advantageous to energise the AUT with a transmitter or transceiver and measure the field strength using a sensitive FSM (the FSM designed by G4VSO, described in Chapter 4, would be suitable) or a receiver with an inefficient antenna and/or attenuator. The FSM meter or receiver S-meter is then viewed while rotating the antenna. These measurements are best performed using an arrangement similar to that illustrated in Fig 5.6 for VHF test measurements. The only difficulty is that the distance between the AUT and the FSM can be quite considerable at HF, making it difficult to view the signal level meter while rotating the antenna. There are two ways this difficulty can be overcome:

1. View the signal level meter through binoculars. I have used this method using an old professional HF FSM (Radio Interference Measuring Set Model No: RMSI made by EMI). This instrument had the advantage of having a very large signal-strength meter calibrated in decibels. The FSM was placed on the flat roof of the house extension about 2λ from the antenna.

2. Connect a meter to the FSM via a long cable so that it is more easily viewed, as shown in Fig 5.6. This method is more accurate but it does mean that you have to break into the FSM and find somewhere to connect the remote meter. This extra meter, if connected in series or parallel with the existing meter, will affect the calibration. The best method is to remove the existing meter and use it as the remote meter.

It must be stressed that these measurements are concerned only with directivity and not gain. Although gain varies considerably at different angles of radiation, directivity remains fairly constant – see the sections through a polar diagram on p62.

PARASITIC BEAM ANTENNA ADJUSTMENT
The importance of optimisation of a beam antenna

A few sentences on the adjustment of beam antennas so far discussed are included because they answer one of the most frequently asked questions when I have given lectures at radio clubs.

All installations benefit from some tuning and most well-known DX operators have spent a considerable amount of time adjusting the antenna for maximum efficiency, particularly when a new one is constructed.

It is almost impossible to get complete reproducibility of any design. All installations are located in different environments, made of slightly different materials and situated at different heights. For example, if you use bare copper wire instead of plastic-insulated wire for wire elements it will be necessary to multiply the wire dimension figures, given in the design data on the wire double-D in Chapter 7, by 1.04. (Plastic-covered wire appears to have a velocity factor of about 0.96. Try measuring the resonance of two identical lengths of wire, one with insulation and the other without to check this.) Wire element resonances can also be dependent on types of insulator and methods of connecting the wire to the insulator.

If the performance of an antenna is not optimised a promising new design can be prematurely abandoned because of an unwarranted inferior performance.

Ideally, the antenna should be adjusted *in situ*. In the case of a VHF antenna it may be adjusted at a height of 1λ without any difficulty and there will be very little change when it is raised to 10λ. Adjusting an HF antenna *in situ* is only possible if the antenna is mounted on top of a flat roof or on a fixed tower with a working platform at the top of it, with the antenna element lengths and feeder matching adjustments easily accessible.

Before an antenna is adjusted ensure that the dimensions of the elements and spacings are correct, either by checking the lengths with available design data or by measuring resonances with a GDO (see Chapter 3). If you are working with a new design adjust the driven element to the resonant frequency, the reflector to 5% lower than resonance and directors 5% higher as a starting point.

When measuring the driven element resonance, disconnect the feeder and short the feedpoint. When the feeder cable is connected it may cause many very deep false resonances.

Adjusting element length

Metal elements

Elements made of different-diameter telescoped tubes clamped with hose clamps are easy to adjust. Just loosen the clamp and slide the tube to the required length. It is a good idea to make a mark on one of the tubes to provide a reference in case it is necessary to return to this point during the adjustments.

Wire elements

Often, design data does not include the extra length of wire that may be needed to fix it to the insulator. The best way of making adjustments is to make the element too long and to fold the excess wire down along the element. In this way the elements can be made adjustable. Tape the excess wire back along the element away from the insulator so it can be cut off when the adjustments are completed.

Adjusting an antenna *in situ*

This is relatively simple:

1. Adjust the matching of the antenna to the feeder. If the feeder is connected directly to the element this adjustment is achieved by altering the length of the driven element. If a matching device is used, such as a gamma match, then this should be adjusted. Optimise the matching using the noise bridge, as described in Chapter 2, or by aiming for the lowest standing wave ratio using an SWR bridge.
2. Adjust the parasitic elements for maximum front-to-back ratio or maximum gain.
3. Readjust the driven element for the best match to the feeder.

Adjusting an HF antenna on a fold-over mast

It is not possible to adjust an HF antenna on the ground, then install it on top of a mast and hope that it will give optimum performance. In practice, the antenna is adjusted, hauled up into position, then the performance is checked. The antenna is then brought down again for further adjustment. The whole process can be very laborious unless you have a fold-over mast; this is the reason that the construction of these is given in Chapter 6.

1. Fold the mast over so that the antenna reflector element is nearest the ground, with the beam pointing upwards, as shown in Fig 6.5 (dotted outline) of Chapter 6. The driven element matching system (gamma match), or length

adjustment, should then be accessible using step ladders.
2. Adjust the driven element as described above in step 1 of 'Adjusting an antenna *in situ*'.
3. Raise the antenna and check the performance as described later in this chapter – see 'Performance assessment of full-size HF antennas'.
4. Repeat these adjustments as often as is necessary to optimise the antenna.
5. If the antenna has director element(s), lower the mast so that these elements are nearest the ground. Adjust the length(s), raise the antenna and check the performance.
6. When the parasitic element adjustments are complete, re-adjust the driven element feeder matching.

All stages of antenna adjustment should be documented, including element lengths and performance. This is essential to follow the trends in change of performance, and to be able to go back to the previous settings if a different set of adjustments are to be tried.

Once the antenna is adjusted for optimum performance, record all antenna dimensions, element resonances and performance figures. This information is very important because it is the reference for further work. Also, if you come up with a new design this information will be crucial if you wish to make it the subject of an article for a radio magazine.

Increasing the feed impedance of wire elements

It is possible to make compact versions of wire antennas, such as the double-D, accepting that they may be not as efficient as the aluminium-tube versions. The main difficulty is matching the driven element to the feeder. Although a gamma match can be used, wire elements are more conveniently fed by connecting the feeder cable direct, particularly if any multibanding is involved.

At resonance the impedance will be too low and a degree of mismatch will occur. The difficulty can be overcome by increasing the length of the elements until the resistive component is 50 or 75Ω, depending on the impedance of the coaxial cable. The reactive component will now be inductive and can be cancelled out using two capacitors, connected in series with the elements, each side of the feedpoint. The value of these capacitors can be determined using variable capacitors which are then replaced with a fixed ones once the values have been found. An impedance measuring method, as described in Chapter 2, will greatly simplify these adjustments.

REFERENCES

[1] 'Assessing HF aerials using VHF aerials', Peter Dodd, G3LDO, *Radio Communication* December 1972.

[2] 'Element lengths for three-element Yagis', *ARRL Antenna Handbook*, 1970 edn. (These graphs have been repeated in all subsequent editions and appear on page 11-11 of the 1988 edition.)

[3] *Radio Communication Handbook*, 5th edn, ed D Biddulph, G8DPS, RSGB, 1994, Chapter 12.

[4] *Antenna/RCS Measurement Products*, Hewlett Packard publication 5958-0396.

[5] 'Field strength meters', Doug DeMaw, W1FB, *QST* March 1985.

[6] *ARRL Handbook*, 1990 edn, pp25-36 to 25-38.

[7] *ARRL Antenna Handbook*, 15th edition, pp27-31 to 27-36.

[8] 'Data acquisition using an IBM computer', Mike Gray, N8KDD, *73 Amateur Radio Today* August 1991.

[9] *ARRL Antenna Compendium*, Vol 4. A computer disk with the antenna plotting software (plus many more programs) accompanies the book.

6 Materials, masts and coaxial cable

THIS chapter discusses materials and construction techniques for experimental antennas and masts. Experimental antennas need not be constructed to a high engineering standard for many years of trouble-free use, as is the case with commercial antennas. However, they should be constructed to a standard that is safe and does not compromise the performance of a particular configuration. Any structure that allows the geometric dimensions of the antenna to change appreciably in a moderate wind, or when the antenna is being rotated, should be avoided.

Antenna support systems are also described in detail. The wisdom of describing home-made antenna masts when there are many such items on the market may be questioned. There are two reasons – cost and suitability.

Commercial masts are normally of lattice construction and have a telescoping and fold-over capability. Many antenna experimenters do use these types of masts but a drawback to experimental work with these types of support is that they take some time and effort to raise and lower. Additionally, the winch cables are not designed for the continual raising and lowering normally encountered when a lot of antenna experimental work is being done over a period of time. For this reason I advocate the use of a home-made structure that is easy to raise and lower; two such simple designs are described in this chapter. Another advantage of the fold-over mast is that it can be quickly folded over if gale force winds are forecast. Antenna masts that discourage experimenting with the antennas should be avoided.

The choice of materials for antennas is important, the most common being aluminium, copper wire and copper tube. The material used for the elements should have conductivity commensurate with the radiation resistance and be both strong and lightweight.

A knowledge of the length and the quality of transmission line, particularly coaxial cable, is very important when experimenting with antennas. A description on how to measure electrical length and loss of coaxial cable is given, using test equipment described in earlier chapters.

MATERIALS

Material for masts and antennas may be bought from dealers in steel and aluminium piping and tubing. The diameters of this material can be selected so that sections telescope into each other to make up long masts or elements.

I generally buy antenna material from scrap metal yards. Antenna construction and experimenting costs can be reduced considerably by using materials from these sources because they are sold at scrap weight values. A disadvantage of scrap material is that it very rarely comes in sections whose diameters fit neatly into each other or lengths that are convenient; methods are described later in the chapter for dealing with the construction difficulties caused by this. If you are really into antenna experimenting in a big way then it pays to visit the scrap metal yard regularly because specific items are rarely found during one visit. Sometimes a scrap structure will inspire an idea to overcome an antenna design problem, or even form the basis for an entirely new structure, for example the roof rack mobile antenna in Chapter 7.

The policy of some scrap metal dealers is to reduce tubing and pipes to short lengths when it arrives on site so as to make it more manageable. Others keep long lengths because they consider it as a more marketable commodity in this form.

The best scrap metal yards are those located near an industrial estate. These contain a much more useful selection of material for antenna experimenters. Materials obtainable from scrap metal yards which are useful for antenna work are as follows:

Fig 6.1. Method of fixing the mast-to-boom and boom-to-element using aluminium plate and U-clamps

- Steel tubing (for antenna masts)
- Steel casing (for mast foundations)
- Steel angle material (for gin poles, clamps and guy rope anchors)
- Copper and aluminium tubing (for elements and booms)
- Paxolin, Bakelite or plastic sheet (insulators)
- Electrical wire (antenna elements)
- Electric motors and gearboxes (for rotators)
- Aluminium angle stock (quad and double-D spreaders)
- Aluminium plate (couplers for joining elements to booms and booms to masts, see Fig 6.1)

Steel tubing for masts

Steel tubing is the most common material found in a scrap metal yard. Tubing used for antenna masts should be free from damage and excessive corrosion.

The lower sections of a 12m (40ft) high steel self-supporting mast should be at least 100mm (4in) in diameter, with a wall thickness of 5mm.

Steel tubing is often available, threaded, with screw couplers. These couplers are fine for the purpose for which the tubing was designed, ie piping liquid or gas. When tubing is used for antenna supports it is often under some bending stress.

Couplers only have a short length of screw thread and will be a source of weakness when tubing is employed as an antenna mast, so do *not* be tempted into making a mast using these couplers.

Steel tubes should only be joined by employing lengths that telescope into each other, with at least 300mm (12in) of overlap and secured with a nut and bolt. Do not weld the sections together – a 12m section of steel tubing is very heavy and difficult to manage. It is much easier to assemble a mast in sections.

Ensure the tubing lengths will fit into each other. I once bought a length of tube for a section of an antenna mast. The smaller diameter tubing would not fit into this new section because the inside wall was partially furred with a hard calcite deposit caused by its previous use.

When a small-diameter pole is joined to larger-diameter pipe, eg scaffolding pole into 80mm (3in) pipe, metal strip or angle iron shims should be used to pack any space between the differing diameters before securing with a nut and bolt.

Copper tubing

Copper tubing is also relatively plentiful at scrap metal yards because of changes to central heating systems. Copper has a very good conductivity but is rather heavy so is not suitable for large HF antennas. It is, however, suitable for small compact HF antennas, mobile and VHF antennas. A further advantage of copper for the antenna experimenter is that there are a good selection of solderable couplings available, making it easy to construct unusual antenna geometries. In the UK the most common copper tubing diameters available are 16 and 22mm but some old scrap tubing may have

Fig 6.2. The Mk 1 mobile DDRR antenna constructed from copper tube. Dimensions of the Mk 2 are shown in Chapter 7

imperial dimensions so check these if the tubing is to be integrated with an existing structure.

Aluminium tubing

With the exception of scaffolding poles, aluminium tubing is the scarcest material in a scrap metal yard. This is because there are not many commodities in our society using this material, and where it is available it only comes in one-off items such as tent poles. Aluminium is normally stored in skips at a scrap metal yard so any aluminium tubing that arrives is quickly chopped up into short lengths. For this reason I usually buy any sensible lengths of lightweight tubing that is available.

There is a further type of material called *duralumin*, commonly used for aircraft construction and boat masts. It has the advantage of being lighter and stronger than aluminium but is more brittle. In fact almost all aluminium tube is an alloy of some sort because pure aluminium is rather malleable.

Copper wire

Most scrap electrical wire is usually heavily insulated and therefore too heavy for antenna elements, but occasionally lighter-weight material is available. Stranded copper wire without insulation is a rare commodity.

A cheap source of hard-drawn material is scrap outdoor telephone twin insulated wire, used (in the UK) to distribute underground cable to subscribers via a telegraph pole.

For long wire antennas the best material is 14 SWG hard-drawn copper wire. For wire beams insulated 14 to 16 SWG multi-strand flexible tinned copper wire is preferred.

Electric motors and gearboxes

Industrial scrap sometimes produces electric motors and gearboxes that may be modified for use as a rotator. Before you buy one of these ensure that the electric motor rotation is reversible. Most industrial motors and gearboxes are too large and heavy to be fitted on the top of a mast and will probably be more suited to a structure where the whole mast is rotated – see the counterweighted fold-over mast later in this chapter. In this case weight can be an advantage.

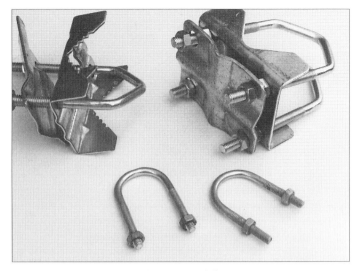

Fig 6.3. Selection of commercial antenna fittings

Other materials

The following materials are also very useful for antenna construction but, unlike the previously mentioned items, should be purchased new.

- *Hose clamps (Jubilee clips)*, the antenna experimenter's friend. They can be used for joining different-diameter sections of elements, joining sections of mast, joining wire to metal elements, joining quad spreaders to angle stock – the list is endless. They are readily available at all hardware, DIY and car (auto) part stores. When a clamp is used as part of an outdoor antenna structure, always coat it with a film of grease to prevent corrosion. Never use paint or varnish because this will make it unusable for further experimental projects.

- *Exhaust pipe clamps* (in the USA called *muffler clamps*). These are used to construct boom-to-mast and element-to-boom fittings.

- *TV-type fittings*. These fittings are convenient for connecting small-diameter booms to larger diameter masts so their use is normally restricted to VHF antennas.

- *Spreaders for wire beams*. Cane (lightweight bamboo) or glass-fibre rod – see Fig 6.4. Glass-fibre rods are preferred because they are lightweight and weather well. In addition they have excellent insulating properties.

- *Polypropylene rope*. Used as halyards and guys for pulling up, and keeping up, mast and antenna structures.

ANTENNA SUPPORTS

Experimenting with HF or large VHF antennas is much easier if a well-designed supporting structure is used. Placing a large antenna 10 to 25m (30 to 70ft) into the air with access for adjustment and tuning is a minor civil engineering project, unless of course the antenna is mounted on top of a building.

House chimney

The house chimney can be used for an antenna support as shown in Fig 6.5. Its main disadvantage is that adjustment and tuning can be difficult, and possibly dangerous to one not experienced with a life on the tiles.

This discourages experimentation unless access to the roof is easy. A chimney used as an antenna support should be in good repair. A double TV antenna chimney lashing kit will support a large VHF array or a medium-sized HF beam.

Fig 6.5. Example of a chimney lashing used to support a 21MHz double-D antenna

CONSTRUCTION OF FOLD-OVER ANTENNA MASTS

Safety

Safety should be a primary consideration when erecting antenna masts. *Never* erect an antenna and mast that could possibly come in contact with electric

Fig 6.4. Construction of a set of spreaders using canes

power lines. Never rush this sort of work. Always stop to consider the implications of the next move, particularly when dealing with heavy sections of steel tubing.

Do not use an antenna support structure that requires the joint efforts of all members of the local radio club to raise and lower it, although help in the construction stages is always welcome. The following are two designs for fold-over masts for single-handed operation.

The G2XK lightweight fold-over mast

Eric Knowles, G2XK, used the method described below to support a 6-element 10m beam on a 11m (36ft) boom at a height of 12m (40ft), using only 80mm (3in) diameter thin-wall duralumin tubing – see Fig 6.6. This large structure weathered many a gale that swept across the Vale of York.

There is nothing new in this method of supporting, or raising and lowering masts using guy ropes. The military have used it for many years for supporting fixed wire antennas.

The description that follows is of a similar mast, suitable for supporting a medium-sized experimental beam antenna. No special tools or welding equipment are required to construct this structure and it is an excellent support for experimental antennas provided the space for the guys is available. Do not

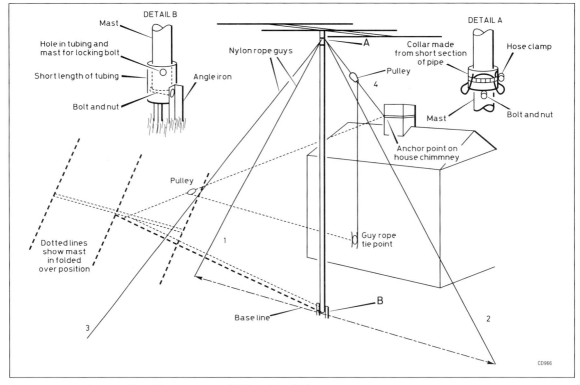

Fig 6.6. Constructional details of the G2XK type of lightweight fold-over mast

use steel tubing for the mast of this design because it is too heavy. Aluminium scaffolding pole is not really suitable either because of the weight/length ratio, although it could be used for short masts of up to 8m (25ft) high.

The layout is illustrated in Fig 6.7. The structure can be used with a fixed mast and rotator, or the mast can be rotated. In this case provision has to be made to allow the mast to rotate and be folded over. A minimum of four guy ropes are used.

The anchor point for guy wire 4 must be above ground level; the chimney of a nearby house is suitable with a lightweight structure. Guy ropes 1 and 2 are anchored along the baseline so that they retain the same tension when the mast is being erected or folded over. The length of guy rope 3 is adjusted so that it is under tension when the mast is in the vertical position. The original G2XK version used two sets of guy ropes but only one set is illustrated in Fig 6.6 for clarity.

This structure gains all its strength from its guys, so it is important that the guy ropes are strong and are connected securely, both at the anchorage and the top of the mast. Polypropylene rope (6mm

diameter) is a suitable material for the guys, which should ideally be at 45° to the mast. This angle can be reduced if space is limited but this increases the downward pressure on the mast in high winds and increases the chances of the mast buckling.

Commercial guy rope-to-mast bearings are available for the top of the mast (see Fig 6.7) and are recommended for this sort of application. The guys should be connected to the bearings with D-clamps.

If a commercial rotatable guy rope support bearing is unavailable, one can be constructed with short length of steel tube, slightly larger in diameter than the mast. Very thick wire loops can be fixed to the tube using one or two hose clamps. The top of the mast is inserted into this tubing. A bolt and nut, through the appropriate point on the mast, holds the guy support collar in position. Detail A of Fig 6.6 illustrates this.

The guy anchorage can be constructed from a 1m (40in) or so length of angle iron, cut to a point one end and a hole drilled in the other. This can be driven into the ground at 90° to the angle of pull. The guy anchorage may need to be more substantial for very large masts and/or if the soil is light and sandy.

Fig 6.7. Above: mast top guy ring bearing suitable for mast diameters up to 2in (upside-down view to show guy connection holes). Right: bearing suitable for base or mast top, for mast diameters up to 90mm (3½in). Supplied with fittings (not shown) to connect guys

The guy rope should be connected to the guy anchorage with a D-clamp. A pulley is required for the halyard to enable the mast to be hauled up; a good-quality clothes line pulley is suitable.

The base pivot point comprises two lengths of angle iron, cut to a point at one end and a hole drilled at the other. The two angle-iron pieces are driven into the ground with the holes aligned so that the pivot bolt can be fitted. If the design calls for a rotatable mast then a small section of tubing, whose internal diameter is slightly larger the outside diameter of the mast, is pivoted to the angle iron. The mast fits inside this section of tubing and is free to rotate. Holes can be drilled through the base tubing and the mast to enable the structure to be locked on any particular heading. Detail B of Fig 6.6 shows how this is done.

Lightweight sections of thin-wall tubing can be joined together using a short joining section, which is sliced longitudinally and sprung open using a screwdriver – see Fig 6.8. The two sections to be joined are forced into the joining section and clamped tight using hose clamps.

Counterweighted fold-over mast

This type of support is heavier and requires more construction effort. Its main advantage is that guy ropes are not absolutely necessary. I have built several masts to the same basic design, which is based on a 18m (60ft) tilt-over support designed by Alfred W Hubbard, K0OHM [1]. The original was designed to support a three-element tri-band beam and a rotator.

In this design all sections of steel tubing of the mast were welded together. It was partially counterweighted by filling the lower half of the tilt-over section with concrete and using a pulley to manage the remaining 160kg (350lb) pull.

The design of the base is interesting. It comprises a section of casing fixed in the ground with a concrete foundation. The gap between the mast and the casing is filled with sand and this removes the

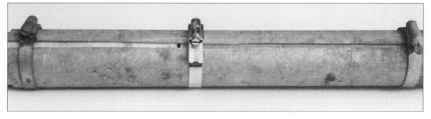

Fig 6.8. Method of joining light-weight tube of equal diameters

Fig 6.9. 12m (40ft) version of the mast in upright position, supporting a 14MHz metal quad antenna

Fig 6.10. 12m (40ft) mast and quad folded over

high-stress point that normally exists if the mast is set directly into concrete.

The sand acts as a buffer and allows the mast to flex within the base during high winds. The internal casing diameter should be around 50mm (2in) greater in diameter than the lowest section of the mast.

The largest mast of this design I have built [2] was 18m (60ft) high and supported an all-metal quad. If constructed using this design then it should

not be fully counterweighted. A top weight imbalance of around 45kg (100lb), controlled with a winch, will enable the momentum of the structure to be more easily managed.

Medium-size 12m (40ft) fold-over steel mast

This mast is counterweighted with approximately 15kg (30lb) of top weight so a pulley is not required. It takes about 15 seconds to raise the antenna mast into the vertical position. The mast is of relatively light weight; the top third of its length is 50mm (2in) diameter scaffolding pole. The whole mast is rotated manually using a handle fixed to the bottom of the mast.

The sections of steel tubing that make up the mast are telescoped into each other for about 300mm (12in) and secured by a bolt and nut. This allows the mast to be assembled, modified or repositioned much more easily than if the section was welded.

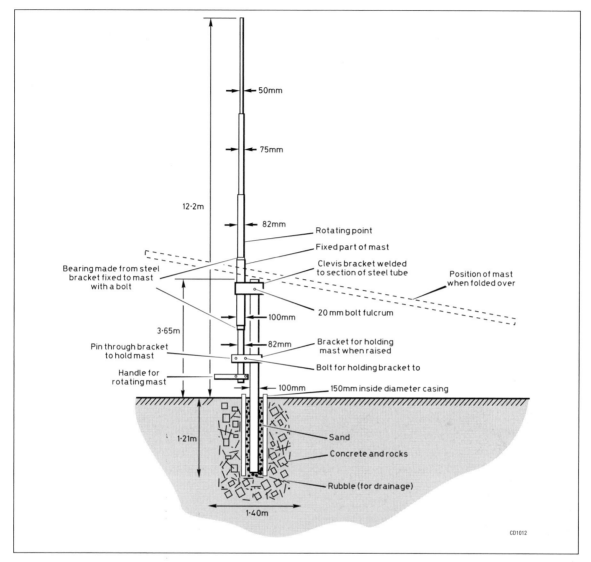

Fig 6.11. Counterweighted, fold-over rotatable 12m mast: constructional details

Although these structures can be built single-handed the following are areas where some assistance would be of help.

- Inserting the lower half of the mast into the base casing. Two ropes are tied to the top of the lower section, using the holes drilled for the pivot bolt. The section can then be placed with the lower end over the base casing and the top supported on a pair of step-ladders. The section can be raised using these ropes; at the same time the lower end is guided into the casing with a section of angle iron.

- Placing the clevis at the top of the mast to enable the bolt to be fitted and inserting the mast into the oversize piping used as the tiltable thrust bearing. These tasks can be eased by using a gin-pole. This can be constructed from steel angle iron and clamped to the mast with additional angle iron pieces or steel straps.

ANTENNA CONSTRUCTION

Antennas can be built using all-metal construction or with wire elements supported on spreaders.

All-metal antenna construction

The boom can be fixed to a tubular mast with a metal plate and car exhaust U-clamps as shown in Fig 6.1. Elements can be connected to booms in a similar manner.

Tapered elements can be constructed from lengths of aluminium alloy tubing with different diameters so that the lengths can be telescoped into each other. If the element sections do not fit snugly, the ends of joining sections may need to be modified as shown in Fig 6.12.

Additionally, if there is a relatively large difference between the two joining sections, a shim can be made from a short section of tubing, slit longitudinally. Any corrosion on any of the metal surfaces that make up the join should be removed with fine sandpaper. The surfaces are then wiped with a cloth and coated with a thin film of grease to prevent corrosion. The join is then clamped tight using a hose clamp. This method is far superior to using a nut and bolt where a new set of holes has to be drilled every time an adjustment to length is made. The hose clamp method also gives the joint a lower contact resistance.

If the antenna is constructed from tubing and insulated copper wire, such as the all-metal quad or the double-D (see Chapter 7) then a short length of the plastic insulation is stripped from the wire element extensions and fixed with hose clamps to the end of the metal elements used to isolate the metals.

It is particularly important that these copper wire/ aluminium tube joins are protected with grease to prevent corrosion. I have not found these sorts of joints to be a problem, possibly because my antennas are in a constant state of change and all

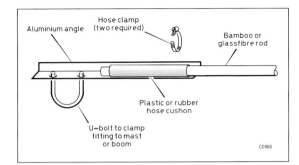

Fig 6.13. Mast to cane/glass-fibre support: constructional details

connections are protected with grease so that parts can be re-used. However, one authority [3] even goes as far as to state that contact between aluminium and copper should be avoided at all costs and that a small stainless steel washer should be used to provide isolation.

Wire beam construction

Insulating spreaders for wire beam antennas or helically wound elements can be constructed using cane (lightweight bamboo) or glass-fibre rod. The main disadvantage of these materials is that they can easily damaged by crushing at the support point. Special support is required to avoid damaging the ends and aluminium angle stock can be used. The length of this aluminium section depends on the size and the frequency range of the antennas to be supported – a 1m (3ft) length is suitable for a conventional multi-band quad or double-D. Two sections are required for a double-D or four for a quad. Two holes are drilled at the centre of each section – the distance apart will depend on the size of the mast or boom and hence the size of the U-bolts.

The canes or glass-fibre rods are fixed to the ends of the aluminium angle using hose clamps as shown in Fig 6.13. Rubber or plastic tubing cushions can be used to prevent the clamps damaging cane or glass-fibre rod supports.

Experimental VHF and UHF antennas

I have built many VHF antennas, mostly for the 144MHz band, usually as models for HF antennas. The simplest method of construction is achieved by fixing 14 SWG hard-drawn copper-wire elements to a wooden boom using netting staples. This is shown in Fig 6.14, which also illustrates how the gamma match is constructed.

The sliding gamma rod is made from two small

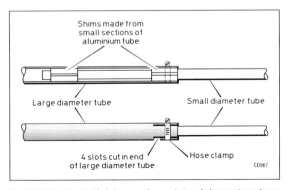

Fig 6.12. Method of joining sections of aluminium tube where the tube diameters present a poor fit. (Top drawing depicts longitudinal section of joint.)

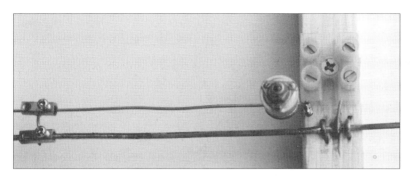

Fig 6.14. VHF antenna construction using copper-wire elements fixed to a wooden boom

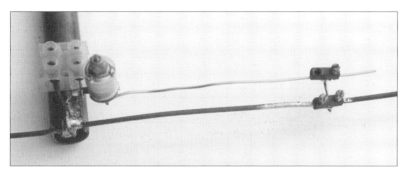

Fig 6.15. VHF antenna construction with a copper-wire element soldered to a copper-tube boom

connector strip inserts with the shorting bar soldered to them. The coaxial cable feeder is connected to the tag-strip with the braid to the centre of the element and the centre to the gamma capacitor.

This construction method is perfectly adequate for obtaining data and is used mostly for making VHF models of HF antennas for performance evaluation. This construction has also been used for a permanent outdoor VHF antenna after the structure had been weather-proofed.

Copper tubing can also be used for an antenna boom. The elements can be fixed to the boom by soldering them directly onto the surface – see Fig 6.15.

Elements can also be attached to the boom using copper pipe-to-wall plastic fixings and held in position with a self-tapping screw as shown in Fig 6.16. The advantage of this method is that element spacing can be adjusted more easily.

Elements can be fixed to a tubular metal boom using hose clamps. A four-element UHF antenna (with circular elements) is shown in Fig 6.17 using this method of construction.

The antenna elements are made from 14 SWG enamelled-covered copper wire. All the separate

parts of this antenna are fixed together using hose clips (Jubilee clips).

The driven element is fixed to the boom using a hose clamp, with a white plastic connector block having three terminals, to enable the coaxial cable to be connected to the elements. The enamel insulation is then cleaned from the ends of the elements to a distance of 20mm (0.8in) from one end and 50mm (2in) from the other. The ends of the elements are then bent at right-angles, the element formed into a loop, the ends pushed through the connector block and the screws tightened. The long 50mm (2in) end is formed into a loop and pushed back though the third connector. The loop formed by this is used to connect the driven element to the boom.

The parasitic elements should be made 40mm (1.6in) longer than the lengths shown in Fig 6.17. The enamel insulation is then cleaned from the ends of the elements to a distance of 20mm (0.8in) from the ends. Bend the ends of the wire at right-angles and then form the wire into a loop. It is preferable, but not essential, to solder the ends of the wires together. This makes it easier to assemble the antenna.

The hose clamp and wire-type fixing can be used to fix the antenna to the boom as shown in Fig 6.17.

Fig 6.16. Use of a plastic pipe-to-wall fitting for element-to-boom fixing

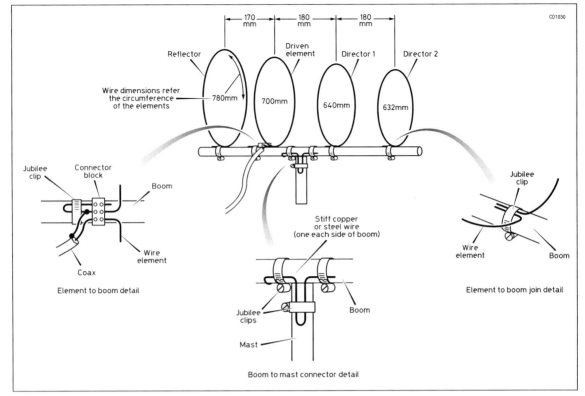

Fig 6.17. A UHF four-element quad antenna constructed by fixing the elements to the boom using hose clamps

Model antennas for 1.3GHz

If you want to go in for table-top antenna modelling then make model antennas for the 1.3GHz band. Throughout this book only the 145MHz band has been considered for VHF modelling because of the availability of test equipment and the problem of scaling from UHF to HF. However, if you can get hold of a UHF signal generator to energise the antenna and use a modified tuneable domestic TV satellite receiver for the FSM then you can have the makings of a miniature antenna range.

The antennas shown in Fig 6.18 were constructed by Allen Grey, G8LCO. It is important that all the antenna dimensions are scaled down. This results in very thin wire being used for the elements of these antennas.

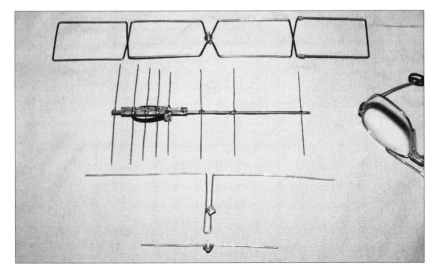

Fig 6.18. Model antennas for 1.3GHz, constructed by Allen Grey, G8LCO

TRANSMISSION LINE

A transmission line is a means of transferring RF power from one point to another. At HF and VHF it usually takes the form of the familiar coaxial cable or twin-wire feeder. When experimenting with antennas it is often important that you know the characteristics and the electrical length of the feeder that you are using. Sometimes things are not what they seem. You would expect that coaxial cable with an RG number printed on outer insulation would have the characteristics quoted in coaxial cable literature, a simplified version of which is given in Table 6.1.

The dielectric material in all the above cables is polyethylene, with a velocity factor of 0.66. Cables marked with an asterisk (*) come with foam polyethylene dielectric with a velocity factor of 0.80.

However, as pointed out by Ian White, G3SEK [4], these RG numbers are for cables that conform fully to the US MIL-C17D specification. Of a couple of samples discussed by Ian White, one was bought as 'RG58', and it even said 'RG58' all along the outer cover, but the dielectric between the inner and outer conductors was white foamed plastic instead of translucent solid polyethylene. This had two consequences: the velocity factor was significantly higher than the correct value of 0.66, which explained the incorrect resonant lengths, and furthermore the cable was slightly thinner overall than real RG58 (cable that conforms fully to the US MIL-C17D specification).

Sample number two was called 'RG213/U - BX', and once again it wasn't proper RG213. The dielectric did appear to be solid polyethylene, as it should be, but the outer braid and jacket were rather loose and this increased the velocity factor to about 0.68 according to measurements by G4SWX. More important, the characteristic impedance appeared to be nearer 55Ω than 50Ω. Most important of all, the outer diameter was only about 9mm instead of 10.3mm, so standard connectors designed for real MIL-spec RG213 did not grip the cable sheath properly.

What both these cables have in common is that they are of cheaper construction than the real RG ones. They are actually quite good examples of 'value engineering', in the sense that they achieve loss figures similar to the full-specification cables, or even lower, and at a reduced manufacturing cost. However, just one aspect of a coaxial cable cannot be changed without affecting something else as well. For example, if a foamed dielectric is used instead of solid polyethylene, then the impedance must change unless the inner conductor is made thicker

Table 6.1. Popular coaxial cable characteristics		
RG/U number	Nominal impedance (Ω)	Cable diameter (in)
RG-8A*	52	0.405
RG-11*	52	0.405
RG-174	50	0.405
RG-213	50	0.405
RG-58*	53.5	0.195
RG-58C	50	0.195
RG-59A	75	0.242
RG-59B	75	0.242

or the outer conductor diameter smaller – and then you've got a different cable that no longer fits a normal plug. There are also some doubts about the wear and water resistance of the outer sheath in the cheaper cables, and if that sheath fails the cable is ruined.

The 'RG' cables are very tightly specified in MIL-C17D, and the 'UR' cables in BS2316. These are well-made quality products. However, the 'RG and 'UR' designations are not trademarked and there appears to be little to prevent manufacturers from selling cables with identical or very similar markings. As soon as the old 52Ω RG8 cable was replaced by 50Ω RG213, the obsolete RG8 designation became devalued by a flood of less expensive so-called 'equivalents'. It now looks as if RG213 is going the same way but prematurely. As mentioned, these new cables may be near-equivalents and they may provide very similar electrical performance at a lower price than the real thing, but they cannot be the same in every respect. Increasingly, it's a case of 'buyer beware'. If you want the real thing, not only will you have to pay for the higher quality, but also you'll need to check very carefully what you're buying.

Measuring resonant lengths of coaxial cable

It is very useful to be able to measure the resonant length (electrical length) of a length of coaxial cable. Sometimes it is necessary to avoid resonant lengths of transmission line to reduce the effects of antenna currents on the line. On the other hand, resonant lengths are needed to make a coaxial balun or a phasing network for a directional array or for a circularly polarised Yagi. The need for identical electrical lengths of cable also arises whenever there is a requirement to feed two or more antennas in phased arrays.

Usually a precise number of electrical half-wavelengths or quarter-wavelengths is required. The physical lengths of cable required can be anything

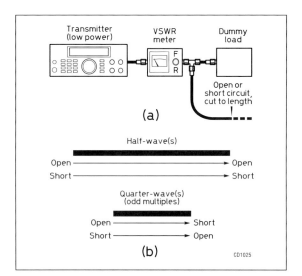

Fig 6.19. (a) Set-up for measuring coaxial cable length using an SWR meter. (b) An electrical λ/2 (or any multiple) shows the same impedance at its far end. An electrical λ/4 (or any odd multiple) shows the 'opposite' impedance at its far end

from, say, 53m (an electrical half-wavelength on Top Band) down to 40mm, an electrical quarter-wavelength for 1.3GHz.

The obvious method of using a ruler is often not practical. Even if the velocity factor of the cable in question is known, it's often difficult to measure an accurate length, especially if the steel tape is as flexible as the cable itself. The electrical length of a section of cable that is already part of an antenna installation or a roll of cable on a drum may also need to be determined.

The methods of measuring the electrical length of coaxial cable that follow use test equipment described in earlier chapters.

Fix a connector to one end of the coaxial cable that is to be measured. A GDO as described in Chapter 3 can be used or one of the following methods described below.

Using an SWR meter

All that is required to make the measurement is the station transceiver and SWR meter. Connect the cable to a T-adapter between the VSWR meter and a dummy load as shown in Fig 6.19(a). The VSWR meter is fed from the transmitter, at sufficiently low power that the transmitter won't be damaged by strange load impedances. One or two watts is usually plenty. Without the cable connected at the T-adapter, the VSWR meter 'sees' the matched dummy load, so the indicated VSWR should be very low. If

a random length of cable is connected at the T-adapter, its reactance appears in shunt across the dummy load and the VSWR will rise. The exception is when the shunt reactance at the end of the cable is very high, almost as high as if the cable were unplugged.

This only happens in two circumstances; when the cable is an exact electrical half-wave (λ/2) long and open-circuited at the far end or when it is an exact electrical λ/4 long and shorted at the far end. The situation repeats itself every λ/2 with the open-circuited cable, and for odd numbers of λ/4 with shorted cable.

Let's take the λ/2 example first. All you have to do is plug in an over-length cable, and snip short lengths off the open-circuited end until the 'reflected' reading on the VSWR meter falls back to zero; the electrical λ/2 point.

An antenna analyser such as the Autek RF-1 MFJ-249/259 could of course be used. An example of measurements made using one of these instruments is shown in Fig 6.20.

Using a noise bridge or similar impedance bridge

Prepare the coaxial cable with a connector as described above. The other end should be open-circuited. Plug it into the noise bridge (set up as described in Chapter 2), set the reactance to zero and and tune the receiver for a null in the noise. The null will occur at $R = 0$ and $X = 0$.

Although noise bridges do not have a reputation

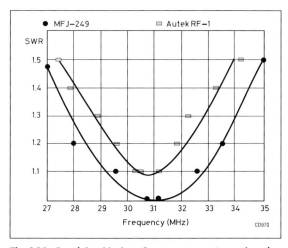

Fig 6.20. Coaxial cable length measurements made using Autek RF-1 MFJ-249/259. Note that the exact length cannot be defined and is estimated using graphical interpolation

for accuracy they can be used to measure coaxial line length accurately. This is because the $X = 0$ point on the reactance scale is easy to calibrate using a resistive load soldered into a coaxial plug. The reactance scale is very sensitive to the changes in coaxial length so the method is accurate.

Table 6.2. Two impedance measurements on a λ/2 length of coaxial cable, using terminating resistors values greater and less than coaxial cable impedance								
INPUT PARAMETERS					**RESULTS**		**+/- ERRORS**	
FREQ	Ea	Ecz	Ec	Ez	RES	jX	RES	jX
20.93	122.8	73.7	37	69.2	69.6	+11.7	1.9	7.3
21	125	76	37	70.3	71.2	+9.2	2.3	8.4
21.1	127	78.7	37	71.3	72.3	+4.7	2.1	6.5
21.2	127.8	80.2	36.5	71	71.9	-0.1	2.1	5.7
21.3	128.6	81.4	36.4	70.5	71.4	-4.1	2.7	6.9
21.4	127.2	81.5	36	69	69	-8.2	1.4	3.2
21.5	126.6	81.4	35.6	67.3	66.8	-12.1	2.2	5.1
INPUT PARAMETERS					**RESULTS**		**+/- ERRORS**	
FREQ	Ea	Ecz	Ec	Ez	RES	jX	RES	jX
20.93	85	48	36.4	23.7	23.1	-6.5	1.1	2.2
21	83.7	46.5	37	23.5	23.3	-3.3	0.1	0.2
21.1	82.6	45	36.4	23	22.9	-2.4	0.1	0.1
21.2	81.6	43	36.4	23	23	+0	0.1	0.1
21.3	82	42	36.6	23.2	23.6	+1.3	1	1.6
21.4	80.4	40	36.3	23.2	23.2	+3.4	0.4	0.7
21.5	80.2	38.5	36	23.7	23.7	+5.1	0.8	1.4

Using the 3-M method impedance bridge

Prepare the coaxial cable with a connector as described above. The far end of the transmission line must be terminated with a resistor that is approximately twice or half the value of the transmission line characteristic impedance; the value is not critical. Its purpose is to prevent the reflected impedances from being too wild and beyond the range of the 3-M bridge. Plug the cable into the 3-M bridge (set up as described in Chapter 2).

Resonance is indicated by the zero reactance, which in the case of printout in Table 6.2 is 21.2MHz. The electrical length in metres is obtained by dividing 300 by the frequency.

As can be seen from Table 6.2, the 3-M method is sensitive to frequency or coaxial cable length.

Measurement of coaxial cable loss

The classic method of measuring coaxial cable loss is to terminate the cable with a dummy load that is equal to the Z_0 of the line. Then use a power meter, first at the transmitter end and then the load end, ensuring that the transmitter power is maintained at a constant level during the test. Finally, calculate the loss from the difference in power readings using the formula:

$$\text{Decibel loss} = 10 \log (P_1/P_2)$$

where P_1 is the power at the transmitter end and P_2 is the power at the dummy load.

An SWR meter can also be used to measure line loss using the same method described above. Measure the SWR at the transmitter and at the load. Use the graph in Fig 6.21 to determine the cable loss.

A quick check of coaxial cable loss, described by K5ED, can be done without leaving the shack or even disconnecting the cable from the antenna.

Use a Autek RF-1 or an MFJ-249/259 and look for the SWR peaks at non-resonant antenna frequencies. Then use the graph in Fig 6.21 to find the cable loss. The graph is calibrated from the equation:

$$\text{Loss (dB)} = 10 \log [(SWR + 1)/(SWR - 1)]$$

The Autek gives up at an SWR of 14:1 and the MFJ-249/259 is very inaccurate at SWRs greater than 3:1 so the method can only be used as a quick check for a suspect cable.

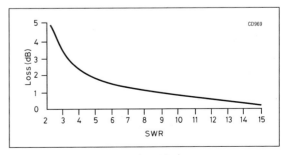

Fig 6.21. SWR versus mismatched line loss

Fig 6.22. The 'Flintstone Special', a rotatable beam antenna and foldover mast, all made from thick bamboo

The method was originally described in the *ARRL Antenna Book* (1995 edn) to be used with shorted or open line. If you use the method with a transceiver, use an ASTU to match the unpredictable impedances that may occur at the transmitter end of an unterminated line.

THIRD-WORLD ANTENNA ENGINEERING MATERIALS

While I was in Sierra Leone (9L1HX) my operation was restricted by a home-made transceiver to 14MHz. It was decided to make a beam antenna for this band but the project was hampered by the lack of material – no aluminium tubing and no lightweight cane for quads. The area was surrounded by thickets of long bamboos so this material was used to construct the antenna shown in Fig 6.22.

The bamboo spreaders support a ZL Special (two-element all-driven array). These bamboo spreaders are 10m (33ft) wide, supported on a bamboo mast, which is rotatable and can be folded over. The

antenna exhibited a good pattern but was not really high enough. I would have been much better off fixing a mast high up in one of the nearby mango trees. A simple dipole at twice the height would probably have been just as effective!

BALUNS

I do not generally use baluns with my experimental antennas. The reason is that the antenna is matched so that its impedance is close to that of the feeder. Under these circumstances the matched antenna can be considered as a terminating resistor, which absorbs all the power. This begs the question; does a terminating resistor need to be balanced or unbalanced? The transformer balun introduces additional circuit complexity and introduces additional reactive components into the feedline.

However, there are circumstances where antenna currents (current flowing on the outside of the feeder) can occur even when the antenna is correctly matched, and that is when the feeder is resonant (the feeder is equal to, or a multiple of, $\lambda/2$). Because it is often convenient to use $\lambda/2$ of coaxial cable to connect the antenna to an impedance measuring instrument to maintain an approximate 1:1 impedance transformation, a method of suppressing these antenna currents is desirable. Antenna currents appear to upset impedance measurements.

The simplest method is to use a choke (current) balun, which should be placed as close to the antenna feedpoint as possible. Two of these devices will be briefly described.

W1JR toroid balun

A simple HF broad-band balun by W1JR [5] comprises a short length of about 1m (39in) of thin coaxial cable of the required impedance, wound on a toroid core – see Fig 6.23.

I use RG-58A with an outside diameter (OD) of 0.195in for antenna impedance measurements. When used with a high-permeability Q1 material (μ = 125 to 400) ferrite toroid, put on as many turns as you can get on to it. This will give good results on the higher-frequency HF bands with reduced efficiency on 3.5 and 1.8MHz. The main difficulty with this arrangement is that it is difficult to get a sufficiently tight wrap of coaxial cable around the toroid and the loss of coupling makes it impossible to utilise the full value of the core permeability. It is also possible to damage the coaxial cable if you try to wind the balun too tight.

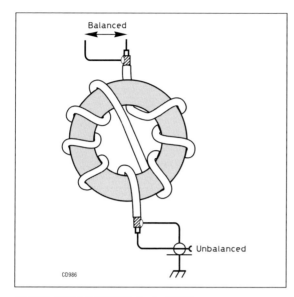

Fig 6.23. Broad-band HF balun by W1JR

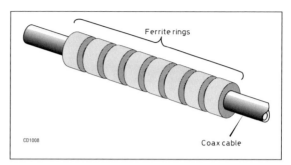

Fig 6.24. The W2DU choke balun constructed from ferrite beads or toroids

The W2DU balun

The W2DU choke balun [6] is far more effective and mechanically more elegant. It is constructed by slipping ferrite beads or toroids whose internal diameter is slightly larger than the coaxial cable. In general, the impedance of the outer coaxial braid surface increases almost proportionately with the number of beads placed over it. Cores of various materials can be used in combination, permitting construction of baluns over a very wide frequency range.

Further reading

An excellent description of the action of baluns is given in 'Baluns, what they do and how they do it', R W Lewallen, W7EL, *ARRL Antenna Compendium*, Vol 1.

REFERENCES

[1] 'The Paul Buyan whip', Alfred W Hubbard, K0OHM, *QST* March 1963,
[2] 'Fold-over mast for beam support', P G Dodd, 9L1HX, *Short Wave Magazine* August 1966.
[3] *Protection Against Atmospheric Corrosion*, Karel Barton, John Wiley, 1976.
[4] 'In Practice', Ian White, G3SEK, *Radio Communication* July 1995.
[5] 'A simple and efficient HF broad-band balun', Joe Reisert, W1JR, *Ham Radio* September 1978.
[6] *Reflections, Transmission Lines and Antennas*, M Maxwell, W2DU, ARRL.

7 Experimental antennas

THIS chapter describes experimental antennas, most of which are based on work that has continued intermittently over a period of many years.

It also describes, where applicable, how assessment and measuring techniques, described in earlier chapters, were used or could have been used. The antenna designs investigated in this chapter are:

- Design of an all-metal quad
- Development of small compact beam antennas with useful gain over a $\lambda/2$ dipole
- A low-profile HF mobile antenna
- A compact toroid antenna

Whenever possible construction details and dimensions are given so that the antenna can be reproduced. In some cases construction of VHF models of the experimental antenna are also described.

DESIGN OF AN ALL-METAL QUAD
Construction

This all-metal version of the quad evolved as an attempt to make a more simple, weather-proof version. Two models have been tried, one for 14MHz, and the other for 145MHz to allow comparative measurements to be done relative to a dipole.

The antenna for 14MHz looks like two 10m two-element beams stacked at $\lambda/2$. The tips of the elements of the bays are joined by 14 SWG stranded copper wire, making 1λ loops for 20m.

The lengths of the elements and the distance between the booms were initially set at approximately 5.5m (18ft), this dimension being determined by the quad formula obtained from the W6SAI *Quad Antenna Book* [1]:

L (total element length in metres) = 306.3/f(MHz)

or

L (total element length in feet) = 1005/f(MHz)

With these dimensions the resonant frequency of

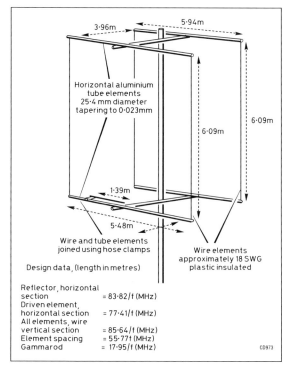

Fig 7.1. All-metal two-element quad for 14MHz, with design data for other frequencies

each metal quad loop was around 15.4MHz; this is probably due to the construction. When wire is added to the end of an aluminium tube it represents an extreme diameter taper, which causes the above formula to be inappropriate.

When the spacing between the bays and the vertical sections of the elements are increased to 6m (20ft) the quad element resonances move down into the 14MHz band. The dimensions for a 14MHz quad are shown in Fig 7.1.

With this type of construction the reflector element can only be made longer by increasing the length of the aluminium tube horizontal sections –

98

the final dimensions for 14MHz are 5.5m (18ft) for the driven element and 5.94m (19ft 6in) for the reflector. The driven element can be fed directly in the centre with 50Ω coaxial cable or via a matching system such as a gamma match.

The physical dimensions of this quad are greater than that of a conventional wire quad. All measurements indicate that the gain is also greater than that of a conventional quad – see Fig 5.11 in Chapter 5.

This structure is neater, and has a smaller windage, than the conventional wire quad on spreaders – see Fig 6.9 in Chapter 6. The main disadvantage of this configuration is that it requires a section of unguyed mast above the rotator. The unguyed rotating mast described in Chapter 6 is the most suitable support for this antenna.

DEVELOPMENT OF A COMPACT HF BEAM ANTENNA

Very few houses in the UK are now built with a plot of land large enough to take a full-size tri-band three-element antenna, so the design of a compact, easy-to-build antenna with a satisfactory performance is a worthwhile aim.

A number of tests at VHF showed that a good compromise between simplicity and gain could be based on a two-element parasitic beam. With this type of array the largest dimensions are the element lengths, which need to be shortened if the antenna is to be reduced in size.

While making measurements on VHF models, described in Chapter 5 ('Examples of Tests on VHF Models of HF Antennas'), I noticed that the elements of the two-element parasitic beam could be bent without any appreciable deterioration of gain or directivity. I did not pursue that line of enquiry at the time because I was investigating VHF modelling rather than the antennas themselves. VHF models of well-known HF antennas, whose performance were already known, were being used to assess the VHF modelling technique. Normally, of course, the VHF model is used to assess the HF antenna.

A two-element VHF antenna with a parasitic reflector is shown in Fig 7.2. This model has been included, with construction details, because it forms the basis of an investigation into the two-element antennas with bent elements. It is based on the simplest of construction methods – fixing the elements to a wooden boom using staples.

Other methods of constructing VHF antennas are shown in Chapter 7. The coaxial cable feeder is connected to the element via a connecting block, with

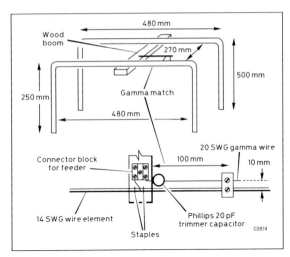

Fig 7.2. Two-element VHF parasitic beam with bent elements

the braid to the centre of the element and the centre to the gamma capacitor.

The gamma match uses a 100mm (4in) length of 20 SWG wire. The adjustable tapping point to the element is made from a small connector block insert. The gamma capacitor used is a 15pF air-spaced trimmer. Any small, easy-to-adjust air-spaced trimmer capacitor is suitable.

The W1QP/W8CPC compact beam

The structure shown in Fig 7.2 performs well but is inherently fragile; ideally, the element ends require support. A solution to the mechanical difficulties of this configuration was brought to my notice by Byron Weaver, WU2J. It was first suggested by John Reinartz, W1QP. A wooden frame is used to support the elements, which allows the element ends to be folded towards each other. A model was constructed for 14MHz by Burton Simson, W8CPC, and described in QST [2].

A simplified diagram of this antenna is shown in Fig 7.3.

The elements were constructed from ¼in copper tubing with brass tuning rods that fitted snugly into the ends of the elements. An additional brass rod was used as a shorting bar for the centre of the reflector. The tuning procedure was interesting. The only test equipment available appeared to be an RF meter (0–5A), the transmitter PA current meter and the receiver S-meter.

An RF meter was connected by short leads to the gap in the reflector and the driven element connected to the link coil of the transmitter by low-impedance

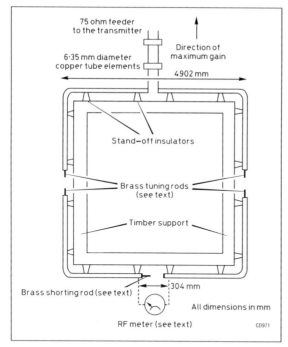

Fig 7.3. The W1QP/W8CPC two-element 14MHz antenna with bent elements

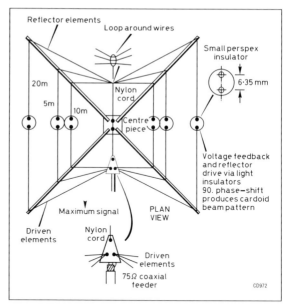

Fig 7.4. VK2ABQ wire two-element beam antenna: G3LZR improved version (from *Amateur Radio Techniques* [5])

twin transmission line. The brass rods at the ends of the driven element were adjusted for maximum transmitter PA current at resonance. The rods at the tips of the reflector were then adjusted for maximum RF current in the reflector. These adjustments are interactive and would have to be repeated.

When the adjustments were complete the RF meter was removed and the gap closed with the brass rod. This tune-up procedure tunes the reflector to transmitter frequency.

According to K1TD [3], if the reflector is resonant at the operating frequency maximum gain occurs when the reflector is spaced λ/4 from the driven element, which is the case with this antenna.

A similar method of tuning can be achieved using the magnetic FSM described in Chapter 4; with this instrument it is not necessary to break the conductor.

The VK2ABQ wire beam antenna

A wire version of the W1QP/W8CPC two-element antenna was described in 1973 by VK2ABQ [4] and an improved derivative is illustrated in Fig 7.4 [5, 6].

In this configuration the tips of the parasitic and driven elements support each other in the horizontal

plane. The insulators are constructed so that the tips of the elements are 6mm (¼in) apart and, according to the description, capacitive end couples the reflector from the driven element. The gap between the tips of the elements is described as 'not critical'. No mention is made of what happens when they get wet in the rain. Gains of 4dB and front-to-back ratios of 12 to 18dB (presumably relative to a dipole) are quoted [4].

My early experiments with VHF models of this antenna were rather disappointing. A model with wire elements laid out on a wooden X spreader was constructed. Various insulators, element tip spacings and wire lengths were tried and success was had in obtaining good directivity but the gain was very little more than that of a dipole. When the elements were just allowed to droop as in Fig 7.2 the gain improved and the antenna became much less critical to adjust.

The difficulty experienced in modelling this antenna at VHF is possibly due to this capacitive end coupling. With VHF modelling, described in Chapter 5, the wavelengths, capacitances and inductances in the VHF scale model are reduced in proportion to the linear dimensions while gains and impedances are unchanged. However, the insulator represents a fixed capacitor whose reactance is frequency dependent. If a value of around 0.2pF is assumed for the wires held in the insulator by knots, ¼in apart,

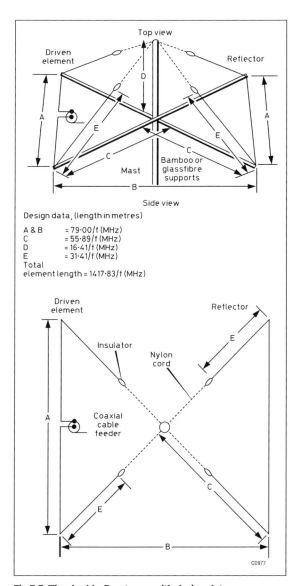

Design data, (length in metres)

A & B $= 79 \cdot 00/f$ (MHz)
C $= 55 \cdot 89/f$ (MHz)
D $= 16 \cdot 41/f$ (MHz)
E $= 31 \cdot 41/f$ (MHz)
Total
element length $= 1417 \cdot 83/f$ (MHz)

Fig 7.5. The double-D antenna with design data

the coupling reactance is 38kΩ at 21MHz and 5.5kΩ at 145MHz. See Note [1] at the end of the chapter.

Development of the wire double-D antenna

The VHF model shown in Fig 7.2 was tried with the elements bent in different directions. It would give the gain of a two-element Yagi provided the elements were not folded too far back on themselves, or directly towards each other on the same plane. The antenna structure in Fig 7.5 illustrates the limit to the degree of bending that could be imposed on

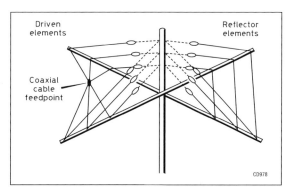

Fig 7.6. The multiband double-D antenna

the model shown in Fig 7.2 without a noticeable deterioration in gain and directivity.

The ends of the elements can be folded back towards the mast and down to an angle of 20° from the horizontal before the gain starts to deteriorate. This shape proved to be a simple and stable mechanical arrangement, and an all-metal derivative 21MHz model survived the hurricane which hit the south coast of England in October 1987. The antenna has been christened the 'double-D' and it will provide 3–4dB of gain over a dipole and a front-to-back ratio better than 14dB.

The double-D is also amenable to multibanding. A number of these antennas for different bands can be mounted on the same support. Use the formula in Fig 7.5 to obtain the wire lengths.

Use plastic tape to fix the wire to the canes; I have never noticed any detuning using this method when using plastic-covered wire. The simplest method of feeding turned out to be the best: paralleling the driven elements and feeding them with the one coaxial line as shown in Fig 7.6.

All-metal double-D antenna

This design was the result of experiments to find a neater derivative of the wire double-D for 21MHz to fix to the chimney of my house. The largest 'wing-span' practicable was around 3.5m (12ft) because the house is not very big. The final design is shown in Fig 7.7. The vertical support for the ends of the elements was also used successfully as a 2m J-type vertical. An attempt to use the vertical section as a 28MHz vertical was a failure due to the interaction between the two antennas.

Ground-wave tests with local amateur radio station some miles away showed a front-to-back ratio of about 2.5 S-points measured on the S-meter of a Drake R4C (one S-point = 6dB power).

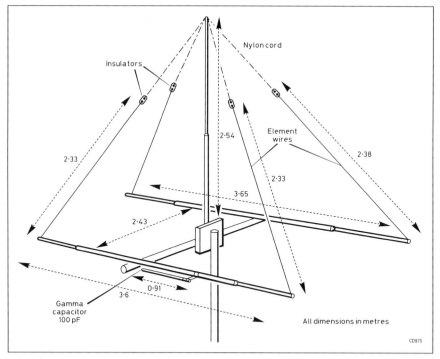

Fig 7.7. A metal double-D for 21MHz. This version is neater and more compact that the full-size wire version

There are no hard and fast rules regarding the horizontal and vertical dimensions of this antenna. If the horizontal dimension is increased then the vertical dimension is decreased; the converse also applies of course.

The compact metal double-D

Further VHF modelling tests on a double-D element indicated that the horizontal sections could be reduced to around 0.16λ before the performance really started to deteriorate.

The implications of these experiments were that a 7MHz beam could be constructed having the same horizontal area as a three-element beam for 15m. The actual construction would, however, depend on the radiation resistance. Reducing the length of an antenna element reduces its radiation resistance, but by how much?

Compact antennas have a reputation for being inefficient and the following measurements show why. I measured the feed impedance (and hence the radiation resistance because the elements were connected directly to the feeder) of a dipole, a standard double-D element and a compact double-D element. These measurements were performed via 1λ

of 50Ω coaxial cable using the 3-M method described in Chapter 2. The centres of all elements were approximately λ/4 above the ground and were measured at frequencies between 28 and 29MHz. The results are illustrated in Fig 7.8.

The current flowing in an antenna element is inversely proportional to the square root of the radiation resistance. This can cause the relatively high resistance of wire elements to dissipate a significant proportion of the transmitter power. The addition of a parasitic element would reduce the radiation resistance (and the efficiency of the driven element) still further. It was therefore decided to use tubing for the high-current sections of the elements.

VHF double-D model

This VHF model of the double-D element was assembled using 'plumbers delight' construction, with

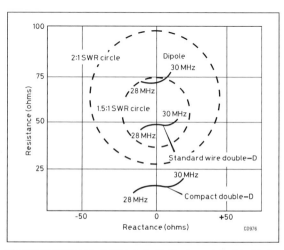

Fig 7.8. Impedance of elements of dipole and double-D elements compared

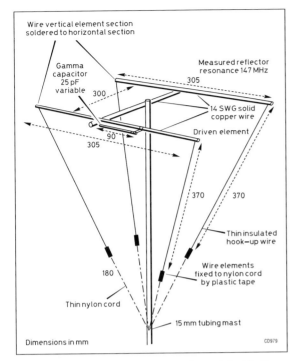

Wire vertical element section
soldered to horizontal section

Gamma
capacitor
25 pF
variable 300

Measured reflector
resonance 147 MHz
305

14 SWG solid
copper wire

90

305

Driven element

370   370

Thin insulated
hook-up wire

180

Wire elements
fixed to nylon cord
by plastic tape

Thin nylon cord

15 mm tubing mast

Dimensions in mm   CD979

Fig 7.9. VHF model of a compact two-element double-D

14 SWG solid copper wire for the horizontal section and thin 26 SWG plastic-covered wire for the end sections. The element was gamma matched and the element fed with 50Ω coaxial cable. A parasitic element was then added using the same construction as the driven element.

Initially an element spacing of 0.1λ was used but the antenna was very difficult to set up. Any slight adjustment of the parasitic element, as either a director or reflector, or the slightest movement of the wire sections of the elements, caused large changes in feed impedance. The spacing was increased to 0.15λ and the model proved much more docile. The final model is illustrated in Fig 7.9 and appears to have a gain of around 3dB relative to a reference dipole.

Compact double-Ds: HF models

The first large-scale model was constructed for 14MHz and used aluminium tubing for the horizontal section of the elements and plastic-covered wire for the vertical end sections.

The initial sizes chosen for the elements were 3.66m (12ft) for the tubular horizontal section and 4.14m (13ft 8in) for the wire sections. The aspect ratio of these elements is slightly different to the

VHF model but, as the model predicted good results for horizontal sections longer than 0.16λ, no problems were foreseen. The elements were then adjusted for resonance at 14.15 and 13.8MHz for the driven element and reflector respectively. The driven element was connected to the feeder via a gamma match.

All the tests were performed at a frequency of 14.15MHz. The antenna exhibited poor directivity and the business of reflector adjustment commenced. The gamma match was adjusted without any difficulty. The front-to-back ratio continued to be very poor in spite of many adjustments of the reflector. Reflector resonances between 13.9 and 13.1MHz were tried with no improvement in antenna performance. If a HF model of this antenna had been constructed first it would have been concluded that the antenna configuration was unsound. However, because the VHF model predicted that the configuration would work I did not give up hope. The parasitic element was shortened to try it as a director and at 14.0MHz the element commenced to work as a reflector! At 14.1MHz the front-to-back ratio improved. The element continued to operate as a reflector, with a reduced front-to-back ratio, up to 14.45MHz. The final reflector resonance chosen was 14.1MHz because it appeared to give the greatest front-to-back ratio.

A double-D has also been constructed for 10MHz. From these two antennas a set of design data has been obtained and this, together with general construction information, is shown in Fig 7.10.

One point should be made regarding the double-D antenna; it is horizontally polarised and requires the same height above ground as a full-size beam to get a similar performance. However, it is considerably easier to support an antenna with an element span of around 5m (16ft) than one of 12m (40ft).

The difficulties regarding front-to-back ratio adjustment encountered with the 14MHz beam were not foreseen with the VHF model. The reason was that no method of measuring element resonance accurately at VHF was at hand at the time. Even so, the VHF model was capable of showing that the configuration would work and does show the value of VHF modelling. The technique can be improved by measuring VHF antenna resonance accurately using a GDO with a frequency counter – see Chapter 3.

The compact double-D has good bandwidth characteristics for a compact beam and SWR plots are

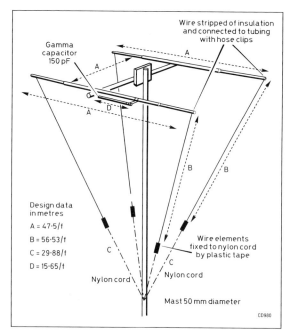

Fig 7.10. Perspective diagram showing the construction of a HF compact double-D antenna

shown in Figs 7.11 and 7.12. This antenna was described in *Radio Communication* [7].

On 14MHz the compact double-D antenna exhibited reasonable directivity and a lot of DX was worked, but the signal was rather outclassed by those from three or more element beams at more than 1λ in height. On 10MHz it was a different matter. Most amateur radio stations on 10MHz use 100W to either a dipole or a vertical. It was surprising what one (theoretical) S-point difference made on transmit. Also the improvement in signal-to-noise (and QRM) ratio was well worthwhile.

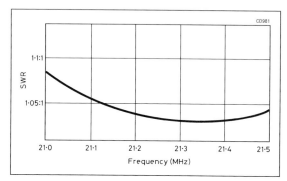

Fig 7.11. 21MHz compact double-D SWR curve. This shows that the element length and gamma match adjustment are not optimum

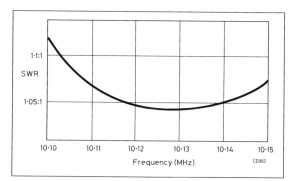

Fig 7.12. 10MHz compact double-D SWR curve

The experiments with the compact double-D described above were done in 1989 [8]. Since then I have acquired and used the computer modelling methods described in Chapter 8. See the frequency sweep analysis on this antenna; the results are very similar to those actually measured. If the EZNEC program had been available then it would have saved months of work.

DDRR MOBILE ROOFRACK ANTENNA

This antenna is based on the DDRR antenna described in the *ARRL Antenna Book* [9].

Note: be aware that mobile antennas in general and magnetic antennas in particular can induce RF currents into vehicle wiring. While this is not a problem with older vehicles it could affect the running of modern ones using microprocessor-controlled engine management systems.

This version of the DDRR antenna was constructed from 2mm copper tubing. The square configuration was used because I didn't have bending equipment suitable for constructing a circular one as described in the *ARRL Antenna Book*. This had two advantages:

1. A square or rectangle can be made up using straight sections of tubing, with the ends joined using 90° angle joints.
2. A rectangular configuration looks more like a roof rack, and if constructed well enough can even be *used* as a roof rack!

After reading the mathematical analysis of this antenna by Robert Dome, W2WAM, (see Appendix 1), I increased the vertical height to 250mm (10in), which was as high as practicable if it was to masquerade as a roofrack.

The antenna is fixed to the roof of the car by a bar roof rack – the sort used to transport ladders or timber, and is illustrated in Fig 7.13. As well as

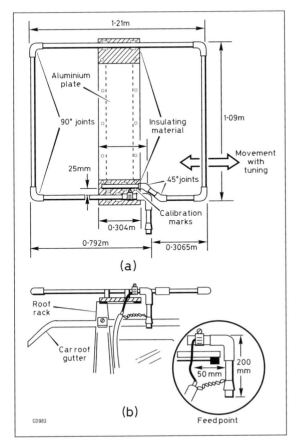

Fig 7.13. DDRR mobile roof rack antenna for 14MHz: top and side views

supporting the DDRR antenna, this rack also provides facilities to mount more conventional antennas.

The bars are set about 350mm (12in) apart and a sheet of aluminium is bolted to them. The roof rack support leg nearest to the vertical section of the antenna is removed to reduce RF absorption by the roof rack support.

Two pieces of Bakelite (or any other suitable insulating material) are fitted to the ends of the rack for mounting the DDRR element. The copper tubing elements are mounted to the insulated roof rack sections with plastic tube-to-wall fittings. Additionally the elements were drilled and bolts and nuts used to secure the elements, but not the variable capacitor section to the insulated section. (This additional securing is only necessary if you require the antenna to double as an actual roof rack.)

The feed end of the element is flattened to sit in the roof gutter and is attached to the roof gutter using the leg clamp removed from the roof rack leg.

Additional electrical contact with the car metalwork is provided with copper braid, soldered to the flattened bottom of the antenna element and attached to the door post with self-tapping screws. This ground connection can be placed so that it is covered when the car door is closed. A thick piece of wire is also soldered to the ground end of the element to enable the screen of the coaxial cable to be connected.

The antenna is shunt fed by tapping the feed-line centre up from the ground end of the element.

To keep the radiation resistance as high as possible the tuning capacitor should only be large enough to tune the band. The capacitance in this case is provided by overlapping the top end of the element with the lowest part of the horizontal section. The capacitance is adjusted by sliding the top end of the element along the tube-to-wall fittings, thereby adjusting the overlap. These fittings offer just enough friction to retain the element in the desired position. Calibration marks are used so that the overlap position can be set at any frequency within the tuneable range. This antenna is described in detail in *QST* [10].

AN OMEGA-MATCHED 14MHz VERTICAL

The antenna design illustrated in Fig 7.14 was originally designed to overcome the problem of not having suitable materials at hand to construct a base insulator and loading coil.

The antenna is basically a λ/4 loaded vertical. It was designed for mobile use and can be used with radials or fixed directly to the metalwork of the car. The prototype was fixed directly to the metal bumper of the car with two thick copper braid straps to the main bodywork to ensure the lowest possible resistance.

The break in the vertical section of the loading coil is provided using a CB antenna base fitting mounted on a steel bracket. This bracket is fixed to the lower vertical section using a hose clamp.

The loading coil is made of thick copper wire and constructed as shown in Fig 7.14, with one end connected to the CB antenna base and the other to the lower vertical section by yet another hose clamp. The top section was initially made from the base section of a military vehicle antenna; the screw fitted the CB antenna fitting. The top section uses a piece of telescoping antenna, as used in portable radios, for tuning the antenna.

The loading coil is air spaced but uses thin strips

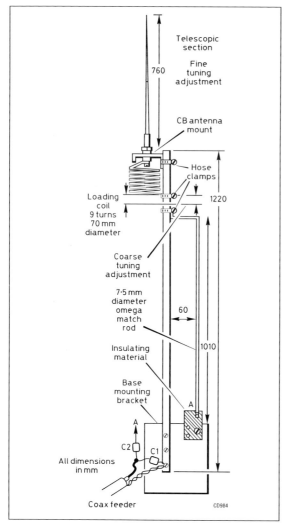

Fig 7.14. λ/4 loaded vertical which can be used with radials or fixed directly to the metalwork of the car for mobile use. The break in the vertical section of the loading coil is provided using a CB antenna base fitting mounted on a steel bracket.

of insulating material to make its structure more rigid.

The omega match is constructed from aluminium tube with a small piece of insulating material to support the feed point and the omega matching capacitors. The other end is connected to the lower section of the antenna with yet another hose clamp.

The antenna matching is adjusted in two stages:

1. Ensure the feeder is disconnected. Then, using a GDO, set the resonance to the required frequency by adjusting the length of the telescoping top section. If necessary the lower connection of the coil

to the mast can be moved up or down to change the resonant point.
2. Connect 500pF variable capacitors at C1 and C2. Using the noise bridge described in Chapter 2 adjust the feedpoint impedance.

C2 will cause changes in X and C1 changes in R, although the adjustments are interactive. Measure the capacitors, as described in Chapter 2, and replace them with fixed ones. My model used 200pF for C1 and 150pF for C2, which gave an SWR of around 1.3:1.

This antenna was first described in the QRP magazine *Sprat* [8].

THE TOROIDAL ANTENNA

To my knowledge the toroid antenna was first mentioned in amateur radio literature by Pat Hawker, G3VA [11]. He referred to a European Patent Application EP 0 043 591 AI on a toroidal antenna (see Appendix 2), made by James Corum, K1AON. It was claimed that of toroid antennas, by virtue of their construction, possess a greater radiation resistance than known antennas of similar electrical size not having the slow-wave winding features. For example, they possess greater radiation resistance and radiation efficiency than loop antennas of similar size.

A theory of how the toroid antenna works, plus some working models, was described by Roger Jennison, G2AJV [12]. The following is a description of the construction and tests on end-fed double-toroid versions. It is done to show how to use measurement techniques, already described in earlier chapters, can be used to gain some insight into the characteristics of an unfamiliar antenna.

This assessment of the toroid antenna was first described in *Radio Communication* [13].

Although this is essentially an LF band antenna all the experimental work on this antenna was carried out on the higher HF bands with the antenna fixed to a vehicle (mobile operation). Although this mobile experimental work was successful it does not imply that the toroid antenna configuration is necessarily considered the best solution for amateur mobile operation. At the time I was working away from home and didn't have access to my garden 'antenna range'.

It was felt that an HF double toroid would allow investigation of the matching problem because the physical parameters of a larger structure could be measured more easily.

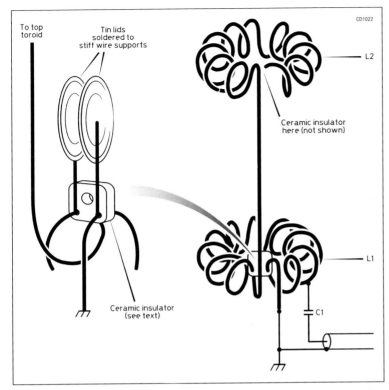

Fig 7.16. Mk 1 shunt-fed antenna (14MHz) fixed to four-footed mag-mount

Fig 7.15. Mk 1 double toroid antenna using shunt feed and parallel capacitor tuning

In all, three HF versions of the double toroid antenna were made:

- The Mk 1 (14MHz) was used to investigate the double toroid feasibility.
- The Mk 2 (14MHz) was built specifically for obtaining data on the original design.
- The Mk 3 (21MHz) was built to investigate construction methods different from the Mk 1 and Mk 2.

The Mk 1 toroid

A diagram of the Mk 1 14MHz toroid mobile antenna is shown in Fig 7.15. It was constructed from hard-drawn 16 SWG antenna wire, supported in a cylindrical cage made from *white* plastic garden fencing, using plastic tie-wraps. The construction of the complete antenna is shown in Fig 7.16. The structure was mounted on metal plate, which in turn was fixed to a four-footed mag-mount – see 'Antenna mounting' later.

Each toroid was constructed separately and joined together when installed in the plastic support. Each toroid was constructed by winding approximately $\lambda/4$ of wire on a 50mm (2in) diameter plastic former,

then removing it from the former and looping the coil into a toroid. The ends of the toroid were held together with ceramic insulators made from old air-spaced capacitors with most of the metal parts removed. Each toroid was adjusted so that it was 200mm (8in) in diameter, by tensioning it to the plastic frame using the plastic tie-wraps. Note that the direction of winding for the top toroid is opposite to the bottom one.

Initially, the lowest SWR at resonance was around 5:1 and no amount of playing around with its physical dimensions made much difference to this figure. Preliminary impedance measurements indicated a feed impedance of around 5Ω at resonance. Additionally, not enough turns had been put on the toroids (28 turns) and the resonant frequency was about 500kHz too high.

Capacitors were built from tin lids and fixed them to the ceramic insulators across the toroids to bring the antenna into resonance into the 14MHz amateur band. It was later found that only one capacitor was required across the lower toroid as shown in Fig 7.15.

To match the antenna to the feeder, a well-tried technique for matching low-impedance antennas was used; a shunt feed arrangement was built and

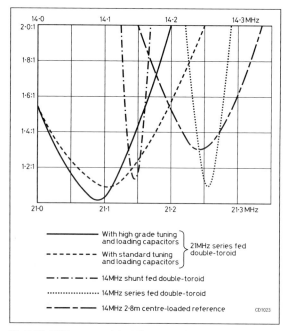

Fig 7.17. SWR curves of the Mks 1, 2 and 3 antennas together with a 14MHz reference antenna

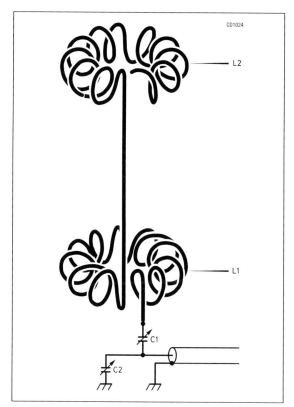

Fig 7.18. Mk 2 double toroid antenna using series feed, shunt capacitor matching and series tuning

aimed for the correct impedance by tapping up the coil. The inductive reactance of the shunt feed was neutralised with a series 100pF capacitor.

Now, at last, things started happening and strong signals were heard on the mobile transceiver when this antenna was connected to it. The antenna proved easy to load and the first short-skip QSO reports ranged from 5/5 to 5/9. My first SSB DX contact was a reply to a CQ from VK6ADP in Perth. Although the signal report was only 5/1 the band was quiet and it was possible to chat for around 10 minutes.

The measured SWR bandwidth of this antenna was found to be rather narrow (see Fig 7.17) and it was felt that this was due to the capacitance across the lower toroid.

In a conversation with G2AJV he suggested the capacitance would reduce the efficiency of the antenna and that I should persevere with the series-fed arrangement, so a further version was made.

The Mk 2 toroid

The Mk 2 double toroid antenna was then built as shown in Fig 7.18. Because this antenna was designed for obtaining data it was constructed so that most parameters, such as the distance between the toroids and the inductance of them, were variable.

Each toroid was constructed from 30 turns of 16 SWG enamelled insulated wire and the construction of the antenna was almost the same as for the Mk 1. The diameter of the Mk 2 toroids was 150mm (6in), smaller than the Mk 1. The reason was that the Mk 1 elements were made from uninsulated copper wire and it was important that the adjacent coil loops did not touch. Two sections of a plastic terminal block was used to support the ends of the toroids.

The antenna was connected to the coaxial cable exactly as shown in the original article [11]. As with the Mk 1 it would not load. The reason for the high SWR at resonance became plain when an impedance plot was made, which was around 5Ω at resonance as shown in Fig 7.19.

A series variable capacitance was added as suggested by G2AJV. This did alter loading slightly although it affected the resonant frequency far more.

I decided to try a shunt capacitor – a method sometimes used to match a conventional loaded mobile whip antenna. With this matching arrangement the

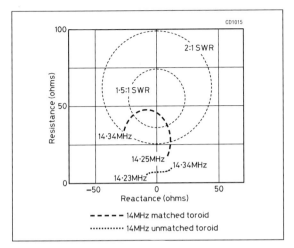

Fig 7.19. Impedance signatures of the series-fed double toroid with and without capacitor matching and tuning capacitors

antenna is made longer than an electrical λ/4 to increase the resistance (and the positive inductive reactance) at the feedpoint. A shunt capacitor is then used to cancel the inductive reactance.

The final matching and tuning arrangement is shown in Fig 7.20. The series capacitor (fine tuning) and parallel loading capacitors are variable, enabling the antenna resonance and the matching to be set quite easily. The impedance plot of the matched 14MHz double toroid is shown in Fig 7.19. This is confirmed by the SWR plot of the series tuned double toroid in Fig 7.17.

The base of this antenna and the method of connecting it to the car is described under 'Antenna mounting'.

Mk 3 toroid

The Mk 3 was used to investigate construction using different materials and conductor diameters and to see what effect this would have on antenna performance.

At the local scrap yard I searched for suitable copper tubing but was out of luck. However, among the scrap electrical cable some material called 'Pyro' (mineral-insulated electrical wire) was found. This material has an outer copper tubing sheath with inner conductor wire(s) in magnesium oxide. It is easy to bend and shape and seemed a promising material for the toroid antenna. It comes in various diameters and 3mm was used for the Mk 2 double toroid for 21MHz. Pyro turned out to be excellent material for winding coils. Because the copper tube sheath is filled with oxide material it can be bent

Fig 7.20. Mk 2 series-fed antenna (14MHz) using home-made mobile roof mount. The clamping magnets are not shown

into shapes having a small radius without the tube kinking.

The Mk 3 toroid was constructed for 21MHz, rather than 14MHz, by accident rather than design. I had only enough Pyro material to make a 21MHz model!

This antenna is shown in Fig 7.21. The coils of the toroid are self-supporting with a resonant frequency of around 20MHz. Fixed silver mica capacitors were used for the series tuning and parallel loading capacitors; their values were 18pF and 150pF respectively. These values were extrapolated from the experimental work on the Mk 2 antenna. This 21MHz antenna worked straight away; it was resonant at 21.2MHz and the SWR was less that 1.7:1.

As can be seen in Fig 7.17 the bandwidth of this tiny antenna seemed suspiciously wide, implying losses. It was assumed that it was being caused by the relatively lossy tuning and matching fixed capacitors and these were replaced by higher-grade capacitors – an air-spaced 50pF variable as the series tuning capacitor and a fixed 180pF Steafix fixed capacitor for parallel loading.

This allowed the SWR to be adjusted to a lower

Fig 7.21. Mk 3 self-supporting structure (21MHz) fixed to a gutter mount

value at resonance and produced a slightly narrower bandwidth, see Fig 7.17. There was no real noticeable improvement in the antenna performance. The conclusion is that the wider bandwidth is the result of using a larger-gauge material in the construction of the toroid, although more experimental work is required to verify this.

Antenna mounting

The way in which these antennas were mounted on the car had a profound effect on their tuning and loading. G2AJV's HF models used mag-mounts and these introduce capacitance between the earth point of the antenna (and the coaxial screen) and the body of the car. This capacitance may not be significant at VHF but with a low-impedance feedpoint HF antenna the results will be unpredictable. One of these unpredictable effects is that there are antenna currents on the feedline. Even with the Mk 1 antenna,

with its large four-footed mag-mount, performance was improved with direct earth connection.

The 21MHz antenna was fixed to the car using an antenna gutter clamp. To get the best antenna/earth connection to the car the paint was scraped away down to bare metal under the clamp and the area was coated with grease to prevent corrosion. This earth point then served as a low-resistance point for all other antennas tested and proved useful for testing the effectiveness of magnetic base clamps for HF antennas.

The base for the Mk 2 was made from a sheet of aluminium (theoretically the larger, the better) clamped to the roof of the car with magnetron magnets. This base fixing method also reduces the base/car roof capacitance – see Fig 7.20.

Eight holes are drilled in the base plate in groups of two. The metal between the holes is lifted so that tie-wraps can be inserted to fix the plastic cage to the base without touching the roof of the car.

A hole is drilled for the earth point, which should be close to the antenna feedpoint when the antenna is assembled. The hole is countersunk so that the countersunk head of the earthing bolt is flush with the bottom of the base.

The outside edges of the base, facing the roof of the car, are faced with strips of plastic tape to prevent the base scratching the roof. The base clamp magnets can be used with plastic sheet protection.

As already mentioned, the base has some effect on the antenna tuning. The Mk 2 antenna was tried fixed and earthed to the aluminium frame of a greenhouse. The antenna resonant frequency had shifted from 14.2MHz (when fixed to the car) to 14.8MHz, although its performance was good when the antenna was retuned.

Antenna performance comparisons

Some comparison signal-strength tests of the 14MHz toroid antenna were made using an 2.5m (8ft) homemade centre-loaded vertical as a reference. This antenna has a lower section constructed from 22mm copper tubing and the air-spaced loading coil is 760mm (3in) in diameter. This reference antenna was fixed to the rear of the car, level with the bumper, with a good earth connection to the car chassis.

The Mk 2 toroid was fixed to the roof, as already described, and both antennas remained in place during the tests. It was reasoned there would be little interaction because the unused antenna is detuned when the feeder is disconnected from the transceiver (load) when the antennas are changed over (the feeder was not a multiple of λ/4 at the test frequency).

Short-skip contacts to Europe were inconclusive; sometimes the vertical antenna outperformed the toroid and at other times the toroid was the better performer.

Ground-wave tests were then tried with GB3RS, the RSGB HQ station. At distances of between a quarter and half a mile away a carrier was transmitted, carefully monitored on a power meter. John Crabbe, G3WFM, the senior station operator, made measurements using the S-meter on the IC781.

Most of the measurements gave the vertical a half to one S-point advantage. The exception was when the car was facing the HQ station, when the toroid antenna had the one S-point advantage.

Conclusions

The double toroid design appears to work very well once the problems of matching are overcome. The implications are that the toroid antenna is particularly useful for low-band HF, particularly where space is at a premium.

Areas for experimentation

There are a number of areas where the additional experimenting would be useful and interesting. An analysis of toroid antennas, using the MFJ-248 antenna analyser, indicates that there are higher-order resonances. The third resonance looks promising because of its wide bandwidth, although the performance as an antenna in this mode is unknown.

Other unknowns regarding antenna performance are: the ratio of series capacitor to coil, capacitance of base to earth, spacing of top and bottom toroids and the diameter of toroids. The effect of earth on an end-fed double toroid also requires more investigation.

The limitations of small antennas have been studied in depth and published – see references [14] and [15].

NOTE

[1] The VK2ABQ antenna can only be modelled using ELNEC or EZNEC (see Chapter 8) by connecting the tips of the driven element and

reflector together and inserting a capacitor 'load'. A capacitor reactance of 5kΩ produces the same results as observed on the VHF model.

REFERENCES

[1] *Cubical Quad Antennas*, William Orr, W6SAI, and Stuart Cohen, W2LX.

[2] 'Concentrated directional antennas for transmission and reception', John Reinartz, W1QP, and Burton Simson, W8CPC, *QST* October 1937.

[3] 'Two element beam spacing versus parasitic element length change', *ARRL Antenna Book*, 15th edn, p11-3, Fig 5.

[4] 'VK2ABQ antenna', Fred Caton, VK2ABQ, *Electronics Australia* October 1973.

[5] '2ABQ and 3APB – fun with a simple beam', Bill Rice, VK3APT, and Harry Caspey, VK2OQ, *Amateur Radio* (Australia) October 1990.

[6] 'VK2ABQ antenna', *Amateur Radio Techniques*, Pat Hawker, G3VA, RSGB.

[7] 'Wire beam antennas and the evolution of the double-D', Peter Dodd, G3LDO, *QST* October 1984. See also *Radio Communication* June/July 1980.

[8] 'Further evolution of the double-D', Peter Dodd, G3LDO, *Radio Communication* April 1990.

[9] 'The DDRR antenna', *ARRL Antenna Book*, 15th edn, p6-9.

[10] 'The mobile roofrack antenna', Peter Dodd, G3LDO, *QST* November 1988.

[11] 'Toroidal helix antennas', Pat Hawker, G3VA, in 'Technical Topics', *Radio Communication* June 1994.

[12] 'The G2AJV toroidal antenna', Roger Jennison, G2AJV, *Radio Communication* April and May 1994.

[13] 'Evaluation of the G2AJV toroidal antenna', Peter Dodd, G3LDO, *Radio Communication* August 1994.

[14] 'Fundamental limitations of small antennas', Harold A Wheeler, *Proceedings of the IRE* December 1947.

[15] 'Physical limitations of omni-directional antennas', L J Chu, *Journal of Applied Physics*, Vol 19, December 1948.

8 Mathematical modelling

"As far as the laws of mathematics refer to reality they are not certain; and as far as they are certain they do not refer to reality." – Albert Einstein, 1922

This chapter describes mathematical modelling and computer analysis of antennas. Mathematical modelling is assessed by looking at some of the antenna modelling programs available and examining their strengths and limitations. This subject is extensive and cannot be covered in one chapter of a book this size. Coverage has therefore been restricted to two examples:

- Mathematical modelling the DDRR antenna for efficiency, showing how the model was devised and the results it produced.
- An introduction to modelling antenna gain, directivity and environment using a computer using easily available antenna modelling software.

MODELLING THE EFFICIENCY OF THE DDRR ANTENNA

The efficiency of a transmitting antenna is the ratio of power applied to the antenna to the power radiated from it. The difference between the applied and radiated power represents power loss, which is dissipated as heat.

The *QST* article by Robert Dome, W2WAM, in Appendix 1 describes the development and use of a mathematical model to investigate the efficiency of the DDRR antenna [1, 2].

This article illustrates the thoroughness in which all aspects of the problem need to be addressed when setting up a mathematical model. The DDRR antenna represents an extreme case of how losses can consume much of the transmitted power. The mathematical model is probably the most convenient way of examining these losses and the efficiency of the antenna.

Although the W2WAM article is included as an illustration of mathematical modelling, it is eminently practical. The article illustrates that once the model (formula) has been developed, it is easy to use. All that is required is a scientific calculator and a basic knowledge of mathematics.

MODELLING ANTENNA RADIATION PATTERN AND GAIN

A mathematical model of radiation pattern, gain and interaction between the antenna and its environment is infinitely more complex than the antenna efficiency model already described.

Method of moments (MoM)

One way of surmounting this complexity is to calculate values at selected points, such as the ends of the antenna and some specified intermediate points. The accumulation of errors at the points not specified can be controlled and is known as its *moment*. A number of numerical procedures were unified into a general moment method by R F Harrington and published in 1968 [3]. The method of analysis came to be known as the *method of moments* (MoM).

The antenna structure is divided into a number of straight wires and each of these wires are divided into segments.

The current in each of the segments of each wire is calculated by assuming a known level of RF voltage or current to the antenna feed points(s).

If we consider the simplest of antennas, the centre-fed $\lambda/2$ dipole, the actual current distribution is approximated by segments of constant current. This means that the actual current on the element (which approximates half a sine wave with the current maximum at the centre and zero at the ends as shown in Fig 8.1) is modelled by a series of steps of constant current. It can be seen that the greater the number of segments, the more closely the model will represent the real current distribution.

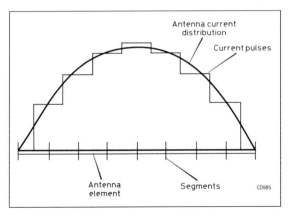

Fig 8.1. Real and modelled current distribution over a λ/2 dipole

Once the magnitude and phase of the current is known, almost all the properties of the antenna can be calculated. The total antenna electromagnetic field pattern can be built up from the magnitude and phases of the currents in the individual segments.

Conversely, current in a conductor segment, located in an electromagnetic field of known intensity, can be calculated from the current amplitudes and phases in these segments.

Calculation of magnitudes and phases of these currents should enable the model, provided that it is sophisticated enough, to represent any antenna configuration or environment.

Antenna systems are often made up of more than one element. These additional elements or wires may be excited by direct connection to the wire or element energised by the source, or connected parasitically as in a Yagi.

The radiation pattern and input impedance of an antenna can be calculated, provided that the current distribution on the structure is known. The current distribution on short, thin wires, where the wire radius is a very small fraction of a wavelength, approximates to a sinusoid with a minimum at the free end of the wire. However, if the wire is thick, an appreciable fraction of a wavelength long, or close to other conductors, the current distribution deviates considerably from the sinusoidal.

This method of mathematical modelling is complex and only really became useful with the advent of the computer. Of the first programs to use the MoM technique, NEC (Numerical Electromagnetic Code) is the most well known. NEC is now in its fourth revision but at the time of writing only NEC-2

is available in the public domain and derivative forms – see 'EZNEC' later in this chapter.

Other methods

For the upper UHF and microwave frequencies the Geometrical Theory of Diffraction (GTD/UTD code) can be used but is beyond the scope of this chapter and is only mentioned to illustrate how computer simulation is now the dominant tool in the field of antenna design.

COMPUTER MODELLING PROGRAMS

With all the calculations necessary to model an antenna it is not surprising that the method was difficult to implement until the advent of the computer.

My first encounter with an antenna computer modelling program was not very auspicious. Early in 1989 I received a letter from a reader in the USA, regarding an article I had written in the *Sprat* magazine [4]. This article described an antenna I had devised called the *double-D* and gave some performance measurements for it. The correspondent wrote that my VHF model polar diagrams were suspect because I did not give details of test methods and my full-sized HF model ground-wave tests with a local radio amateur were "irrelevant" because they were not taken at the elevation angle of maximum radiation.

The correspondent then gave figures that had been obtained from a computer program called MININEC 3 that gave the 'correct' results and showed that the reflector of my antenna design was in fact working as a director. Meanwhile my antenna on the roof, totally unaware of MININEC 3, continued to operate with the parasitic element working as a reflector.

A year later a derivative of MININEC became available called MN. Over a period of time I was able to explore the limitations of this program and obtain later versions and other derivatives as they became available.

The original MININEC program will be briefly described first. Much antenna analysis software available to the radio amateur today is based on MININEC so it is important to understand its limitations.

MININEC

MININEC is a moment methods program developed for the personal computer [5].

MININEC was originally visualised as a cut-down version of NEC, described later, but a considerable amount of original development has gone into this program. The authors had to reduce some of the complex mathematical operations to a level that a PC (in the late 'eighties) could handle in a reasonable amount of time. A number of compromises were necessary and most of the program's limitations are due to these consciously chosen compromises.

There are significant differences between these two codes. Both codes use the method of moments to solve for currents on electrically thin wires. However, each code starts with a different version of the integral formulation for the currents and fields for wires, and follows significantly different algorithms for implementation of the method of moments. NEC calculates for the currents on segments. MININEC calculates based on currents at the nodes defining the segments. Because of its ability to run on a PC, MININEC was very popular and there became thousands of users of it and its derivatives.

An antenna is modelled in three stages. In the first part the user describes the antenna geometry using a text editor.

Key words and a carefully structured input enable the second part of the program to recognise both the variables and their values. This part of the program computes the antenna performance using the MoM method described earlier.

The third part of the program allows the calculated data to be displayed as an azimuth or elevation plot to give a graphic representation of antenna performance.

Constructing a model

All antenna modelling programs require the user to be able to visualise the objects in three-dimensional space. The antenna is modelled as a set of straight conductors called *wires*, the ends of which are

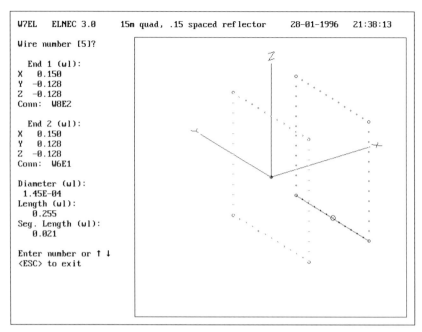

Fig 8.2. Three-dimensional view of a two-element quad antenna showing the *xyz* axis. The small circles at the corners of the loop are wire connecting points. The dots along the wire are segments, described in Fig 8.1. The circle in the centre of wire 6 is the feedpoint (source). This display was created using the ELNEC program (a MININEC derivative described later)

specified in space using *x*, *y* and *z* co-ordinates. A bent or curved wire is modelled by connecting two or more straight wires.

Wires are considered to be connected when their ends share the same *xyz* co-ordinates. For example, each loop of a cubical quad antenna is described by four separate wires whose end points lie at four points. A two-element quad (see Fig 8.2) is thus modelled by eight wires, even though a real quad antenna actually has only two continuous wires strung around the spreaders.

Overlapping wires are not automatically connected by the program. For example, four wires are required to model an X-shaped structure if the conductors are connected at the centre of the X. A Yagi element composed of tapered sections of telescoping tubing may be modelled by using several connected wires having different diameters.

Number of segments

Because the results become more accurate as the number of segments is increased (see Fig 8.1) there is a natural tendency to use a larger number of segments. However, the analysis time and the complex impedance matrix calculated by the program goes up as the square of the number of segments.

Therefore MININEC and all its derivatives have some limit on the allowable number of current pulses.

Generally, using more segments results in higher accuracy, but the analysis takes longer. The number of segments required depends on the geometry of the antenna and on the accuracy required. For example, 5–25 segments are generally used for dipole elements and 20–100 for full-wave loop elements. Many segments are required for very closely spaced wires, such as with folded dipoles or embedded transmission lines, but this in turn can bring other problems.

Algorithm limitations

The MININEC antenna analysis algorithm is accurate for many antenna situations. However, the algorithm does have limitations that can affect analysis accuracy under certain circumstances.

Wire diameter

MININEC shows a slight frequency offset when wire diameter is large (greater than approximately 0.001λ). Normally this effect is significant only at VHF and UHF, although it can be observed at HF as well. Gain, pattern and impedance characteristics of real antennas occur slightly lower in frequency than modelled. Most practical designs using large-diameter wire should be biased slightly high in frequency to compensate for this effect.

Closely spaced wires

Closely spaced wires, whether parallel or forming a V, require many more segments to model accurately than do the same wires separated by a greater distance. This makes it impractical to model antennas containing embedded transmission lines, such as log-periodic arrays.

Ground losses

For antennas modelled over ground, MININEC calculates wire currents assuming perfectly conducting earth. Horizontal antennas located less than about 0.25λ over real earth will incur ground losses not calculated by MININEC.

Wires connected at a non-zero angle

Wires connected at non-zero angles, such as a quad (where the wires are connected at 90°) require additional segments. A reasonable estimate of gain and pattern can be achieved with four segments per quarter-wavelength of a full-wave square loop but there will be a frequency offset and impedance

inaccuracy. (Frequency offset is a point where the program indicates resonance that is different from the true resonance of the real antenna.) The model of a three-element quad (designed by the late Al Slater, G3FXB) whose optimum performance occurred at 14.15MHz, exhibited optimum performance at 14.6MHz when modelled on MN using six segments per wire.

With wires connected at acute angles, such as the double-D antenna described in Chapter 7, the errors increase unless even more segments are used. The straightforward solution in this situation is to increase the number of segments. However, doing so increases computation time and may require more than the permitted maximum of 127 total pulses. There is a technique for improving the accuracy with a smaller total number of pulses or segments known as *tapering*. This technique is described under 'Segment tapering for wires joining at an angle' on p118.

Element mounting and boom effects

The method used to mount Yagi elements to a boom can greatly affect antenna performance, particularly at VHF and UHF. Conductive mounting plates and through-the-boom mounting raise the resonant frequency of an element.

Very short wires

MININEC can exhibit reactance errors when a very short wire is connected to a longer one. The length of each segment should be both greater than 0.0001λ and greater than the wire diameter.

THE ELNEC MININEC DERIVATIVE

There are a number of MININEC derivatives available (see Appendix 2) that are easier to use than MININEC. Although there are generally no mathematical changes to these programs they all have additional features, with each new version introducing additional enhancements. Rather than try to describe them all, the discussion is limited to ELNEC and EZNEC (a NEC-2 derivative described later in this chapter), both written by Roy Lewallen, W7EL. In a chapter this size only a brief description can be given – the on-disk user manuals that come with these programs are 90 pages for ELNEC and 130 pages for EZNEC. Much of the information that follows is based on these manuals.

The ELNEC program is one of the easiest to use if you are new to antenna modelling using a computer. It does not require a great deal of computer power by today's standards. An IBM PC compatible computer with a hard disk drive and at least 640k of RAM is all that is required. ELNEC is available with a coprocessor option, which runs much faster when a coprocessor is installed.

Antenna geometry

ELNEC uses the same Cartesian co-ordinate system to refer to points in space as MININEC. *x* and *y* are in the horizontal plane and *z* is height. The antenna model in Fig 8.2 is taken from a three-dimensional view of the antenna geometry, which can be displayed on the graphics screen after the antenna file has been created.

This ability to view the antenna geometry is an important feature. With a geometric display misplaced wires may be easily identified. The antenna can also be rotated and viewed from any angle, and scaled in size.

ELNEC operation involves the constant revision of the last file used in the previous session. All the variables appear on the main screen or subscreens and reference to the manual is only required occasionally. The method of entering antenna parameters is illustrated in Fig 8.3, which shows a spreadsheet-type display into which the data is entered.

```
                 ELNEC  ver. 3.0 / MaxP option
                 (c) 1994  by Roy Lewallen, W7EL

TI  TITLE:                    14MHz Double-D, free space
FR  FREQUENCY:                14.2 MHz. (wavelength = 21.11215 m.)

WI  WIRES:                    46 Wires          WL  WIRE LOSS: Zero
SO  SOURCES:                  1 Source          UN  UNITS:     Wavelengths
LO  LOADS:                    0 Loads
GT  GROUND TYPE:              Free Space            LAST FILE SVD/RCLD:
                                                    LAST.EN

PT  PLOT TYPE:                Azimuth           AR  ANAL RES:   1 Deg.
PA  ELEVATION ANGLE:          0 Deg.            RF  REFERENCE:  0 dBi
PR  PLOT/TABLE RANGE:         0 - 360 Deg. (full) SZ SWR Z0:    75 ohms
SS  STEP SIZE:                5 Deg.
OR  OUTER RING OF PLOT:       Automatic scaling
FI  FIELD(S) TO PLOT:         V, H, and Total

(BR)owse file   (DE)lete, (RE)call, (SA)ve desc   (Freq S)wp   <RET> = Plot
(AN)alyze   (CU)rrents   (Load D)ata   (OP)tions   (Print D)esc   (Src D)ata
(TA)ble   (View A)ntenna        (EX)it pgm without saving desc   (QU)it
```

Fig 8.3. Spreadsheet-type display entry into ELNEC. A two-letter abbreviation is used to enter any submenu. For example, keying in 'WI' will take you into the 'Wires' subscreen where the model is built. 'VA' allows you to 'View the Antenna' to confirm that model has the configuration you originally envisaged

```
               --------------- WIRES ---------------

Wire Conn. --- End 1 (x,y,z : m)    Conn. --- End 2 (x,y,z : m)    Dia(mm)  Seg

 1  W2E1  -3.048,  1.829,  0.000  W3E1   3.048,  1.829,  0.000  1.91E+01  18
 2  W1E1  -3.048,  1.829,  0.000        -1.143,  0.508,  2.134    # 18    18
 3  W1E2   3.048,  1.829,  0.000         1.143,  0.508,  2.134    # 18    18
 4  W5E1  -3.175, -1.829,  0.000  W6E1   3.175, -1.829,  0.000  1.91E+01  18
 5  W4E1  -3.175, -1.829,  0.000        -1.143, -0.508,  2.134    # 18    18
 6  W4E2   3.175, -1.829,  0.000         1.143, -0.508,  2.134    # 18    18
                                                            Tot segs: 108

(number) = wire to change   (A)dd wires   (D)elete wires   (G)roup edit
chg ant (H)t   (R)enumber wire   (T)aper segments   chg (U)nits   (V)iew antenna
Preserve Connections = OFF; X to turn ON            <ESC> = ret to main menu
```

Fig 8.4. An example of the ELNEC Wires subscreen. The numbers indicate the *x*, *y* and *z* co-ordinates of 'end 1' and 'end 2' of each wire. The two bent elements of the double-D geometry are each constructed with three wires. Wire connections of wire 1 to other wires are confirmed by 'W2E1' (Wire 2, End 1) and 'W3E1' (Wire 3, End 1) respectively

The antenna *x*, *y* and *z* co-ordinates are created using the WI Wires subscreen; an example is shown in Fig 8.4. All the entries are numeric. The double-D antenna, described in Chapter 7, has been used in many of the following examples. This antenna is essentially a two-element Yagi with bent elements and provides an interesting example of antenna modelling using a computer.

For complex antenna geometries ELNEC has a 'group edit' feature which allows you to copy, move, add, or delete groups of wires, sources, loads, or media. You also can fill any block of data with a common value. Another feature permits changing the units of measure. This is particularly useful for switching between wave-lengths and other units, or for converting a design from metric to Imperial units or vice-versa.

ELNEC only saves a file when requested, except for the last file of a session.

Wire currents may be viewed after the impedance is calculated. Fig 8.5 shows a three-dimensional view of the antenna geometry of a two-element VHF Yagi. Wire currents are displayed directly in relation to the wires in the geometry and show currents in their true physical context. The currents may be displayed as phasors or as magnitude only. With phasors, the distance from a wire to the current trace represents magnitude, and the rotation angle of the trace around the wire represents phase. This aspect can be seen more easily when the antenna model is rotated so that the elements are viewed end-on the phase and amplitude of the currents can be seen.

Loads and lumped circuits

ELNEC can model lumped circuits with different load models such as impedance loads or Laplace Transform loads. The impedance load is a resistor in series with reactance. This model can be used to model antennas containing a resistive load, such as a rhombic or a Beverage.

Fig 8.6 illustrates the current components of a travelling wave on a rhombic antenna which is terminated with a resistor. Wires with travelling-wave currents exhibit spiral current traces when current phase is displayed. The circular

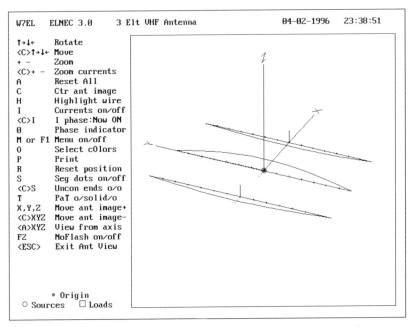

Fig 8.5. Three-dimensional view of a three-element VHF Yagi, showing relative current distribution and phase on the driven element and the parasitic elements. Small markers, showing 0° and 90° are used as phase references. If the model is rotated and tilted so that it can be viewed down the y axis the currents appear as phasors

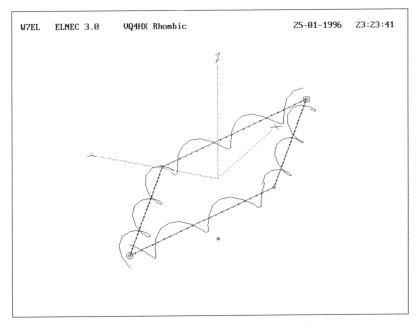

Fig 8.6. The current components of a travelling wave on a rhombic antenna

symmetry of a phasor spiral, which depends on the value of the termination resistor, can be viewed by sighting down a wire axis.

The Laplace Transform is a special polynomial representation of a lumped circuit. It enables the program to model multiband trap antennas and loaded dipoles and whips. It also enables a simple inductor or capacitor to be modelled without having to specify a new reactance value when the frequency is changed.

Segment tapering for wires joining at an angle

Wires joining at an angle must have shorter segments than single straight wires or wires joining in a line. This is because of the way MININEC handles the currents at wire junctions. Instead of making the entire wires out of short

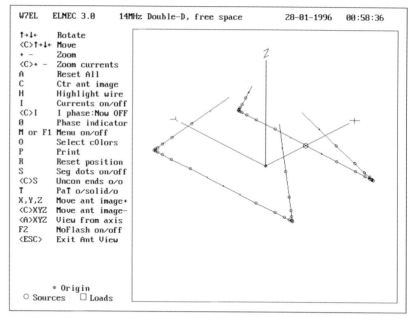

Fig 8.7. Wire taper segmentation used on a model of the double-D antenna as automated by ELNEC

segments, the segments can be made short near the junction, tapering to a longer length away from the junction. Both programs automate this process but it is useful to know how the procedure works so you can optimise it for your particular purpose. The basic procedure is to replace the original wire with several wires of different lengths. The new wire closest to the junction is made very short and with one segment. The second wire is made twice the length of the first, also with one segment. This process is continued until the segment length becomes long enough (say, $\lambda/20$), and the remainder of the original wire is made up of a multiple-segment wire of approximately this segment length.

Fig 8.7 shows a model of the double-D antenna and the arrangement of the tapered connections.

Plotting

The far-field azimuth and elevation patterns are plotted directly on the screen in polar co-ordinates. These can be plotted in ARRL log periodic or linear log – see Chapter 4 for more details on the meaning of these plots.

The plots can be saved and viewed later without repeating the analysis. The forward gain, front-to-back ratio, maximum sidelobe level and beamwidth can be displayed as an overlay as shown in Fig 8.8.

Once the gain and pattern have been computed

the element currents and pattern may be superimposed over the view of the model as shown in Fig 8.9.

Frequency sweep

With ELNEC the plots from data calculated at specified frequencies can be overlaid in colour on one display, giving a very good graphic comparison of the performance of an antenna over a given frequency range – see Fig 8.10.

The frequency sweep is set up from a sub-screen – see Fig 8.11.

Additionally the output from this function can be sent to a file for use with the MicroSmith program (see Chapter 2). From this an automatically generated analysis of feedpoint impedance characteristics can be made, together with the design of appropriate matching networks.

Modelling ground

All the polar diagrams shown so far are plotted as free-space diagrams that assume no ground reflection effect. A horizontal section at 0° relative to the x axis through the three-dimensional diagram describes characteristics of the antenna without the complication of taking ground into consideration and is the easiest way to model or compare antenna configurations in the early stages of comparison or development.

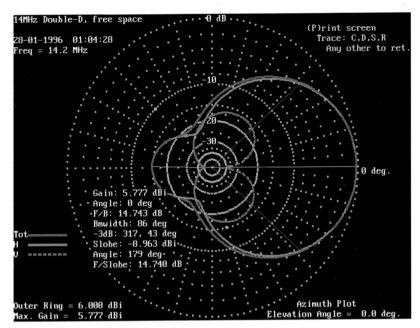

Fig 8.8. Horizontal free-space polar plot of a double-D antenna. Forward gain, front-to-back ratio, maximum sidelobe level and beamwidth are shown superimposed on the plot

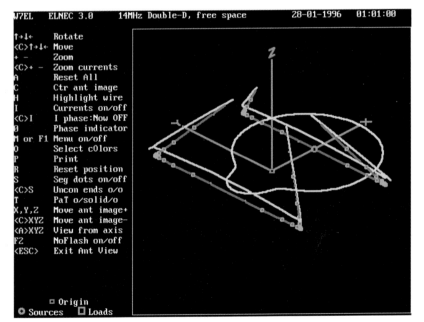

Fig 8.9. The element currents and gain pattern shown superimposed over the view of the model

ground environments. If either a perfect or 'real' ground is specified, ELNEC assumes a perfect ground for impedance and current calculations. The 'real' ground description is used only for determining the shape and strength of the far field (pattern). ELNEC calculates the far field pattern that results from ground absorption or partial reflection due to finite ground conductivity and permittivity.

The diagram in Chapter 5, Fig 5.10, shows how an azimuth polar diagram of a three-element beam near to ground is obtained.

When an azimuth plot is selected (see 'PT Plot Type' in Fig 8.3) the elevation angle must also be selected. The most representative diagram is plotted at an angle of maximum radiation of the vertical main lobe caused by ground. This angle can be obtained by first making an 'Elevation Plot', also selected by 'PT'. Plots at other elevation angles give very similar polar diagrams (see Fig 8.12) but with different gain figures. This illustrates the point that antenna comparison measurements should be made, where possible, at the angle of maximum radiation; if this is not possible then antennas should be compared at the same height above ground.

A wire is connected to ground by specifying a zero z co-ordinate at one end. In Fig 8.13 a four-square array is modelled using four verticals, each fed at the point where it contacts ground.

This popular phased array has several desirable properties. Because of its symmetry, it is easy to

In the real world, ground affects the far-field patterns of most antennas. The effect of ground is described in Chapter 5, Figs 5.9 and 5.10.

ELNEC provides free-space, ideal ground, or 'real'

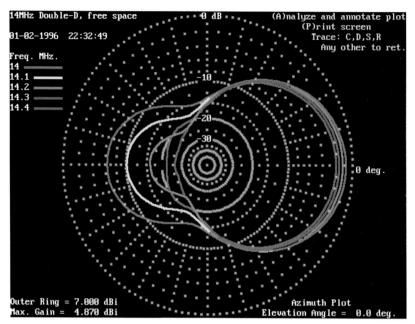

Fig 8.10. The frequency sweep of a double-D antenna, giving a graphic comparison of the performance of this antenna over a given frequency range. The measurement frequencies are shown in the colour legend at the top left-hand corner of the display

```
ELNEC  ver. 3.0 / MaxP option
(c) 1994  by Roy Lewallen, W7EL

These remain in effect until a new file is recalled or ELNEC is ended.

FO  FREQUENCY SWEEP:          ON
      START FREQUENCY:        14 MHz.
FL    STOP FREQUENCY:         14.4 MHz.
      FREQUENCY STEP:         .1 MHz.
PN  PAT PLOT FILES NAME:      DDXTAP.F(#)
SN  MICROSMITH FILE NAME:     MicroSmith files will not be saved
FN  FREQ SWP FILE NAME:       DDXTAP

SF  SAVE IN FREQ SWP FILE:
                              Pattern table:            √
                              Source data (incl SWR):   √
                              Load data:
                              Currents:
                              Pattern analysis:

(DE)lete, (BR)owse freq sweep file
                                  <ESC> to return to Main Menu
```

Fig 8.11. The frequency sweep sub-screen. The frequency sweep range and step are selected with 'FL'. Each time a plot is calculated it is saved on a .F(#) file and all files are displayed at the end of the frequency sweep

switch in four directions. The forward lobe is broad enough to ensure that four-direction switching gives good coverage to all directions. Good rejection of signals occurs over a broad region to the rear. The small rear nulls can be eliminated and the forward gain increased slightly by increasing the element spacing. However, this may make the physical spacing too great for convenient use of some feedmethods.

The efficiency of a ground radial system cannot be determined using ELNEC, and the impedances given for low (lower than about 0.2λ) horizontal antennas will not be correct. Specifically, the resistive part of the impedance of low horizontal antennas will be unrealistically low, which also results in incorrectly high reported gain. ELNEC shares this limitation with MININEC and all other MININEC-based programs, which was consciously made by the authors of MININEC to limit the code size and computation time.

Note that the pattern of a low horizontal antenna will have the correct shape (although the reported impedance and gain will be wrong) provided that all parts of the antenna are at the same height.

Maximum Pulse Option (MaxP)

The ELNEC Maximum Pulse Option (MaxP) is a program which works in conjunction with ELNEC version 2.20 or higher to increase the complexity of antennas which ELNEC can model. Without MaxP, ELNEC is limited to a maximum of 127 pulses. (The number of pulses approximately equals the total number of wire segments.) With MaxP, ELNEC's capability is limited only by the available amount of conventional RAM. Depending on how much conventional RAM (lowest 640k) can be freed, MaxP increases ELNEC's capability to as many as 260 pulses, with at least 230 being obtainable with most systems.

MaxP is the calculation portion of ELNEC, specially compiled to work with the huge arrays generated when analysing antennas with more than 127

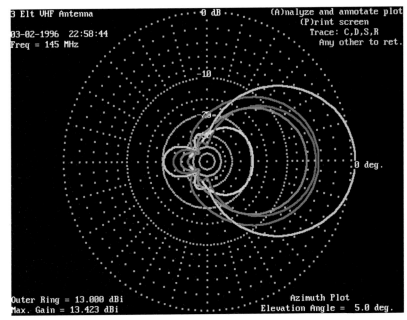

Fig 8.12. Azimuth polar plots at different elevation angles of a three-element beam, 1λ above ground. The purple plot is taken at 5°, light blue at 15°, green at 25°, yellow at 30° and the dark blue plot is at 40°. The antenna has two vertical lobes – see Fig 5.10, Chapter 5

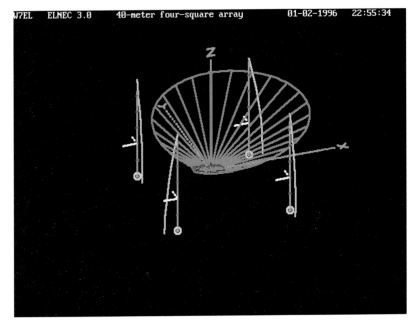

Fig 8.13. A four-square array, modelled using four verticals, each fed at the point where they contact the ground. The maximum gain occurs half-way between the x and the y axis so you would have to set the azimuth angle to 45° to model the elevation plot

pulses. When correctly installed and started, ELNEC detects the presence of MaxP and automatically uses

it for calculation when the number of pulses exceeds 127.

Because of the special compilation, MaxP is much slower than the main ELNEC program in doing calculations. This speed reduction is about two to four times, depending on the antenna. However, the presence of MaxP does not have any effect on ELNEC if the number of pulses is 127 or fewer.

NEC AND EZNEC

EZNEC is a NEC derivative, also written by Roy Lewallen, W7EL. Unlike ELNEC the fundamental computation portion of EZNEC is that of NEC-2, but it uses the operator interface developed for ELNEC.

Again, unlike ELNEC, which will run with only 640k of RAM, the EZNEC memory requirement is determined by the complexity of the antenna being modelled; the most significant factor being the total number of wire segments.

EZNEC requires just under two megabytes of available extended memory (RAM) to load and run. With just this amount, fairly complex antennas can be modelled. To analyse more elaborate antennas, EZNEC requires more resources. It will use additional extended memory if available; if not, it will use the hard disk as 'virtual RAM', writing, reading, and erasing temporary files on the disk as required. Six megabytes of RAM is adequate to run nearly any antenna of 500 or fewer segments entirely in RAM. If less RAM is available and the disk must be used for virtual RAM, over eight megabytes of disk space may be required for a 500-segment antenna.

Since disk operations occur frequently in the course of normal EZNEC operation, a disk cache can speed operation considerably. This may be true even if creating a disk cache reduces the amount of available RAM to the point that EZNEC has to use the disk for virtual RAM.

One of the main differences between ELNEC and EZNEC is in the way ground is modelled. EZNEC includes two new ways to do this which permit accurate modelling of antennas with horizontal wires very close to the ground.

Note that EZNEC cannot model wires in contact with or under the ground. EZNEC is unable to accurately model buried ground radial systems or systems within 0.01λ and 0.05λ of the ground at HF, but it can model elevated systems with an accuracy that increases with height above ground.

Another major improvement over ELNEC is the elimination of the 'cutting corners' problem with wires joining at an angle.

Quads can now be modelled accurately with a relatively small number of segments, and without the necessity of segment length tapering.

EZNEC doesn't suffer from the 'frequency offset' problem of MININEC-based programs. It can also handle transmission line modelling, which simplifies modelling of log-periodic antennas and allows the modelling of phased array feed systems (if the feed systems consist only of transmission lines). Line ends may be left open or shorted to model stubs.

```
                    ┌──────────────────────────────────┐
                    │        EZNEC  ver. 1.0           │
                    │  (c) 1995  by Roy Lewallen, W7EL  │
                    └──────────────────────────────────┘

   TI   TITLE:                Rectangle loop 10'wide x 30'hi
   FR   FREQUENCY:            14.2 MHz. (wavelength = 69.26558 ft.)

   WI   WIRES:                8 Wires          WL  WIRE LOSS: Zero
   SO   SOURCES:              1 Source         UN  UNITS:     Feet
   LO   LOADS:                0 Loads
   TL   TRANSMISSION LINES:   0 Lines
   GT   GROUND TYPE:          Real/Fast Anal       LAST FILE SVD/RCLD:
   GD   GND DESCRIPTION:      1 Medium             \RADIO\EZNEC\ANT\HEN4.EZ

   PT   PLOT TYPE:            Elevation        RF  REFERENCE: 0 dBi
   PA   AZIMUTH ANGLE:        0 Deg.           SZ  SWR Z0:    50 ohms
   PR   PLOT/TABLE RANGE:     0 - 180 Deg. (full)  FI  PLOT FLDS: V, H, Total
   SS   STEP SIZE:            1 Deg.
   OR   OUTER RING OF PLOT:   Automatic scaling

   (BR)owse file    (DE)lete, (RE)call, (SA)ve desc   (Freq S)wp   <RET> = Plot
   (AN)alyze  (CU)rrents  (Guideline C)k  (Load D)ata  (OP)tions  (Print D)esc
   (Src D)ata  (TA)ble  (View A)nt  (EX)it pgm without saving desc  (QU)it
```

Fig 8.14. Spreadsheet-type display entry into EZNEC. It is very similar to the ELNEC display shown in Fig 8.3. The additional features most apparent are TL Transmission Lines and GC Guideline Check

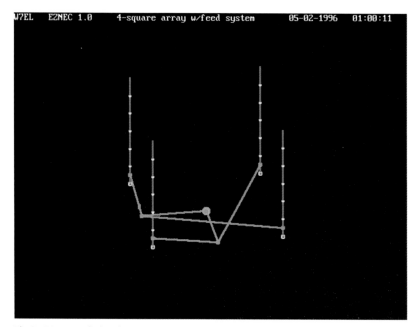

Fig 8.15. Transmission line model of four-square antenna

Four-square with transmission lines

This model uses EZNEC's transmission line models for the feed system. Note that the lengths are not what might be expected because the delay in a transmission line is not equal to its electrical length except in special circumstances – circumstances which don't occur in most phased arrays [8].

As it stands, the model is unsatisfactory for testing the feed system over a range of frequencies. This is because the feedline lengths are specified in degrees and the implied physical length changes with frequency.

NEC-2, and hence EZNEC, is segment-based rather than pulse-based (segment-junction based); it is somewhat more fussy about segment length/diameter ratio and minimum segment length than MININEC. So EZNEC includes a Guideline Check (see Fig 8.14) to notify you if these parameters or some others are beyond limits.

All sources, loads, and transmission lines are placed at segment centres, rather than segment junctions. (Actually, they're distributed over the whole segment.) This is one reason for modifying the information read from ELNEC files. Being segment-based makes it impossible to place a source, load, or transmission line at the junction of two wires. EZNEC contains new 'split' source types which behave just like ordinary sources, but can be placed at wire junctions. It does this by creating two sources, placed on each side of the junction. When using this program it is a good idea to use an odd number of segments for wires, so that sources, loads and transmission lines can be placed on the centre segment if desired. (ELNEC requires an even number in order to place a source or load at the centre.)

Like any other modelling program, NEC-2 (and therefore EZNEC) has limitations of its own. The most severe probably is inaccuracy in modelling wires which change diameter, as in elements made from telescoping tubing. It has a serious effect on Yagis and other sharply tuned antennas (the situation is even worse when modelling wire connected to the end of tubing as in the construction of the all-metal quad antenna and the metal double-D) but isn't generally serious for others. In the EZNEC documentation this is referred to as the 'stepped-diameter' problem. This limitation has been corrected in NEC-4 but, at the time of writing, this code wasn't available for inclusion into EZNEC. However, it does include a 'stepped-diameter correction' to calculate an equivalent length and constant diameter for a combination of collinear wires with different diameters. Results of this approximation are quite good, although they are valid only for elements which are close to resonance.

With the new ground types comes a trap. With ELNEC, the ground is considered perfect for calculation of impedance and currents. With EZNEC, a ground connection to one of the new ground types acts as though the antenna extends into the lossy ground. For a vertical antenna, the connection will look like a single ground stake at the base of the antenna. For that reason, a MININEC- (or ELNEC-) style ground model is also included.

You may want to use it for vertical antenna systems, since its results except for modelling ground loss are valid for vertical antennas.

COMPUTER MODELLING UNUSUAL ANTENNA CONFIGURATIONS
The 21MHz double-D antenna

Earlier on in this chapter an account of a situation was given where a computer model of a double-D for 21MHz (see Fig 7.7) and measurements on the real antenna were at odds. As a result I have followed the development of these programs with interest, and that is why models of this antenna feature so much in this chapter.

When EZNEC became available I wrote to Roy Lewallen, W7EL, for advice on this particular antenna problem and what follows is part of his reply.

"You are certainly correct that the double-D antenna presents a challenge for MoM programs! ELNEC has the known MININEC problem of 'cutting corners' with bent wires, and EZNEC the known NEC-2 problem of having trouble with stepped diameters. I now have a third program which is alleged to be the best yet and without any of these problems. Having spent an evening running variations of the double-D with all three, I can cautiously make some statements.

"1. Minor errors in analysis always show up worst when modelling parasitic elements, because small changes in the analysis can cause large changes in antenna performance. Most noticeable is front/back ratio at a given frequency.

"2. EZNEC, because of its NEC-2 engine, isn't capable of producing extremely accurate results when diameters of connecting wires differ by a large ratio. The ratio in the double-D is about 19:1. This is too large for really accurate results.

"3. This one is really a surprise but true. When modelling antennas with large-diameter steps, best results with EZNEC will be obtained with the smallest number of segments possible. The objective is to get the largest segment length/diameter ratio near the junction where the wires join. Tapering with small segments at the junction makes the program less, not more, accurate. The best method is to use the automatic segmentation feature in the Wires Menu and select (M)in. recommended. Another rule may apply in some circumstances, such as the low vertical with elevated radials, where the diameter of the vertical wire is very different from the radial wires.

"4. ELNEC, with tapered segment (small segments at the junction), is roughly as (in)accurate as EZNEC when large-diameter steps are involved. I'm not sure why this is, unless NEC-4 is in error and ELNEC is correct.

"5. The chief inaccuracy is in the calculated reactance. This means that the programs will show representative performance, but at the incorrect frequency. The frequency sweep option can be used find the frequency at which the desired performance is obtained. This will be representative of what the antenna will deliver, but the actual antenna will have to be adjusted to produce that performance at the desired frequency.

"I ran frequency sweeps with ELNEC, EZNEC and NEC-4 to find the frequency at which the front/back ratio was best, within 50kHz. Here are the results:

EZNEC: 13.55MHz Gain = 5.13dBi, f/b = 21.11dB, feedpoint $Z = 47.07 + j6.93$

NEC-4: 13.85MHz Gain = 5.08dBi, f/b = 21.95dB, feedpoint $Z = 50.42 + j6.08$

ELNEC: 14.20MHz Gain = 5.16dBi, f/b = 23.72dB, feedpoint $Z = 50.88 + j5.19$

"For ELNEC I used the minimum recommended number of segments. The ELNEC model was tapered using the default limits. NEC-4 used the double-D.EN model except for adding one segment to wire 1 to keep the source centred.

"You can see that the reported performance is nearly identical for all three programs, but they disagree at what frequency it occurs. So I have high confidence that you'd be able to achieve this performance by adjusting the parasitic element length for the best f/b at the desired frequency."

The compact metal double-D

The compact version of the double-D was described in Chapter 7. VHF modelling tests indicated that the

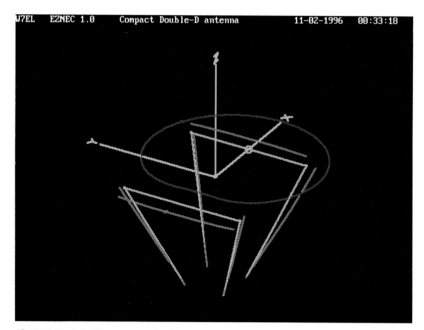

Fig 8.16. Model of the compact double-D antenna. The horizontal elements are only 0.17λ long

horizontal sections could be reduced to around 0.17λ before the performance really started to deteriorate. The implications of these experiments were that a 7MHz beam could be constructed having the same horizontal area as a three-element beam for 15m. The model is illustrated in Fig 8.16.

A frequency sweep of the compact double-D is shown in Fig 8.17. Compare this with the larger model of the same antenna shown in Fig 8.10.

The HF skeleton slot antenna

This antenna was first designed and described by Bill Sykes, G2HCG, in 1956 [8]. It was brought to my attention by Bill Capstick, G3JYP, who had used one with some success for many years (his work was described by G3VA [9] in 1969 and more recently in [10]). The antenna comprises three 3.05m (10ft) horizontal elements spaced 4.57m (15ft) vertically apart. The ends of the elements are connected and the antenna is fed at the centre of the centre horizontal element – see Fig 8.18.

The skeleton slot antenna has some interesting characteristics and the antenna analyser programs already discussed are very suitable for analysing them. One of these characteristics is that it has similar azimuth polar diagrams over a wide range of frequencies – see Fig 8.19.

The real performance of this antenna can be seen

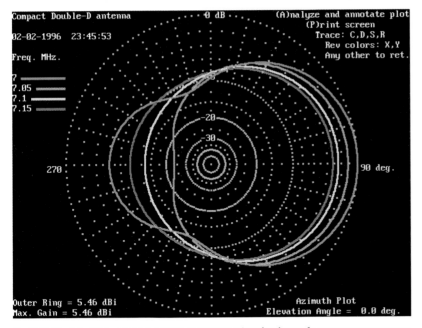

Fig 8.17. Model of the compact double-D antenna showing its performance over a range of frequencies

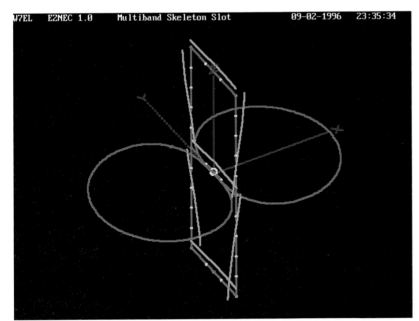

Fig 8.18. The HF skeleton slot antenna showing the general configuration. The currents in the vertical section are equal and opposite and there is no vertical radiation component; hence the vertical elements can be regarded as high-impedance twin-wire transmission line

looking at the elevation polar plots during a frequency sweep as shown in Fig 8.20. These plots

were calculated for a model whose lowest element is 4.8m (15ft) high.

I built a full-size version using the dimensions from the computer model. The self-supporting mast described in Chapter 6 (see Fig 6.11) is very suitable for this type of antenna configuration.

The horizontal elements were made from 25mm aluminium tubing (tapering to 20mm) insulated from the mast using plastic tubing. 14 SWG stranded copper wire was used for the vertical elements, fixed to the horizontal elements with hose clamps. and the antenna was fed at the centre horizontal element using 450Ω heavy-duty slotted twin line.

The antenna appears to perform as predicted by the model and resulted in my first taste of DX operating in the 18MHz band.

USING MATHEMATICAL MODELS

I have in the past always used a practical and empirical approach to designing antennas. My conversion to the use of the mathematical model was precipitated by the *QST* article by W2WAM, mentioned earlier and reproduced in Appendix 1. I had built a mobile version of the DDRR antenna (see Chapter 7) to the design and dimensions in the *ARRL Antenna Book* [1]. I subsequently modified this antenna after reading the *QST* article and the improvement in its performance was very noticeable.

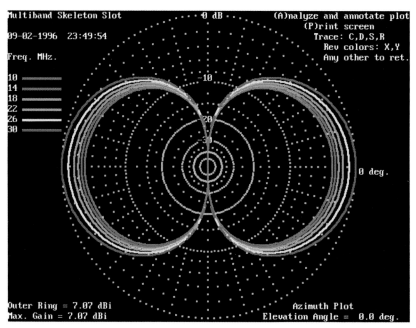

Fig 8.19. The azimuth polar plots of a skeleton slot antenna, calculated for a free-space model

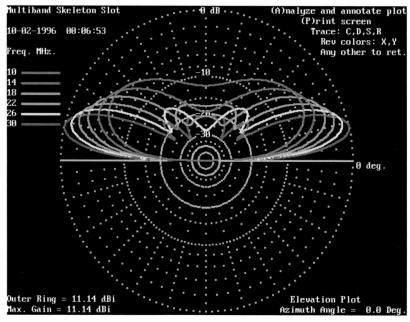

Fig 8.20. Elevation frequency sweep polar plots of a skeleton slot antenna, calculated over average ground

This is because I had already discovered the limitations in these programs described in item 1 of Roy Lewallen's letter, described earlier.

Note that the computer modelling programs described are little more than numerical experiments. The programs often have to be run repeatedly (often automatically) to gain insight into an antenna's performance. They do not generate analytical formula or expressions to gauge how the result might change with an alteration of antenna configuration.

Modelling guidelines of a program must be followed and algorithm limitations noted.

Unfortunately many of the rules can be ignored and the program will still give results – usually wrong.

Beware of antenna articles and books that rely exclusively on a computer program for the data on the described antennas; unless, of course, they are just exploring ideas.

Ideally, a computer analysis should be the prelude to a real design.

These antenna analysis programs have considerable value and have had a significant impact on antenna design methods.

If you have a computer and an interest in antennas it is thoroughly recommended that you try one. Not only can you model your favourite antenna but you can learn a lot about antennas in general.

Information regarding the range and availability of these programs is given in Appendix 2.

With regard to the computer models based on MININEC, I have tended to use computer modelling to explore trends of various antenna configurations rather than expect specific and accurate answers.

FURTHER READING

'Comparing MININECS, a guide to choosing an antenna optimization program', L B Cebik, W4RNL, *Communications Quarterly* Spring 1994.

REFERENCES

[1] *The ARRL Antenna Book,* 15th edn.

[2] 'A study of the DDRR antenna', Robert B Dome, *QST* July 1972.

[3] *Field Computation by Moment Methods,* R F Harrington, Macmillan Company, New York, 1968.

[4] 'Further evolution of the G3LDO double-D antenna', Peter Dodd, G3LDO, *Sprat* (*Journal of the G-QRP Club*), No 49, Winter 1986/87.

[5] *The New MININEC (Version 3): A Mini-Numerical Electromagnetic Code,* J C Logan and J W Rockway, Naval Ocean Systems Centre, San Diego, California.

[6] 'MININEC: the other edge of the sword', Roy Lewallen, W7EL, *QST* February 1991.

[7] 'The simplest phased array feed system that works', *ARRL Antenna Compendium,* Vol 2.

[8] 'The skeleton slot aerial system, B Sykes, G2HCG, *Short Wave Magazine* January 1955.

[9] 'Antenna, Skeleton Slot, HF,14/21/28MHz' in 'Technical Topics', *Radio Communication* June 1969.

[10] 'The HF skeleton slot', Bill Capstick, G3JYP, *Radio Communication* July 1996.

1 A study of the DDRR antenna

by Robert B Dome, W2WAM

I WAS very much interested in the article 'A 40-Metre DDRR Antenna' by W E English that appeared on pp28–31 of the December 1971 issue of *QST*. My analysis indicates that the main advantage of the DDRR is its low profile or inconspicuousness, but that the efficiency is rather low as compared to conventional half-wave dipoles suspended high above the earth.

The DDRR antenna may be described in the more familiar terms as being a short grounded vertical antenna having a horizontal or flat-top extension to provide quarter-wave resonance. As such, the radiation resistance may be determined from existing technical sources. With the resistance known, and from a computation of the surge impedance, it is possible to compute the feedpoint impedance, the open-end voltage, and the Q and bandwidth of the antenna. Any actual variation from the calculated impedance would indicate added losses and hence decreased Q, efficiency and end voltage. It will also be shown that lengthening the vertical section will improve the efficiency. A word also will be given regarding the effect of a shunt-tuning capacitor at the end of the antenna and why its capacitance should be held at the minimum possible value.

RADIATION RESISTANCE

The radiation resistance is made up of two parts, namely, that owing to the vertical section and that owing to the horizontal section.

(a) Radiation resistance of vertical section

The antenna under study is one which is a quarter-wave in overall length resulting in a current loop at the ground point. The radiation resistance of the vertical portion, referred to the base of the antenna, may be determined from reference [1]. On p475 of this reference is found Table I. For the quarter-wave antenna, the radiation resistance of the vertical

portion is obtained by adding R_1 and R_2 because in Eq 107, p474, for such an antenna length $q = \pi$ radians and cos $q = -1$ and sin $q = 0$; likewise:

$$\sin^2\left(\frac{q}{2}\right) = 1.0$$

Thus:

$$R_v = R_1 + R_2 \text{ ohms} \tag{1}$$

where R_v is the radiation resistance of the vertical portion. This is shown plotted as curve 1 of Fig A1.1 as a function of vertical height expressed in degrees, where $90° = $ a quarter-wave.

It will be observed that this curve is a straight line for very short vertical lengths with a slope of 2 on the log-log paper used, thereby indicating that the resistance varies directly as the square (or the second power) of the vertical length. For the straight line portion of the curve, the radiation resistance may be computed without reference to the curve using the equation:

$$R_v = 1578\left(\frac{H}{\lambda}\right)^2 \text{ ohms} \tag{2}$$

where H is the antenna vertical length in metres and λ is the wavelength of resonance in metres.

Example: If a 7MHz (40m) antenna has a height of $H = 0.303$m (12in) then:

$$R_v = 1578\left(\frac{0.303}{40}\right)^2 = 0.0902\Omega \tag{3}$$

This height corresponds to an angular height of:

$$\phi = 360°\left(\frac{H}{\lambda}\right) = 360°\left(\frac{0.303}{40}\right) = 2.72° \tag{4}$$

An inspection of the curves shows that at $H = 2.72°$, $R_v = 0.09\Omega$, in agreement with the calculated value. Incidentally, the coefficient 1578 also agrees with the figure given in Eq 26, p795, of reference [2].

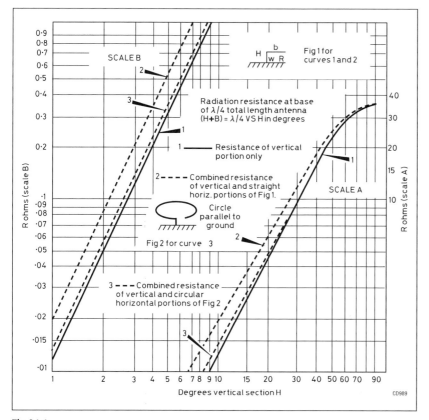

Fig A1.1

Since a 40m wavelength in feet is 132, it is seen that in Eq 3 above that if H is measured in wavelengths, $H = (1/132)\lambda$ or 0.00758λ, which is, of course, a very short antenna. It can be shown that Eq 2 yields results correct to within 1% for $H \leq 8.55°$ or $H \leq 0.0237\lambda$ which at 40m wavelength is 3.12ft. At $H = 8.55°$, the radiation resistance $R_v = 0.89192\Omega$ from reference [1], while from Eq 2 the result is 0.900Ω, a 1% discrepancy.

(b) Radiation resistance of horizontal section

The horizontal section may be regarded as approximately half of a dipole in the horizontal plane and therefore will have radiation resistance. The radiation is directed upward and will not contribute to the field strength along the ground but may be useful to achieve short skip. The radiation resistance is obtained from reference [1], Table II on p475 or Fig 11 on p476. These data apply only to a straight run for the horizontal portion. It was more convenient to use the curves than to carry out the more tedious

calculations involving r_2, r_3 etc. This was done accordingly and the resulting resistances were added to the vertical radiation resistance to obtain curve 2 of Fig A1.1.

For very short vertical lengths, the *total* radiation resistance is given by the asymptotic equation:

$$R_T = 2620 \left(\frac{H}{\lambda}\right)^2 \text{ ohms} \quad (5)$$

where R_T is the total radiation resistance and H and λ are defined as for Eq 2.

The results are in error by less than 1% if the vertical length $H \leq 0.0237\lambda$.

When the horizontal section is curved into a a circle as in the DDRR antenna, two effects cause the radiation resistance of the horizontal section to decrease. The first is the partial cancellation of the field from the side of the circle opposite the first. The second is the shortening of the overall length of the horizontal from a straight wire into a circle. The average current over a diameter may be expressed by:

$$I_{avg1} = \frac{4I_0}{\pi - 2\theta_1} \left[\int_{\theta_1}^{\theta_2} \cos\theta \, d\theta - \int_{\theta_2}^{\pi/2} \cos\theta \, d\theta \right] \quad (6)$$

where the total horizontal wire length is:

$$\frac{\pi}{2} - \theta \text{ radians}$$

and I_0 is the current maximum (at the ground point) and:

$$\theta_2 = \frac{1}{2}\left(\frac{\pi}{2} + \theta_1\right) = \frac{\pi}{4} + \frac{\theta_1}{2}$$

Integrating Eq 6, there results:

$$I_{avg1} = \frac{4I_0}{\pi - 2\theta_1} \left[\sin\theta \Big|_{\theta_1}^{\theta_2} - \sin\theta \Big|_{\theta_2}^{\pi/2} \right] \quad (7)$$

Example: If the horizontal length is $\pi/2$ then $\theta_1 = 0$ and $\theta_2 = \pi/4$. Substituting these limits in Eq 7:

$$I_{avg1} = \frac{4I_0}{\pi}[0.707 - 0 - 1 + 0.707] = 0.527I_0 \quad (8)$$

The average current in a straight horizontal wire is given by:

$$I_{avg2} = \frac{2I_0}{\pi - 2\theta_1} = \int_{\theta_1}^{\pi/2} \cos\theta \, d\theta = \frac{2I_0}{\pi - 2\theta_1}\left[\sin\theta \Big|_{\theta_1}^{\pi/2}\right] \quad (9)$$

with the same definitions as in Eq 6 for θ_1 and I_0.

Substituting in the same limits as in Eq 8, namely $\theta_1 = 0$:

$$I_{avg2} = \frac{2I_0}{\pi} = 0.636I_0 \quad (10)$$

In order to cause equal fields for the two examples, the current must be increased in the circular top by the ratio of:

$$\frac{I_{avg2}}{I_{avg1}} = \frac{0.636}{0.527} = 1.21 \quad (11)$$

The radiation resistance of the circular antenna must be that of a straight wire divided by 1.21^2, or:

$$\frac{R_{\text{H circular}}}{R_{\text{H straight}}} = \frac{1}{1.21^2} = 0.68 \quad (12)$$

As θ_1 increases from 0 upwards (as the vertical height increases), this ratio approaches 1.0.

The second effect requires that the current in the circular antenna be π times that in the straight wire because of the decreased 'effective height', where π is the ratio of the circumference of a circle to its diameter; hence the ratio of the resistances is the square of π, or:

$$\frac{R_{\text{H circular}}}{R_{\text{H straight}}} = \frac{1}{\pi^2} = 0.1013 \quad (13)$$

Thus for very short vertical lengths, the combined effect of Eqs 12 and 13 is:

$$\frac{R_{\text{H circular}}}{R_{\text{H straight}}} = 0.68(0.1013) = 0.069 \quad (14)$$

This gradually approaches 0.1013 (or Eq 13) as the vertical height increases. For example at $\theta_1 = 8.55°$, Eq 8 yields:

$$I_{avg1} = 0.515I_0 \quad (15)$$

while Eq 10 becomes:

$$I_{avg2} = 0.600I_0 \quad (16)$$

and thus Eq 14 becomes:

$$\frac{R_{\text{H circular}}}{R_{\text{H straight}}} = \left(\frac{0.515}{0.600}\right)^2(0.1013) = 0.075 \quad (17)$$

Over the range from 0 to 8.55° for the vertical, an average of 0.072 may be used. The radiation resistance of the DDRR system may be approximated by the value of R_v in Eq 2 plus 0.072 times the difference between Eq 5 for R_T and Eq 2 for R_v, or:

$$R_{\text{H DDRR}} \cong [1578 + 0.072(2620 - 1578)]\left(\frac{H}{\lambda}\right)^2$$

$$\cong 1652\left(\frac{H}{\lambda}\right)^2 \text{ ohms} \quad (18)$$

This radiation resistance is shown plotted as curve 3 in Fig A1.1.

SURGE IMPEDANCE

The surge impedance is determined principally by the vertical portion of the DDRR if the vertical length is kept short and the mutual effect of one side of the circle on the other side is neglected. From transmission line equations the surge impedance is expressed by:

$$Z_0 = 138\log_{10}\left(\frac{2H - r}{r}\right) \text{ ohms} \quad (19)$$

where H is the height of centre of conductor above ground and r is the radius of the conductor (in the same units). Thus from p31 of the *QST* article, which gives $H = 12$in and $r = 1$in:

$$Z_0 = 138\log_{10}\left(\frac{2(12) - 1}{1}\right)$$

$$= 138\log_{10} 23$$

$$= 188\Omega \quad (20)$$

TAP-POINT RESISTANCE

In matching the feeding transmission line to the DDRR antenna it is important to know how far up from the ground a given resistance is encountered. The radiation resistance is seen from the open end of the antenna is given by:

$$R_e = \frac{Z_0^2}{R_B} \text{ ohms} \quad (21)$$

where Z_0 is the surge impedance, R_B is the total resistance at base of antenna including radiation and ohmic-loss resistance and the antenna overall length is 0.25λ.

If ϕ is the angle from ground to tap point and 90° is the total antenna length (0.25λ), then the resistance at ϕ is given by:

$$R_\phi = R_\varepsilon \sin^2 \phi \text{ ohms} \qquad (22)$$

Substituting in Eq 21 for R_ε in Eq 22:

$$R_\phi = \frac{Z_0^2 \sin^2 \phi}{R_B} \text{ ohms} \qquad (23)$$

Solving Eq 23 for $\sin \phi$:

$$\sin \phi = \frac{\sqrt{R_\phi R_B}}{Z_0} \qquad (24)$$

But $\sin \phi = \phi$ for small angles; making this substitution in Eq 24:

$$\phi = \sin^{-1}\left(\frac{\sqrt{R_\phi R_B}}{Z_0}\right) \cong \frac{\sqrt{R_\phi R_B}}{Z_0} \text{ radians}$$

$$\cong \frac{57.3\sqrt{R_\phi R_B}}{Z_0} \text{ degrees} \qquad (25)$$

Conversely, if ϕ is given (as by test or experiment) then R_B may be solved for in Eq 24 as:

$$R_B = \frac{Z_0^2 \sin^2 \phi}{R_\phi} \text{ ohms} \qquad (26)$$

Q AND BANDWIDTH OF DDRR ANTENNA

The quarter-wave antenna may be regarded as consisting of a resistance R_B in series with an inductor L and a capacitance C, where the reactive components balance out at resonance. The inductive reactance is given in reference [3] as:

$$X_L = 2\pi f_0 L = \frac{Z_{01}\pi}{2} \qquad (27)$$

where f_0 is the resonant frequency and Z_{01} is the surge impedance as found by Eq 20 above.

The Q of the antenna is thus:

$$Q = \frac{X_L}{R_B} = \frac{Z_{01}\pi}{2R_B} \qquad (28)$$

The antenna frequency bandwidth, BW, at the -3dB points is given by

$$BW = \frac{f_0}{Q} = \frac{2f_0 R_B}{Z_{01}\pi} \text{ hertz} \qquad (29)$$

where f_0 is the quarter-wave resonant frequency in hertz.

RADIATION EFFICIENCY OF DDRR ANTENNA

If the total base resistance is R_B and is made up of radiation resistance R_T and ohmic loss resistance R_L then:

$$R_B = R_T + R_L \qquad (30)$$

If a certain power W is fed into the antenna system:

$$W = I_0^2 R_B = I_0^2(R_T + R_L) \text{ watts} \qquad (31)$$

where I_0 is the antenna current in the base in amperes. Of this power, the useful radiated power is $I_0^2 R_T$, hence the power efficiency is:

$$\eta = \frac{\text{Useful power}}{\text{Total power}}$$

$$= \frac{I_0^2 R_T}{I_0^2(R_T + R_L)}$$

$$= \frac{R_T}{R_T + R_L} \qquad (32)$$

Expressed in decibels:

$$\eta = 10\log_{10}\left(\frac{R_T}{R_T + R_L}\right) \text{ decibels} \qquad (33)$$

Expressed as a field strength ratio:

$$\eta = \frac{E_B}{E_T} = \sqrt{\frac{R_T}{R_T + R_L}} \qquad (34)$$

VOLTAGE AT OPEN END OF ANTENNA

If the transmitted output power delivered to the antenna is W_0 and the open-end resistance of the antenna is that given by Eq 21, then:

$$W_0 = \frac{E^2}{R_\varepsilon} = \frac{E^2 R_B}{Z_0^2} \text{ watts} \qquad (35)$$

where E is the RMS voltage across the open end, R_B is the total base resistance $R_T + R_L$ and Z_0 is the surge impedance.

Solving Eq 35 for E:

$$E = Z_0\sqrt{\frac{W_0}{R_B}} \text{ volts RMS} \qquad (36)$$

The peak voltage is $\sqrt{2}$ times the RMS voltage, so:

$$E_{peak} = Z_0\sqrt{\frac{2W_0}{R_B}} \text{ volts (peak)} \qquad (37)$$

If the power W_0 represents the carrier power of an amplitude modulated (AM) wave, and the modulation factor is m, then the peak voltage (at modulation peaks) is given by:

$$E_{peak} = (1+m)Z_0\sqrt{\frac{2W_0}{R_B}} \text{ volts} \qquad (38)$$

PERFORMANCE OF IDEAL DDRR ANTENNA

The performance of an ideal DDRR antenna may be determined from various of the above equations, assuming that the loss resistance is zero, ie that $R_L = 0$.

Assuming that the antenna is designed for 40m, and that the feed line has a surge impedance of 50Ω and is matched to the antenna at the feed point; and that the dimensions are as in the *QST* article, ie $H = 1$ft and $\lambda = 132$ft, the following may be calculated using the indicated equations.

(a) $R_T = 1652\left(\dfrac{1}{132}\right)^2 = 0.095\Omega$ (from Eq 18)   (39)

(b) $\qquad\qquad Z_0 = 188\Omega$ (40)

(from Eq 20 assuming conductor radius is 1in)

(c)   Tap point $\phi = \dfrac{57.3\sqrt{52 \times 0.095}}{188} = 0.675°$ (41)

(from Eq 25)

$$\text{Distance above ground} = \frac{\lambda\phi}{360°}$$
$$= \frac{132 \times 0.675°}{360°}$$
$$= 0.248\text{ft} = 3\text{in}\quad (42)$$

(d) Resistance at open end of antenna

$R_\varepsilon = \dfrac{Z_0^2}{R_B} = \dfrac{188^2}{0.095} = 372,000\Omega$ (from Eq 21) (43)

(e) Radiation efficiency

$\eta = \dfrac{R_T}{R_T + R_L} = \dfrac{0.095}{0.095 + 0} = 1.0$ (from Eq 32) (44)

(f) Q of antenna

$Q = \dfrac{Z_{01}\pi}{2R_B} = \dfrac{188\pi}{2(0.095)} = 3120$ (from Eq 28) (45)

(g) Bandwidth of antenna

$$BW = \frac{f_0}{Q} = \frac{7,200,000}{3120} = 2300\text{Hz}\quad (46)$$

(from Eq 29)

(h) Voltage at open end of antenna. Assume 1000W input to an AM transmitter modulated 100%, or when $m = 1.0$. If the transmitter is 70% efficient, 700W carrier power is transmitted. From Eq 38, the peak voltage on positive crests of modulation becomes:

$$E_{\text{peak}} = (1+1)188\sqrt{\frac{2 \times 700}{0.095}} = 45,500\text{V peak}\quad (47)$$

PERFORMANCE OF *QST* DDRR ANTENNA

Since the dimensions are the same as in the previous section, $R_T = 0.095\Omega$ and $Z_0 = 188\Omega$.

Assuming that the feed tap is at the 52Ω point or that $R_\phi = 52$, the following are calculated.

(a) The tap point per Table I in *QST* is 18in (1.5ft) from the ground, or at an angle of:

$$\phi = 360°\left(\frac{1.5}{132}\right) = 4.09°\quad (48)$$

(b) The base resistance R_B from Eq 26 is:

$$R_B = \frac{188^2 \sin^2 4.09°}{52} = 3.45\Omega\quad (49)$$

From Eq 30 the loss resistance is:

$$R_L = R_B - R_T = 3.45 - 0.095 = 3.355\Omega\quad (50)$$

(c) The open-end resistance is from Eq 21:

$$R_\varepsilon = \frac{188^2}{3.45} = 10,200\Omega\quad (51)$$

(d) The efficiency is from Eq 32 and Eq 33:

$$\eta = \frac{0.095}{3.45} = 0.0275 = 2.75\%\quad (52)$$

$$\text{or } \eta = 10\log_{10}0.0275 = -15.6\text{dB}\quad (53)$$

or the field strength ratio is:

$$\frac{E_B}{E_T} = \sqrt{\frac{0.095}{3.45}} = 0.166\quad (54)$$

(e) The Q of the antenna is, from Eq 28:

$$Q = \frac{188\pi}{2(3.45)} = 85.6\quad (55)$$

(f) The bandwidth of the antenna is, from Eq 29:

$$BW = \frac{7,200,000}{85.6} = 84,000\text{Hz or 84kHz}\quad (56)$$

(g) The voltage at the end of the antenna is, from Eq 38, assuming a carrier of 700W 100% modulated:

$$E_{\text{peak}} = (1+1)188\sqrt{\frac{2 \times 700}{3.45}} = 7600\text{V peak}\quad (57)$$

PROBABLE CAUSES OF LOSSES

The fact that the total resistance referred to the base of the antenna appears to be 3.45Ω whereas the radiation resistance is but 0.095Ω leaves 3.355Ω of loss resistance to be accounted for. The losses are probably divided between the ohmic losses in the antenna conductor and the losses in the ground system. The ohmic losses in the antenna conductor may be computed if the length, diameter and metal of the antenna are known.

From p35, Eq 7, of reference [2] the AC resistance of a *copper* rod or tube is given by:

$$R_{ac} = \frac{83.2\sqrt{f}\ 10^{-9}}{d} \text{ ohms /centimetre length (58)}$$

where *f* is the frequency in hertz and *d* is the conductor outside diameter in centimetres.

Using the dimensions of the DDRR antenna at 40m, *d* = 2in or 5.08cm and *f* = 7,200,000, and substituting in Eq 58:

$$R_{ac} = 4.4 \times 10^{-5} \text{ ohms / cm} \qquad (59)$$

Now the length of the antenna from ground to the far end is 10m or 1000cm; therefore, multiplying Eq 59 by 1000:

$$R_{ac} = 0.044\Omega \qquad (60)$$

for the total resistance of the 10m long copper tube.

If the metal used is something other than copper, and particularly if it is magnetic, the resistance may be quite a bit greater than 0.044Ω. Table A1.1 has been calculated for several different materials, based on the AC resistance being proportional to the square root of the resistance of a cubic centimetre of each material, and also proportional to the square root of the magnetic permeability μ.

The last column of Table A1.1 represents the resistance, which when multiplied by the square of the current at the base of the antenna, will yield total loss in the antenna (neglecting insulator and capacitor dielectric losses). This may be arrived at by integrating the losses over the antenna length $\pi/2$ (or 90°) as follows.

Assuming a sinusoidal current distribution so that the current at any point may be expressed as $I = I_0 \cos \phi$, where ϕ proceeds from 0 to $\pi/2$, then the watts consumed is given by:

$$I_0^2 R_{ac\ effective} = \frac{R_{ac}}{\pi/2} \int_0^{\pi/2} I_0^2 \cos^2\theta\ d\theta$$

$$= \frac{2R_{ac}I_0^2}{\pi}\left[\frac{\phi}{2} + \frac{\sin 2\phi}{4}\right]\Big|_0^{\pi/2} \qquad (61)$$

where R_{ac} is the total AC resistance of the line in Eq 60 and $R_{ac\ effective}$ is the effective resistance.

Material	μ	R_{ac}	$R_{ac\ effective}$
Copper	1.0	0.044	0.022
Aluminium	1.0	0.0562	0.0282
Brass	1.0	0.0912	0.0456
Zinc	1.0	0.0812	0.0406
Tin	1.0	0.1132	0.0566
Iron	1.0	0.1044	0.0522
Iron	10	0.330	0.165
Iron	20	0.468	0.234
Iron	50	0.74	0.37
Iron	100	1.044	0.522
Iron	200	1.48	0.74
Iron	500	2.34	1.17

Table A1.1

Substituting in the limits:

$$I_0^2 R_{ac\ effective} = \frac{2R_{ac}I_0^2}{\pi}\left(\frac{\pi}{4}\right) = \frac{R_{ac}I_0^2}{2} \qquad (62)$$

Solving Eq 66 for $R_{ac\ effective}$:

$$R_{ac\ effective} = \frac{R_{ac}}{2} \qquad (63)$$

The last column in the table is therefore one-half the value of the third column.

In the *QST* article it was stated that the material was steel. Now assuming a value of 100 for μ, which seems reasonable, the resultant effective ohmic resistance becomes 0.522Ω.

The remainder of the 3.355Ω of ohmic resistances, or 2.833Ω, probably is accounted for by the effective resistance of the ground system made up of chicken wire of fairly small individual conductors of iron with a zinc dip.

Changing to a solid copper ground sheet would undoubtedly lead to a very much lower effective ground resistance.

EFFECT OF CURRENT THROUGH THE TUNING CAPACITOR

Any current that flows through the tuning capacitor from the open end of the DDRR antenna to ground is detrimental and should be minimised for this reason. If the current is assumed to be of like phase throughout (and it should be over one quarter-wave from current maximum), then the current flows upward at the antenna base but downward through the tuning capacitor leads. The opposing current directions cause the far field effect of the main vertical section to be partially cancelled by the far field set up by the capacitor lead current.

It can readily be shown that the effective current causing radiation is thus:

$$I_{eff} = I_0 - I_0 \cos\phi = I_0(1 - \cos\phi) \qquad (64)$$

where ϕ is the length of antenna in degrees and I_0 is the current at antenna base.

Now in order for the system to provide its rated field for a given power, the current at the base must be increased so that the new current I_n satisfies the equation:

$$I_0 = I_n(1 - \cos\phi) \text{ or } I_n = \frac{I_0}{1 - \cos\phi} \qquad (65)$$

From the law of the conservation of energy, the radiation resistance referred to the antenna base thus becomes:

$$R_T{}^1 = R_T(1 - \cos\phi)^2 \qquad (66)$$

where $R_T{}^1$ is the new radiation resistance (with capacitor) and R_T is the original radiation resistance (absence of capacitor).

For example, if the antenna at some low frequency in a given band were 80° long ($\phi = 80°$), the radiation resistance of 0.095Ω, as calculated in Eq 39, would instead become:

$$R_T{}^1 = 0.095(1 - \cos 80°)^2$$
$$= 0.095(1 - 0.17635)^2$$
$$= 0.0645\Omega \qquad (67)$$

The use of this antenna, in conjunction with the ohmic losses already discussed, would necessarily lead to even a still smaller efficiency than the 2.75% efficiency found by Eq 52.

It is therefore recommended that the DDRR antenna be constructed to be no shorter than is required to tune with the tuning capacitor at its minimum when tuned to the highest frequency to be used in the band of interest.

CONCLUSION

This study of the DDRR antenna indicates the advantages of the antenna over others are the compactness, low profile and inconspicuousness of the installation. The disadvantages of the antenna are its relative low radiation efficiency and comparatively narrow bandwidth. The efficiency is low because the radiation resistance is very low (0.095Ω) so that conductor ohmic losses consume most of the available power. The narrow bandwidth necessitates the use of a variable tuning arrangement to bring the system to something approaching unity power factor.

It is suggested that increasing the vertical height could improve the radiation efficiency very appreciably because the radiation resistance for a short vertical heights varies as the square of the height. Increasing the height from 12in to 42in would raise the radiation resistance to about 1.16Ω, which, coupled with a ground conductor loss of the same magnitude as in the study (3.355Ω) would increase the efficiency from 2.75% to 25.8%, or provide 9.8dB increase in signal strength.

REFERENCES

[1] *Electric Oscillations and Electric Waves*, G W Pierce, McGraw-Hill Book Co, New York, 1920.
[2] *Radio Engineers' Handbook*, F E Terman, McGraw-Hill Book Co, 1943.
[3] *Television Principles*, R B Dome, McGraw-Hill Book Co, New York, 1951, p104, Eq 5-10.

Availability of computer programs, components, equipment and kits

NOTE that quoted prices and availability were correct at the time of publication – check first before placing an order.

ANTENNA MODELLING PROGRAMS

ELNEC and EZNEC, described in Chapter 8, can be obtained from Roy Lewallen, W7EL, PO Box 6658, Beaverton, Oregon 97007, USA. Prices are $49 for ELNEC and $89 for EZNEC. Add $3 outside US and Canada. Visa and Mastercard accepted.

My first MININEC derivative program was MN from Brian Beezley, K6STI, which I described in the first edition of this book. I liked this program but found the copy protection could be a problem under some circumstances. According to the latest advertisements MN is no longer available and consequently was not described in Chapter 8. However, new programs are available as follows:

AO 6.5. Automatically optimises antenna designs for best gain, pattern and impedance, SWR and resonance.

NEC/Wires. Models true earth losses, surface waves and large antennas.

YO 6.5. Automatically optimises monoband Yagi designs for maximum forward gain, best pattern, and minimum SWR.

NEC/Yagis 2.5. For modelling large Yagi arrays such as those used for EME.

TA 1.0. Plots elevation patterns for HF antennas over irregular terrain.

The minimum hardware requirements for these programs are a 386 with coprocessor and a VGA monitor.

In July 1995 K6STI dropped the copy protection and lowered prices for bundles of his programs. Each program is $60, or $120 for three or $200 for all five; plus $5 shipping outside USA. Visa and Mastercard accepted.

A Macintosh version of MININEC is available; MacMININEC 4.4 from Chris Smolinski, N3JLY, 40 South Lake Way, Reistertown, Maryland 21136.

MININEC Professional for Windows (available as a commercial product) from EM Scientific Inc, 2533 N Carson Street, Suite 2107 Carson City, NV 89706, USA. Tel: 702 888-9449. Fax: 702 883-2384.

ANTENNA ANALYSERS

In the UK the MFJ-249 and MFJ-259 are available from Waters and Stanton, 22 Main Road, Hockley, Essex, SS5 4QS. The price is £249. The MFJ-66 dip meter coils (price £25.95) will convert the analyser to a wide-range dip meter.

Until recently, the RF1 was available only from the US manufacturers. However, it is now available in Europe from Eastern Communications, Cavendish House, Happisburgh, Norfolk, NR12 0RU. Tel: 01692 650077. Fax: 01692 650925. The price is £139.95 inc P&P within Europe.

DOCUMENTATION

The James Corum patent on the toroid antenna is available from The British Library, Science Reference and Information Service, 25 Southampton Buildings, London WC2A 1AW; enclose a cheque for £10 and quote Patent Application EP 0 043 591.

A/D CONVERTERS

Information regarding analogue-to-digital converters for IBM PCs, used for plotting polar diagrams in Chapter 5, is as follows.

The Pico ADC-10 is the size of a printer cable connector and is self-contained. It plugs into the parallel printer port and requires no external power. It has a resolution of 8 bits and a input voltage range of 0–5V. The signal is connected to the ADC-10 via a standard BNC coaxial socket. It is supplied with software routines in C, PASCAL and BASIC. Pico

Technology Ltd, Broadway House, 149–151 St Neots Road, Hardwick, Cambridge, CB3 7QJ. Tel: 01954 211716. Fax: 01954 211880. Price around £50.00. Pico Technology accepts credit cards, sterling cheques and banker's drafts.

A similar ADC is described in an article 'High Speed Data Acquisition' by Mike Gray, N8KDD. It also interfaces the IBM PC via the parallel printer port. A printed circuit board is available and parts are available from Radio Shack. Software information (BASIC) is also supplied.

Another solution is given in *Linear Technology Design Notes* June 1990. This circuit uses the LTC1290 ADC and interfaces the IBM PC via the serial COM port. Software information (BASIC) is also supplied. The address is: Linear Technology Corporation, 1630 McCarthy Blvd, Milpitas, CA 95035-7487.

The subject of signal/IBM PC interfaces is described in *Interfacing Sensors to the IBM PC* by W J Tompkins, published by Prentice-Hall. It also describes a low-cost data acquisition system (ADC) that interfaces with the expansion bus. A circuit is given together with a BASIC program.

COMPONENTS

The receiver noise bridge (Chapter 2) and the FET dip meter (Chapter 3) can be obtained in kit form from Derek Pearson, G3ZOM, 6 Fellows Ave, Kingswinford, West Midlands, DY6 9ET. Derek used to run a kit manufacturer called 'Jandek' but has since given it up. He has, however, offered to continue supplying the two kits.

A comprehensive range of coaxial cable and coaxial plugs and sockets, plus 300 and 450Ω balanced twin feeders are obtainable from W H Westlake, West Park, Clawton, Holdsworthy, Devon, EX22 6QN.

3 Computer listings

EXTRACTING RF IMPEDANCE FROM 3-M BRIDGE VOLTAGES

These programs are all based on an algorithm by the late Tom Lloyd, G3TML/9L1TL – see notes later.

Program ZSMALL is for use with small BASIC calculator such as the Casio PB110.

Program ZSMALL

```
10 B=50
20 INPUT "A",A
30 INPUT "C",C
40 INPUT "D",D
50 INPUT "E",E
60 F=(B*B+C*C-A*A)/(2*B*C)
70 G=ACS F
80 H=(C*C+D*D-E*E)/(2*C*D)
90 J=ACS H
100 K=(A*A+B*B-C*C)/(2*A*B)
110 L=ACS K
120 M=(D*D+E*E-C*C)/(2*D*E)
130 N=ACS M
140 I=E*M
150 Q=ATN (B/D)
160 T=B/SIN Q
170 P=ACS((T*T+E*E-A*A)/(2*T*E))
180 S=P-Q
190 IF (L+Q)>(PI/2) THEN S=(2*PI)-(P+Q)
200 IF H>0 THEN W=D-A*SIN L
210 IF H<=0 THEN W=D+A*SIN L
220 Y=E*COS S
230 O=A*K-B
240 M=E*SIN N
250 U=E*SIN S
260 X=(W+I+Y)/3
270 R=(O+M+U)/3
280 IF X>=0 THEN GOTO 360
290 X=-X
300 Z$="-"
310 R=INT(10*R+.5)/10
320 X=INT(10*X+.5)/10
330 PRINT "R = ";R
340 PRINT "Xj = ";Z$;X
350 END
360 Z$="+"
370 GOTO 31
```

All the following programs have been written for an IBM PC compatible computer using GW BASIC or Q-BASIC.

Program ZCALC can be used as a stand-alone program for making single impedance measurements.

Enter the items of data when prompted by the program. (The exception is Er (B) which the program assumes to be 50, although a modification to the program is given at the end of the ZCALC listing if you wish to change this.)

The program prints the solution as soon as the last item of data is entered. It will amend any data resulting in a geometric non-intersection and will inform you of the change in an item of data.

The program can be used for making displaying the results of multiple measurements with the programs listed below. Data files have been included at the end of the program for testing.

MENU   Menu program to control all these programs

TODISK   For creating files of impedance data (see data files on p143) for use with TABLE and GRAPH. Alternatively you can create a data file by typing them in using a simple text editor. You could use a word processor but remember to save it as a text or ASCII file.

TABLE   To make a table of several measurements over a given frequency range.

GRAPH   To plot an impedance signature over a given frequency range. This program uses a low-resolution CGA screen. If you want a higher resolution screen use GRAPHEGA instead of GRAPH.

Processing batches of data to calculate an antenna characteristic is achieved by storing the data in .DAT files using program TODISK. You can enter the data more quickly using an editor, such as the one that comes with XTREE. Look at existing .DAT files to get the format.

Data should be run through ZCALC to check that they are free of errors before making data files.

The data can be displayed in a tabular form, together with an approximation of errors using program TABLE.

The data can be displayed as a graph using GRAPH.

Program ZCALC

```
10 ON ERROR GOTO 740
20 CLS : PRINT "    Program for Calculating
Impedance Values "
30 PRINT "    from 3-Meter Data. Copyright
Peter Dodd, G3LDO. ": PRINT
40 PRINT "    Use this program to make a
single impedance measurement, or"
50 PRINT "    to verify data before it is
entered into a .DAT file."
60 PRINT "    The program assumes the value
of Er (B) to be 50.": PRINT :PRINT
70 B = 50: PI = 3.1416:ENO=0
80 INPUT "    Ea    (A) ", A
90 INPUT "    Ecz (C) ", C
100 INPUT "    Ec    (D) ", D
110 INPUT "    Ez    (E) ", E
120 PRINT "If there is more than one line
of data below then the data has been
corrected"
130 PRINT "Last line indicates corrected
data used to determine impedance." :PRINT
140 PRINT "Ea (A)=";A; ", Ecz (C)=";C; ",
Ec (D)=";D;", Ez (E)=" ;E
150 F = (B * B + C * C - A * A) / (2 * B * C)
160 IF F = 0 THEN G = PI / 2: GOTO 180
170 G = ATN(SQR(1 / (F * F) - 1)): IF F < 0
THEN G = PI - G
180 H = (C * C + D * D - E * E) / (2 * C * D)
190 IF H = 0 THEN J = PI / 2: GOTO 210
200 J = ATN(SQR(1 / (H * H) - 1)): IF H < 0
THEN J = PI - J
210 K = (A * A + B * B - C * C) / (2 * A * B)
220 IF K = 0 THEN L = PI / 2: GOTO 240
230 L = ATN(SQR(1 / (K * K) - 1)): IF K < 0
THEN L = PI - L
240 M = (D * D + E * E - C * C) / (2 * D * E)
250 IF M = 0 THEN N = PI / 2: GOTO 270
260 N = ATN(SQR(1 / (M * M) - 1)): IF M < 0
THEN N = PI - N
270 Q = ATN(B / D)
280 T = B / SIN(Q)
290 ZZ = (T * T + E * E - A * A) / (2 * T *
E )
300 IF ZZ = 0 THEN P = PI / 2: GOTO 320
310 P = ATN(SQR(1 / (ZZ * ZZ) - 1)): IF ZZ
< 0 THEN P = PI -P
320 S = P - Q
330 IF (L + Q) > (PI / 2) THEN S = (2 * PI)
- (P + Q)
340 IF H > 0 THEN X1 = D - A * SIN(L) ELSE
X1 = D + A * SIN(L)
350 X2 = E * M
360 X3 = E * COS(S)
370 R1 = A * K - B
380 R2 = E * SIN(N)
390 R3 = E * SIN(S)
400 X = (X1 + X2 + X3) / 3
410 R = (R1 + R2 + R3) / 3
420 V1 = ABS(X1 - X)
430 V2 = ABS(X2 - X)
440 V3 = ABS(X3 - X)
450 W1 = ABS(R1 - R)
460 W2 = ABS(R2 - R)
470 W3 = ABS(R3 - R)
480 IF V1 >= V2 THEN GOTO 500
490 IF V2 >= V3 THEN EX = V2: GOTO 520
500 IF V1 >= V3 THEN EX = V1: GOTO 520
510 EX = V3
520 IF W1 >= W2 THEN GOTO 550
530 IF W2 >= W3 THEN ER = W2: GOTO 570
540 ER = W3
550 IF W1 >= W3 THEN ER = W1: GOTO 570
560 ER = W3
570 IF X >= 0 THEN P$ = "+": GOTO 590
580 X = -X: P$ = "-"
590 EX = INT(10 * EX + .5) / 10
600 ER = INT(10 * ER + .5) / 10
610 R = INT(10 * R + .5) / 10
620 X = INT(10 * X + .5) / 10
630 : PRINT : PRINT : PRINT "SOLUTION"
640 PRINT " Resistance "; R
650 PRINT " Reactance ", P$; X: PRINT
660 PRINT " ERRORS"
670 PRINT "    R= (+/-) "; ER
680 PRINT "    X= (+/-) "; EX
690 PRINT : PRINT
700 INPUT "Goto Main Menu 1. Repeat this
program 2. "; AA
710 IF AA = 1 THEN CHAIN "MENU"
720 IF AA = 2 GOTO 10
730 END
740 ENO = ENO+1:IF ENO >10 THEN PRINT
"Error in data cannot be corrected":GOTO
700
750 IF ERL = 170 AND ERR=5 THEN
C=C+1:RESUME 140
760 IF ERL = 310 AND ERR=5 THEN
D=D+1:RESUME 140
```

The listing below is a modification to program ZCALC to allow values other than 5V (50) to be used for Ea (B).

```
60 PRINT "   This program requires that the
value of Er (B) is entered.": PRINT
70 PI = 3.1416: ENO = 0
80 INPUT "   Ea   (B) ", B
85 FTR = 50 / B: B = B * FTR
90 INPUT "   Ea   (A) ", A: A = A * FTR
95 INPUT "   Ecz (C) ", C: C = C * FTR
100 INPUT "   Ec   (D) ", D: D = D * FTR
110 INPUT "   Ez   (E) ", E: E = E * FTR
```

Program MENU
Type CHAIN "MENU" to start.

```
10 CLS
20 PRINT "   A SET OF PROGRAMS FOR
EXTRACTING IMPEDANCE VALUES" :PRINT
30 PRINT "   FROM 3-METER IMPEDANCE DATA "
:PRINT
40 PRINT "   Copyright Peter Dodd G3LDO   "
50 PRINT
60 PRINT "   The programs are as follows:
":PRINT
70 PRINT "   1. A program to make a single
impedance measurement. It is also used "
80 PRINT "   to check the data before being
entered into a file, see 2 below."
90 PRINT
100 PRINT "   2. To enter data into a file
to be processed by programs TABLE or GRAPH"
110 PRINT
120 PRINT "   3. Program TABLE. Creates a
table of impedance measurements, from "
130 PRINT "   data obtained from a file."
140 PRINT
150 PRINT "   4. Program GRAPH. Creates a
graphic impedance signature of an antenna
or"
160 PRINT "   component, from data obtained
from a file."
170 PRINT "————————————————
————"
180 PRINT:PRINT
190 INPUT "Select 1, 2, 3 or 4; or select 5
to exit Basic "; AA
200 IF AA = 1 THEN CHAIN "ZCALC"
210 IF AA = 2 THEN CHAIN "TODISK"
220 IF AA = 3 THEN CHAIN "TABLE"
230 IF AA = 4 THEN CHAIN "GRAPH"
240 IF AA = 5 THEN SYSTEM
```

Program TODISK
```
10 CLS:CLEAR
20 ON ERROR GOTO 300
30 PRINT "   TODISK, Copyright Peter Dodd
```

```
G3LDO " :PRINT
40 PRINT "   Enables 3_Meter data to be
entered into a named file "
50 PRINT "   for processing by TABLE or
GRAPH" :PRINT
60 PRINT "The data file name must comprise
max of 8 characters, ending in .DAT"
70 INPUT "Data file NAME for impedance
data? ", NF$:PRINT
80 INPUT "Enter measurement Title "; TITLE$
90 INPUT "How many sets of data? (maximum
of 9) ", M
100 OPTION BASE 1
110 DIM AA(9)
120 DIM CC(9)
130 DIM DD(9)
140 DIM EE(9)
150 DIM FY(9)
160 OPEN "O", #1, NF$
170 PRINT #1, TITLE$
180 FOR Z = 1 TO M
190 PRINT "MEASUREMENT "; Z:PRINT
200 INPUT "FREQUENCY ", FY(Z):PRINT
210 INPUT "Ea (A)", AA(Z)
220 INPUT "Ecz (C)", CC(Z)
230 INPUT "Ec (D)", DD(Z)
240 INPUT "Ez (E)", EE(Z)
250 INPUT "Is this data correct? if not
press N, if OK any other key ", C$
260 IF C$ = "N" GOTO 190
270 IF C$ = "n" GOTO 190
280 PRINT #1, M, FY(Z), AA(Z), CC(Z),
DD(Z), EE(Z)
290 NEXT Z
300 CLOSE #1
310 PRINT : PRINT
320 INPUT "Goto Main Menu 1. Repeat this
program 2. "; AA
330 IF AA = 1 THEN CHAIN "menu"
340 IF AA = 2 GOTO 10
```

Program TABLE
```
10 CLS:CLEAR
20 ON ERROR GOTO 880
30 PRINT "   Program TABLE. Compiles an
impedance table of an antenna over"
40 PRINT "   a range of frequencies, from
data on an impedance .DAT file"
50 PRINT "   Copyright Peter Dodd G3LDO"
:PRINT:PRINT
60 FILES "*.DAT"
70 PRINT "   Enter .DAT file from the above
list."
80 INPUT "Remember to add .DAT after the
file name. ", NF$:CLS
90 PI = 3.1416:B = 50
100 DIM AA(9)
```

```
110 DIM CC(9)
120 DIM DD(9)
130 DIM EE(9)
140 DIM RR(9)
150 DIM XX(9)
160 DIM FY(9)
170 DIM P$(9)
180 OPEN "I", #1, NF$
190 INPUT #1, TITLE$
200 PRINT : PRINT TITLE$: PRINT
210 PRINT "   Input Parameters    Results
+/-Errors"
220 PRINT "Freq    A    C    D    E    Res    jX
Res    jX"
230 PRINT "————————————————————————————————————
"
240 INPUT #1, M
250 MM = M
260 FOR Z = 1 TO MM
270 INPUT #1, FY(Z), AA(Z), CC(Z), DD(Z),
EE(Z)
280 A = AA(Z)
290 C = CC(Z)
300 D = DD(Z)
310 E = EE(Z)
320 F = (B * B + C * C - A * A) / (2 * B *
C)
330 IF F = 0 THEN G = PI / 2: GOTO 350
340 G = ATN(SQR(1 / (F * F) - 1)): IF F < 0
THEN G = PI - G
350 H = (C * C + D * D - E * E) / (2 * C *
D)
360 IF H = 0 THEN J = PI / 2: GOTO 380
370 J = ATN(SQR(1 / (H * H) - 1)): IF H < 0
THEN J = PI - J
380 K = (A * A + B * B - C * C) / (2 * A *
B)
390 IF K = 0 THEN L = PI / 2: GOTO 410
400 L = ATN(SQR(1 / (K * K) - 1)): IF K < 0
THEN L = PI - L
410 M = (D * D + E * E - C * C) / (2 * D *
E)
420 IF M = 0 THEN N = PI / 2: GOTO 440
430 N = ATN(SQR(1 / (M * M) - 1)): IF M < 0
THEN N = PI - N
440 Q = ATN(B / D)
450 T = B / SIN(Q)
460 ZZ = (T * T + E * E - A * A) / (2 * T *
E)
470 IF ZZ = 0 THEN P = PI / 2: GOTO 490
480 P = ATN(SQR(1 / (ZZ * ZZ) - 1)): IF ZZ
< 0 THEN P = PI -P
490 S = P - Q
500 IF (L + Q) > (PI / 2) THEN S = (2 * PI)
- (P + Q)
510 IF H > 0 THEN X1 = D - A * SIN(L) ELSE
X1 = D + A * SIN(L)
520 X2 = E * M
530 X3 = E * COS(S)
540 R1 = A * K - B
550 R2 = E * SIN(N)
560 R3 = E * SIN(S)
570 X = (X1 + X2 + X3) / 3
580 R = (R1 + R2 + R3) / 3
590 V1 = ABS(X1 - X)
600 V2 = ABS(X2 - X)
610 V3 = ABS(X3 - X)
620 W1 = ABS(R1 - R)
630 W2 = ABS(R2 - R)
640 W3 = ABS(R3 - R)
650 IF V1 >= V2 THEN GOTO 670
660 IF V2 >= V3 THEN EX = V2: GOTO 690
670 IF V1 >= V3 THEN EX = V1: GOTO 690
680 EX = V3
690 IF W1 >= W2 THEN GOTO 720
700 IF W2 >= W3 THEN ER = W2: GOTO 740
710 ER = W3
720 IF W1 >= W3 THEN ER = W1: GOTO 740
730 ER = W3
740 IF X >= 0 THEN P$(MM) = "+": GOTO 760
750 P$(MM) = "-"
760 ZZ(Z) = INT(10 * ER + .5) / 10
770 RR(Z) = INT(10 * R + .5) / 10
780 XX(Z) = ABS(INT(10 * X + .5) / 10)
790 EJ(Z) = INT(10 * EX + .5) / 10
800 PRINT FY(Z); TAB(8); AA(Z); TAB(15);
CC(Z); TAB(22); DD(Z); TAB(29); EE(Z);
TAB(37); RR(Z); TAB(45); P$(MM); TAB(46);
XX(Z); TAB(55); ZZ(Z); TAB(62); EJ(Z)
810 NEXT
820 CLOSE #1
830 PRINT : PRINT
840 INPUT "Goto Main Menu 1. Repeat this
program 2. "; AA
850 IF AA = 1 THEN CHAIN "MENU"
860 IF AA = 2 GOTO 10
870 END
880 CLS : PRINT "ERROR IN DATA OR INCORRECT
FILE NAME" :RESUME 820
```

Program GRAPH

```
10 CLS : CLEAR : SCREEN 0
20 ON ERROR GOTO 660
30 PRINT " Program GRAPH. Creates an
antenna impedance signature over a
specified"
40 PRINT " frequency range, from 3-Meter
impedance data. Copyright Peter Dodd G3LDO"
50 PRINT : PRINT : PI = 3.141: B = 50
60 FILES "*.DAT"
70 PRINT " Enter .DAT impedance data file
from the above list"
80 INPUT " Remember to add .DAT after the
file name"; NF$
```

```
90 SCREEN 9: CLS
100 DIM AA(9)
110 DIM CC(9)
120 DIM DD(9)
130 DIM EE(9)
140 DIM RR(9)
150 DIM XX(9)
160 DIM ZZ(9)
170 DIM FY(9)
180 DIM EJ(9)
190 DIM P$(9)
200 OPEN "I", #1, NF$
210 INPUT #1, TITLE$
220 INPUT #1, M
230 MM = M
240 FOR Z = 1 TO MM
250 INPUT #1, FY(Z), AA(Z), CC(Z), DD(Z),
EE(Z)
260 A = AA(Z)
270 C = CC(Z)
280 D = DD(Z)
290 E = EE(Z)
300 F = (B * B + C * C - A * A) / (2 * B *
C)
310 IF F = 0 THEN G = PI / 2: GOTO 330
320 G = ATN(SQR(1 / (F * F) - 1)): IF F < 0
THEN G = PI - G
330 H = (C * C + D * D - E * E) / (2 * C *
D)
340 IF H = 0 THEN J = PI / 2: GOTO 360
350 J = ATN(SQR(1 / (H * H) - 1)): IF H < 0
THEN J = PI - J
360 K = (A * A + B * B - C * C) / (2 * A *
B)
370 IF K = 0 THEN L = PI / 2: GOTO 390
380 L = ATN(SQR(1 / (K * K) - 1)): IF K < 0
THEN L = PI - L
390 M = (D * D + E * E - C * C) / (2 * D *
E)
400 N = ATN(SQR(1 / (M * M) - 1)): IF M < 0
THEN N = PI - N
410 Q = ATN(B / D)
420 T = B / SIN(Q)
430 ZZ = (T * T + E * E - A * A) / (2 * T *
E)
440 IF ZZ = 0 THEN P = PI / 2: GOTO 460
450 P = ATN(SQR(1 / (ZZ * ZZ) - 1)): IF ZZ
< 0 THEN P = PI - P
460 S = P - Q
470 IF (L + Q) > (PI / 2) THEN S = (2 * PI)
- (P + Q)
480 IF H > 0 THEN X1 = D - A * SIN(L) ELSE
X1 = D + A * SIN(L)
490 X2 = E * M
500 X3 = E * COS(S)
510 R1 = A * K - B
520 R2 = E * SIN(N)
530 R3 = E * SIN(S)
540 X = (X1 + X2 + X3) / 3
550 R = (R1 + R2 + R3) / 3
560 IF Z = 1 THEN GOSUB 670: REM plot chart
once only
570 GOSUB 970: REM plot Z
580 NEXT Z
590 CLOSE #1
600 PRINT " Freqs (MHz)"; FY(1); FY(2);
FY(3); FY(4); FY(5); FY(6); FY(7); FY(8);
FY(9)
605 PRINT
610 INPUT "   goto main menu 1. repeat this
program 2."; AA
620 SCREEN 0
630 IF AA = 1 THEN SHELL "menu"
640 IF AA = 2 THEN GOTO 10
650 END
660 PRINT " ERROR IN DATA OR INCORRECT FILE
NAME.": RESUME 610
670 REM Chart
routine...........................
690 PRINT : PRINT TAB(1100); "Plot Title":
PRINT TAB(1100); TITLE$: PRINT
700 PRINT TAB(1100); "Dotted circle=":
PRINT TAB(1100); "2:1 SWR contour"
710 PRINT "100"
720 PRINT TAB(1100); "Lowest frequency"
730 PRINT TAB(1100); "indicated by":
740 PRINT TAB(1100); "double circle"
750 PRINT TAB(1100); "on the plot"
760 PRINT " R" :PRINT
770 PRINT " 50"
780 PRINT TAB(1100); "Measurement"
790 PRINT TAB(1100); "frequencies"
800 PRINT TAB(1100); "shown along"
810 PRINT TAB(1100); "bottom of chart"
820 PRINT: PRINT " 0"
830 PRINT " -100    -50    0    +50    Xj
+100 "
840 FOR V = 30 TO 510 STEP 109
850 LINE (V, 1)-(V, 274), , , &HAAAA
860 NEXT
870 FOR H = 1 TO 280 STEP 91
880 LINE (28, H)-(466, H), , , &HAAAA
890 NEXT
900 FOR RR = 1 TO 100 STEP 2
910 TT = 2 * (PI * RR / 100)
920 VV = (SIN(TT) * 68) + 160
930 HH = (COS(TT) * 84) + 248
940 PSET (HH, VV)
950 NEXT
960 RETURN
970 REM Z plotting
routine......................
980 VP = 274 - (R * 1.8)
990 HP = ((X + 106) / .465) + 20
```

```
1000 CIRCLE (HP, VP), 3: IF Z = 1 THEN
CIRCLE (HP, VP), 5
1010 RETURN
```

Program GRAPHEGA

```
10 CLS : CLEAR : SCREEN 0
20 ON ERROR GOTO 660
30 PRINT " Program GRAPH. Creates an
antenna impedance signature over a
specified"
40 PRINT " frequency range, from 3-Meter
impedance data. Copyright Peter Dodd G3LDO"
50 PRINT : PRINT : PI = 3.141: B = 50
60 FILES "*.DAT"
70 PRINT " Enter .DAT impedance data file
from the above list"
80 INPUT " Remember to add .DAT after the
file name"; NF$
90 SCREEN 10: CLS
100 DIM AA(9)
110 DIM CC(9)
120 DIM DD(9)
130 DIM EE(9)
140 DIM RR(9)
150 DIM XX(9)
160 DIM ZZ(9)
170 DIM FY(9)
180 DIM EJ(9)
190 DIM P$(9)
200 OPEN "I", #1, NF$
210 INPUT #1, TITLE$
220 INPUT #1, M
230 MM = M
240 FOR Z = 1 TO MM
250 INPUT #1, FY(Z), AA(Z), CC(Z), DD(Z),
EE(Z)
260 A = AA(Z)
270 C = CC(Z)
280 D = DD(Z)
290 E = EE(Z)
300 F = (B * B + C * C - A * A) / (2 * B *
C)
310 IF F = 0 THEN G = PI / 2: GOTO 330
320 G = ATN(SQR(1 / (F * F) - 1)): IF F < 0
THEN G = PI - G
330 H = (C * C + D * D - E * E) / (2 * C *
D)
340 IF H = 0 THEN J = PI / 2: GOTO 360
350 J = ATN(SQR(1 / (H * H) - 1)): IF H < 0
THEN J = PI - J
360 K = (A * A + B * B - C * C) / (2 * A *
B)
370 IF K = 0 THEN L = PI / 2: GOTO 390
380 L = ATN(SQR(1 / (K * K) - 1)): IF K < 0
THEN L = PI - L
390 M = (D * D + E * E - C * C) / (2 * D *
E)
400 N = ATN(SQR(1 / (M * M) - 1)): IF M < 0
THEN N = PI - N
410 Q = ATN(B / D)
420 T = B / SIN(Q)
430 ZZ = (T * T + E * E - A * A) / (2 * T *
E)
440 IF ZZ = 0 THEN P = PI / 2: GOTO 460
450 P = ATN(SQR(1 / (ZZ * ZZ) - 1)): IF ZZ
< 0 THEN P = PI - P
460 S = P - Q
470 IF (L + Q) > (PI / 2) THEN S = (2 * PI)
- (P + Q)
480 IF H > 0 THEN X1 = D - A * SIN(L) ELSE
X1 = D + A * SIN(L)
490 X2 = E * M
500 X3 = E * COS(S)
510 R1 = A * K - B
520 R2 = E * SIN(N)
530 R3 = E * SIN(S)
540 X = (X1 + X2 + X3) / 3
550 R = (R1 + R2 + R3) / 3
560 IF Z = 1 THEN GOSUB 670: REM plot chart
once only
570 GOSUB 970: REM plot Z
580 NEXT Z
590 CLOSE #1
600 PRINT " Freqs (MHz)"; FY(1); FY(2);
FY(3); FY(4); FY(5); FY(6); FY(7); FY(8);
FY(9)
605 PRINT
610 INPUT "   goto main menu 1. repeat this
program 2."; AA
620 SCREEN 0
630 IF AA = 1 THEN SHELL "menu"
640 IF AA = 2 THEN GOTO 10
650 END
660 PRINT " ERROR IN DATA OR INCORRECT FILE
NAME.": RESUME 610
670 REM Chart
routine...........................
690 PRINT : PRINT TAB(1100); "Plot Title":
PRINT TAB(1100); TITLE$: PRINT
700 PRINT TAB(1100); "Dotted circle=":
PRINT TAB(1100); "2:1 SWR contour"
710 PRINT "100"
720 PRINT TAB(1100); "Lowest frequency"
730 PRINT TAB(1100); "indicated by":
740 PRINT TAB(1100); "double circle"
750 PRINT TAB(1100); "on the plot"
760 PRINT " R" :PRINT
770 PRINT " 50"
780 PRINT TAB(1100); "Measurement"
790 PRINT TAB(1100); "frequencies"
800 PRINT TAB(1100); "shown along"
810 PRINT TAB(1100); "bottom of chart"
820 PRINT: PRINT " 0"
830 PRINT " -100    -50    0    +50    Xj
```

```
+100 "
840 FOR V = 30 TO 510 STEP 109
850 LINE (V, 1)-(V, 274), , , &HAAAA
860 NEXT
870 FOR H = 1 TO 280 STEP 91
880 LINE (28, H)-(466, H), , , &HAAAA
890 NEXT
900 FOR RR = 1 TO 100 STEP 2
910 TT = 2 * (PI * RR / 100)
920 VV = (SIN(TT) * 68) + 160
930 HH = (COS(TT) * 84) + 248
940 PSET (HH, VV)
950 NEXT
960 RETURN
970 REM Z plotting
routine......................
980 VP = 274 - (R * 1.8)
990 HP = ((X + 106) / .465) + 20
1000 CIRCLE (HP, VP), 3: IF Z = 1 THEN
CIRCLE (HP, VP), 5
1010 RETURN
```

Calibration file for checking the graph display

```
Graph_calibrate
5
50     112    71    50    50
25     90.5   56    50    25
100    158    112   50    100
-50    145    116   56    70
+50    100    50    50    70.6
```

Data file of coaxial cable impedance test

```
Coax_Z_Test
9
1.8    189    154    93    100
3.5    151    115.6  47.2  85.3
7.0    117.4  83     32.8  58.2
10.1   100    67.4   36.8  39.2
14.0   77     32     14    25.5
18.1   76.7   32.8   32.1  27.4
21.0   80.1   32.1   34.1  39
24.9   102.1  55.4   59.7  64.1
29     144    97.4   49    98
```

80m mobile whip antenna file

```
80M_Mobile_Gwhip
9
3.55 120 105 52 53
3.56 115 98 52 47
3.57 109 90 52 40
3.58 102 80 51 31
3.59 95 70 51 24
3.6 89 57 51 22
3.61 87 45 52 34
3.62 94 53 51 61
3.63 118 70 50 102
```

DDRR mobile antenna data file

```
DDRR_Mobile_Antenna
9
14.14   100   52   72   69
14.15   114   64   71   72
14.16   124   76   71   72
14.17   130   86   71   67
14.18   131   91   71   60
14.19   128   92   71   51
14.2    123   90   71   41
14.21   116   86   70   33
14.22   110   82   70   26
```

PROGRAM FOR PLOTTING POLAR DIAGRAMS

The equipment required to plot polar diagrams is described in Chapter 5, 'Plotting antenna polar diagrams using an IBM PC compatible computer'.

The program displays a graticule with heading information to provide a reference for the polar plot; samples analogue data from the FSM and plots it as a polar diagram over the graticule as the AUT is rotated; and saves antenna data to a file and redisplays it when required.

In addition, provision is made for adjusting parameters, such as aligning the plotting time to the AUT rotation speed, and then adjusting the sampled values for the required polar display.

The software is written in BASIC and is given as a listing – it will run in GW-BASIC and QUICK-BASIC. The program is menu driven and straightforward to use. If you save the file using a suffix such as .DAT or .ANT then you will have to add it to the file name when you recall the file.

The program has facilities for calculating polar diagram plotting scales – see Chapter 5, Figs 5.4, 5.5 and 5.6. If these facilities in software are not required leave out lines 1210 to 1240, 1350 to 1370 and 1490 to 1570.

Program IBMPLOT

```
30 PI = 3.14158: MH = 400: MV = 91: REM
global positioning;mv vertical;mh
horizontal
40 CLS : AR = 2.286: REM aspect ratio 2.286
50 DIM A(250): REM dimension array for data
60 SCREEN 2
70 GOSUB 100
80 GOTO 70
90 SCREEN 0: END
100 CLS : REM *******Subroutine to show
menu ***********
110 LOCATE 4, 7: PRINT "   G3LDO Antenna
Polar Plot": PRINT : PRINT
```

```
120 PRINT "   T    align plotting time to
AUT rotation Time": PRINT
130 PRINT "   P    Plot polar diagram":
PRINT
140 PRINT "   S    Save data from antenna
plot to file": PRINT
150 PRINT "   L    Load previous plotted
data to screen": PRINT
160 PRINT "   Q    to Quit program": PRINT
170 PRINT "   Enter appropriate letter"
180 PRINT "   and press ENTER ": PRINT
190 INPUT "", A$
200 IF A$ = "t" THEN GOSUB 260: GOSUB 720
210 IF A$ = "q" THEN GOTO 90
220 IF A$ = "p" THEN GOSUB 260: GOSUB 720
230 IF A$ = "s" THEN GOSUB 1080
240 IF A$ = "l" THEN GOSUB 1460: GOSUB 260:
GOSUB 1170
250 RETURN
260 REM *******Subroutine to draw the
graticule*******
270 STARTSIZE = 22: REM size of first
circle on graticule
280 D = 2: REM Number of dots per line on
graticule
290 CLS : PSET (MH, MV)
300 CS = STARTSIZE: REM cs = circle size
310 FOR R = 0 TO 120 STEP D
320 T = 2 * (PI * R / 120)
330 V = (SIN(T) * CS) + MV
340 H = (COS(T) * (CS * AR)) + MH
350 PSET (H, V)
360 NEXT R
370 CS = 44: REM cs = circle size
380 FOR R = 0 TO 120 STEP (D / 1.666)
390 T = 2 * (PI * R / 120)
400 V = (SIN(T) * CS) + MV
410 H = (COS(T) * (CS * AR)) + MH
420 PSET (H, V)
430 NEXT R
440 CS = 66: REM cs = circle size
450 FOR R = 0 TO 120 STEP (D / 2.5)
460 T = 2 * (PI * R / 120)
470 V = (SIN(T) * CS) + MV
480 H = (COS(T) * (CS * AR)) + MH
490 PSET (H, V)
500 NEXT R
510 CS = 88: REM cs = circle size
520 FOR R = 0 TO 120 STEP (D / 4)
530 T = 2 * (PI * R / 120)
540 V = (SIN(T) * CS) + MV
550 H = (COS(T) * (CS * AR)) + MH
560 PSET (H, V)
570 NEXT R
580 REM Spokes
590 SPOKE = 128
600 FOR CS = STARTSIZE TO (STARTSIZE * 4)
STEP D
610 FOR R = 0 TO SPOKE STEP 16: REM spoke/
STEP = number of spokes
620 T = 2 * (PI * R / SPOKE)
630 V = (SIN(T) * CS) + MV
640 H = (COS(T) * (CS * AR)) + MH
650 PSET (H, V)
660 NEXT R
670 NEXT CS
680 LOCATE 1, 51: PRINT "0": LOCATE 12, 75:
PRINT "90"
690 LOCATE 23, 50: PRINT "180": LOCATE 12,
24: PRINT "270"
700 RETURN
710 PH = 400: PV = 52
720 REM *********Subroutine to read
analogue data from FSM*****
730 REM This subroutine is for the Pico
ADC-10 only and lines 760-790 &
740 REM 850-920 will have to be changed if
a different ADC is used
750 IF A$ = "t" THEN GOSUB 1590: GOTO 820
760 ADDRESS% = &H378: CLOCK% = &H378:
PORTIN% = &H379
770 HIGH% = &HFD: LOW% = &HFC: MASK% =
&H80: SHIFT% = 2
780 OUT ADDRESS%, &HFE: REM power up ADC
790 OUT ADDRESS%, &HFC: REM chip select
800 LOCATE 1, 1: PRINT "Input Scale Factor"
810 INPUT "Default 1.5 "; PSF: PRINT
820 IF PSF = 0 THEN PSF = 1.5: REM Sets
default scale factor
830 PRINT : PRINT "Press RETURN": PRINT
"and start AUT rotator"
840 INPUT "to commence plotting", S$
850 Q = 0
860 FOR R = 240 TO 120 STEP -.5
870   Q = Q + 1
880   BITS% = 0
890   FOR J% = 1 TO 8
900   OUT CLOCK%, HIGH%
910   REM read MSB of register 'portin%'
and add to left-shifted 'bits%'
920   BITS% = (INP(PORTIN%) AND MASK%) +
BITS% * SHIFT%
930   FOR DELAY = 1 TO PT: NEXT: REM pt =
plotting time
940   OUT CLOCK%, LOW%
950   NEXT J%
960   IF A$ = "t" THEN DS = 55 ELSE DS =
(BITS% / MASK% XOR &HFF) * PSF
970   A(Q) = DS
980   T = 2 * (PI * R / 120)
990   V = (SIN(T) * DS) + MV
1000   H = (COS(T) * (DS * AR) + MH)
1010   CIRCLE (H, V), 1: REM points plotted
as small circles
```

```
1020 PSET (H + .2, V + .2)
1030 NEXT R
1040 OUT ADDRESS%, &H10: REM power down ADC
1050 PRINT : PRINT : PRINT
1060 INPUT "RETURN for menu", A$
1070 RETURN
1080 REM ****Subroutine for saving antenna
data to file***
1090 PRINT "Name Antenna"
1100 INPUT "Data File"; ANT$
1110 OPEN "O", #1, ANT$
1120 DTA = Q
1130 FOR Q = 1 TO DTA
1140 PRINT #1, A(Q)
1150 NEXT
1160 CLOSE : RETURN
1170 REM *******Subroutine to read data
from file******
1180 LOCATE 2, 1: PRINT "Scale Factor"
1190 INPUT "(Default 1.5)"; SF
1200 IF SF = 0 THEN SF = 1.5: PRINT
1210 PRINT "L for Linear plot"
1220 PRINT "G for Log plot"
1230 PRINT "A for ARRL plot": PRINT
1240 INPUT "Select plot by letter"; PT$: PRINT
1250 PRINT "Plot of"
1260 PRINT "antenna file"
1270 PRINT ANT$: PRINT : PRINT
1280 PRINT "Press Return"
1290 OPEN "I", #1, ANT$
1300 Q = 1: DS = 1: R = 240
1310 INPUT #1, A(Q)
1320 IF EOF(1) THEN 1430
1330 DS = A(Q)
1340 IF DS = 0 THEN DS = 1
1350 IF PT$ = "g" THEN GOSUB 1490
1360 IF PT$ = "a" THEN GOSUB 1520
1370 IF PT$ = "l" THEN GOSUB 1550
1380 T = 2 * (PI * R / 120)
1390 V = (SIN(T) * DS) + MV
1400 H = (COS(T) * (DS * AR)) + MH)
1410 CIRCLE (H, V), 1
1420 A = A + 1: R = R - .5: GOTO 1310
1430 INPUT "for menu", S$
1440 CLOSE : RETURN
1450 REM *******Subroutine for printing
antenna file list*****
1460 CLS : PRINT : FILES "*."; PRINT
1470 INPUT "Enter Required File"; ANT$
1480 RETURN
1490 REM *****Log Function Plot*****
1500 DS = (LOG(DS) * .4343) * SF
1510 RETURN
1520 REM *****ARRL Plot********
1530 DS = (.01 * (DS) + (LOG(DS) * .4343))
* SF
1540 RETURN
```

```
1550 REM *******Linear Plot**********
1560 DS = DS * SF
1570 RETURN
1580 REM ***********Subroutine for setting
plotting time**************
1590 PRINT "Set Plot Time"
1600 INPUT "(default 30)"; PT
1610 IF PT = 0 THEN PT = 30
1620 RETURN
```

Notes regarding the development of the impedance measurement algorithm by Tom Lloyd, G3TML

"I felt the need for an algorithm which would yield a solution, together with an indication of its reliability; it should also be capable of handling all but the poorest of data.

"The geometry of the vector diagrams, shown in the graphic solution in Chapter 2, Fig 2.21, calls for a trigonometrical approach. However, because I wished to avoid the use of angular functions to allow wider use of the BASIC program I initially examined the possibility of using geometrically derived equations where a solution is given by:

$$R_{es} = \frac{E_a^2 - E_r^2 - E_{cz}^2}{2 \times E_r} \qquad (1)$$

$$jX = \frac{E_{cz}^2 - E_c^2 - E_z^2}{2 \times E_c} \qquad (2)$$

"The real part of the solution (R_{es}) is a function of E_a, E_r and E_{cz} only. Hence any change in the values of E_c or E_z will not affect the value of R_{es}. Similarly, the imaginary part of the solution (jX) is a function of E_{cz}, E_c and E_z only. This means that jX does not respond to changes in the values of E_a and/or E_r.

"Consequently an accurate solution is only possible when ideal data are used, and in no case is an indication of the reliability of the solution given. These disadvantages are aggravated by the fact that the larger the data errors are, the solution is in error disproportionately. For these reasons I did not proceed with this approach.

"It is rare that 'ideal' data are available, by this I mean that the three arcs with radii E_a, E_{cz} and E_z arcs intersect in a common point.

"Generally data are 'well behaved'; by this I mean that the three arcs intersect to give six intersections, some of which may coincide.

"Three of these intersections will lie close to the true solution and form the apices of a small triangle of error. It is the accepted practice to take a solution to lie at the centre of gravity of this triangle. Provided the size of the triangle is small its sides may be approximated to straight lines without introducing other than insignificant errors. I decided that the algorithm would use this procedure to find a solution together with its attendant errors, the latter giving an indication of its reliability.

"There is a further class of data which may or may not have any significant errors; causing one of the smaller arcs not to intersect the other two. This data I have designated 'acceptable faulty data' and the method of dealing with it is described later; however, I must stress that, in practice, most data is well behaved.

"Program ZCALC uses the fundamental trigonometrical algorithm referred to above. There are two regions of the vector diagram where, with particular data, ambiguities result from the procedure used in the program and an additional error, usually small, is introduced. However, the error print out always indicates the reliability of the result.

"This trigonometrical algorithm TOM requires the inverse cosine function; this seems to be available on many early BASICs (Sinclair, BBC) and in calculators using BASIC, but not on BASIC derived from Microsoft BASIC (Amstrad, IBM etc).

"The original voltage designations by W8CGD have been changed within all the programs as follows: $E_a = A$, $E_r = B$, $E_{cz} = C$, $E_c = D$ and $E_z = E$. This is because these variables are used extensively throughout the programs; also the PB110 only allows single-letter variables.

TRANSMISSION LINE IMPEDANCE TRANSFORM

If the impedance of an antenna is measured via a length of coaxial cable the measurement will be affected by the impedance transformation of the feeder; except if the feeder was an *exact* multiple of $\lambda/2$ at the frequency the measurement was made.

The algorithm for this program, by Bert Weller, WD8KBW, calculates this impedance transform. It requires the *electrical* length of the feeder. You will have to calculate this length by multiplying the physical length of the feeder by its velocity factor, or measure it using a dip meter or impedance bridge. The program will also ask for the transmission line characteristic impedance, and the frequency at which the measurement is made.

```
10 INPUT " Transmission line electrical
length in metres? ", L
20 INPUT " Transmission line characteristic
impedance? ", ZO
30 INPUT " Frequency in MHz? ", F
40 F=1000000!*F
50 PRINT: PRINT:PRINT "   Measured
impedance " :PRINT
60 INPUT "   Resistive part? ", RL
70 INPUT "   Reactive part? ", XL
80 ANG = -(2 * 3.142 * (3.333E-09) * L * F)
90 DENOM = (ZO - XL * TAN(ANG)) ^ 2 + (RL *
TAN(ANG)) ^ 2
100 RIN = ZO ^ 2 * RL * (1 + (TAN(ANG)) ^
2) / DENOM
110 XIN = ZO * (ZO *XL * (1-(TAN(ANG))^2)-
(RL^2+XL^2-(ZO^2))*TAN(ANG))/DENOM
120 IF XIN < 0 THEN S$ = "-j" ELSE S$ =
"+j"
130 AXIN=ABS(XIN)
140 RIN = INT(10 * RIN + .5)/10
150 AXIN = INT(10 * AXIN + .5)/10
160 PRINT:PRINT "   Impedance at antenna or
load is "; RIN; S$;AXIN
```

4 Conversion formulae and tables

LENGTH AND WEIGHT CONVERSIONS

Metric unit = Factor × Imperial unit

Metric unit × Factor = Imperial unit

Metric unit	Factor	Imperial unit
Millimetre	25.4	Inch
Centimetre	2.54	Inch
Centimetre	30.48	Foot
Metre	0.3048	Foot
Metre	0.9144	Yard
Kilometre	1.609	Mile
Gram	28.349	Ounce
Kilogram	0.45359	Pound

Some metric/imperial equivalents:

$$18m = 60ft$$
$$12m = 40ft$$
$$160kg = 350 lb$$
$$45kg = 100 lb$$
$$15kg = 30 lb$$
$$8cm = 3in$$

CONVERSION OF RECTANGULAR TO POLAR COORDINATES

Example: Rectangular 40 + j30.

Manual method

Find Z by Pythagoras:

$$Z = \sqrt{(R^2 + X^2)}$$
$$= \sqrt{(40^2 + 30^2)}$$
$$= 50$$

Arc tan (X/R) = 36.87°, phase angle, referenced to the positive real axis.

Automatic method

This assumes your calculator has rectangular to polar conversion (calculator in degree mode). '[ ]' indicates entries to the calculator, '{ }' indicates readout.

[4] [0]	Enter resistive part
[R->P]	
[3] [0]	Enter j, include negative sign if appropriate
[=]	
{50}	Readout of polar Z
[X<->Y]	
{36.87}	Readout of polar angle

If the j term in the rectangular coordinate is negative then the angle in the polar coordinate will be negative.

CONVERSION OF POLAR TO RECTANGULAR COORDINATES

Example: Polar impedance = 50/36.87

$$R = Z \cos \theta$$
$$R = 50 \times \cos (36.87) = 40$$
$$j = Z \sin \theta$$
$$X = 50 \times \sin (36.87) = 30$$

If your calculator has polar to rectangular conversion (calculator in degree mode), then:

[5][0]	Enter Z
[P->R]	
[3][6][.][8][7]	Enter angle
[=]	
{40}	Resistance readout
[X<->Y]	
{30}	j readout

If the the angle in the polar coordinate is negative then the j term in the rectangular coordinate will be negative.

CONVERTING CAPACITANCE VALUES TO REACTANCE FOR IMPEDANCE BRIDGES

The graph (Fig A4.1) is based on a frequency of 1MHz; for other frequencies, simply divide the reactance value by the actual frequency in megahertz.

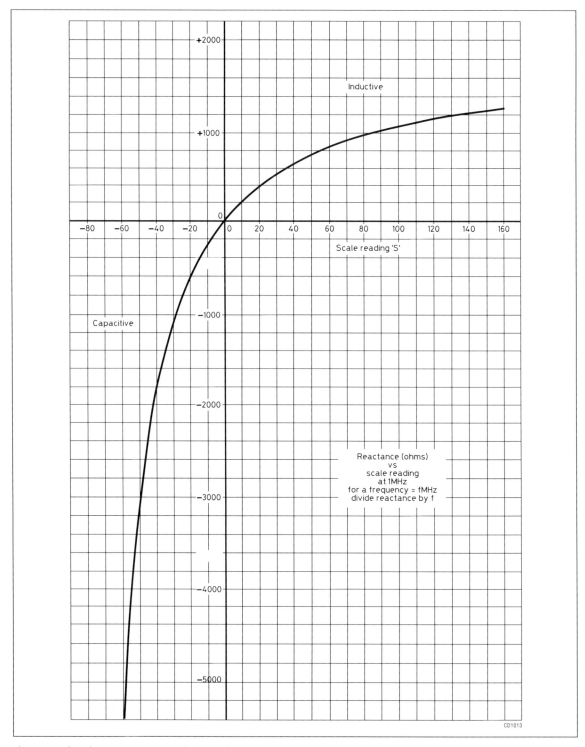

Fig A4.1. Calibration graph for converting capacitance values to reactance (+ or – j)

Table A4.1. Power and voltage ratios in decibels				
Voltage ratio (equal Z)	Power ratio	Voltage ratio (equal Z)	Power ratio	+ or − (dB)
1.000	1.000	1.000	1.000	0
0.989	0.977	1.012	1.023	0.1
0.977	0.955	1.023	1.047	0.2
0.966	0.933	1.035	1.072	0.3
0.955	0.912	1.047	1.096	0.4
0.944	0.891	1.059	1.122	0.5
0.933	0.871	1.072	1.148	0.6
0.923	0.851	1.084	1.175	0.7
0.912	0.832	1.096	1.202	0.8
0.902	0.813	1.109	1.230	0.9
0.891	0.794	1.122	1.259	1.0
0.841	0.708	1.189	1.413	1.5
0.794	0.631	1.259	1.585	2.0
0.750	0.562	1.334	1.778	2.5
0.708	0.501	1.413	1.995	3.0
0.668	0.447	1.496	2.239	3.5
0.631	0.398	1.585	2.512	4.0
0.596	0.355	1.679	2.818	4.5
0.562	0.316	1.778	3.162	5.0
0.531	0.282	1.884	3.548	5.5
0.501	0.251	1.995	3.981	6.0
0.473	0.224	2.113	4.467	6.5
0.447	0.200	2.239	5.012	7.0
0.422	0.178	2.371	5.623	7.5
0.398	0.158	2.512	6.310	8.0
0.376	0.141	2.661	7.079	8.5
0.355	0.126	2.818	7.943	9.0
0.335	0.112	2.985	8.913	9.5
0.316	0.100	3.162	10.0	10
0.282	0.0794	3.550	12.6	11
0.251	0.0631	3.980	15.9	12
0.224	0.0501	4.47	20.0	13
0.200	0.0398	5.01	25.1	14
0.176	0.0316	5.62	31.6	15
0.159	0.0251	6.31	39.8	16
0.141	0.0200	7.08	50.1	17
0.126	0.0159	7.94	63.1	18
0.112	0.0126	8.91	79.4	19
0.100	0.0100	10.0	100.0	20
3.16×10^{-2}	10^{-3}	3.16×10	10^3	30
10^{-2}	10^{-4}	10^2	10^4	40
3.16×10^{-3}	10^{-5}	3.16×10^2	10	50

Table A4.2. Basic antenna dimensions		
Band (MHz)	Length (m)	Length (ft)
1.8	39.6	130
3.5	20.4	66.9
7	10.2	33.5
10	7.14	23.4
14	5.1	16.7
18	3.96	12.9
21	3.4	11.1
24	2.95	9.6
28	2.55	8.3

Lengths of dipole elements or vertical antenna elements.

Table A4.3. The quad beam antenna				
Band (MHz)	L1	L2	S	D
7	10.7	11.0	5.2	7.6
10.1	7.5	7.8	4.4	5.4
14	5.4	5.6	2.6	3.8
18.1	4.2	4.4	2.4	3.1
21	3.6	3.7	1.8	2.6
24.9	3.0	3.2	1.8	2.3
28	2.6	2.8	1.3	1.8
50	1.48	1.54	1.2	1.0

Approximate dimensions for a quad. Lengths in metres.

$$N(\text{dB}) = 10 \log_{10} (P_2/P_1)$$

or

$$N(\text{dB}) = 20 \log_{10} (V_2/V_1)$$

P_2 and P_1 are power ratios being compared; V_2 and V_1 are voltage ratios being compared. A constant impedance is assumed.

A value in decibels only has absolute meaning if the reference level is stated. The expressions dBm and dBw are frequently used for ratios with respect to 1mW and 1W respectively. A power level of 1mW into 50 or 600Ω has become the standard for comparative purposes and has been given the datum 0dBm. Signal levels above and below this datum are expressed in + dBm and −dBm respectively; they correspond to finite voltage or current levels – not ratios.

0dBm into 600Ω resistance corresponds to 0.775V. 0dBm into 50Ω resistance corresponds to 0.225V.

See Table A4.1.

BASIC DIMENSIONS FOR ANTENNAS

The antenna element-length data given in Table A4.2 is for $\lambda/4$ sections of wire for each leg of a dipole or the vertical or radials of a ground-plane antenna. These data are included as a starting point for constructing antennas.

Alternatively, the reactance may be derived using the following formula; a negative answer indicates a capacitive reactance, positive indicates inductive reactance.

$$X = \frac{106}{2\pi f} \times \frac{S}{C_5(S + C_5)}$$

where X is the reactance in ohms, f is the frequency in megahertz, S is the scale reading (+ or −) and C_5 is 82 (the value of C5 in picofarads).

POWER AND VOLTAGE RATIOS IN DECIBELS

Power and voltage ratios are normally expressed in decibels where:

Table A4.4. Wire gauges				
	SWG		**AWG**	
Wire No	**(in)**	**(mm)**	**(in)**	**(mm)**
0000	0.40	10.16	0.460	11.68
000	0.372	9.45	0.409	10.41
00	0.348	8.84	0.365	9.27
0	0.324	8.23	0.325	8.25
1	0.300	7.62	0.289	7.35
2	7.276	7.01	0.258	6.54
3	0.252	6.40	0.229	5.83
4	0.232	5.89	0.204	5.19
5	0.212	5.38	0.182	4.62
6	0.192	4.88	0.162	4.11
7	0.176	4.47	0.144	3.66
8	0.160	4.06	0.128	3.26
9	0.144	3.66	0.144	2.90
10	0.128	3.25	0.102	2.59
11	0.116	2.95	0.091	2.30
12	0.104	2.64	0.081	2.05
13	0.092	2.34	0.072	1.83
14	0.081	2.03	0.064	1.63
15	0.072	1.83	0.057	1.45
16	0.064	1.63	0.051	1.29
17	0.056	1.42	0.045	1.15
18	0.048	1.22	0.040	1.02
19	0.040	1.02	0.036	0.91
20	0.036	0.92	0.032	0.81
21	0.032	0.81	0.028	0.72
22	0.028	0.71	0.025	0.64
23	0.024	0.61	0.023	0.57
24	0.023	0.56	0.020	0.51
25	0.020	0.51	0.018	0.45
26	0.018	0.46	0.016	0.40
27	0.016	0.41	0.014	0.36
28	0.014	0.38	0.013	0.32
29	0.013	0.35	0.011	0.29
30	0.012	0.305	0.010	0.25
31	0.011	0.29	0.009	0.23
32	0.0106	0.27	0.008	0.20
33	0.010	0.254	0.007	0.18
34	0.009	0.229	0.0063	0.16
35	0.008	0.203	0.0056	0.14
36	0.007	0.178	0.0050	0.13
37	0.0067	0.17	0.0044	0.11
38	0.006	0.15	0.0040	0.10
39	0.005	0.127	0.0035	0.08

SWG = Standard Wire Gauge
AWG = American Wire Gauge

Impedance and Smith charts

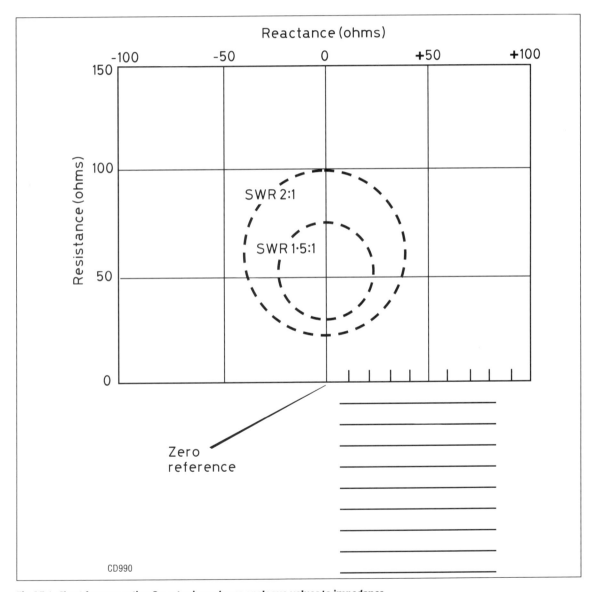

Fig A5.1. Chart for converting 3-meter impedance analogue values to impedance

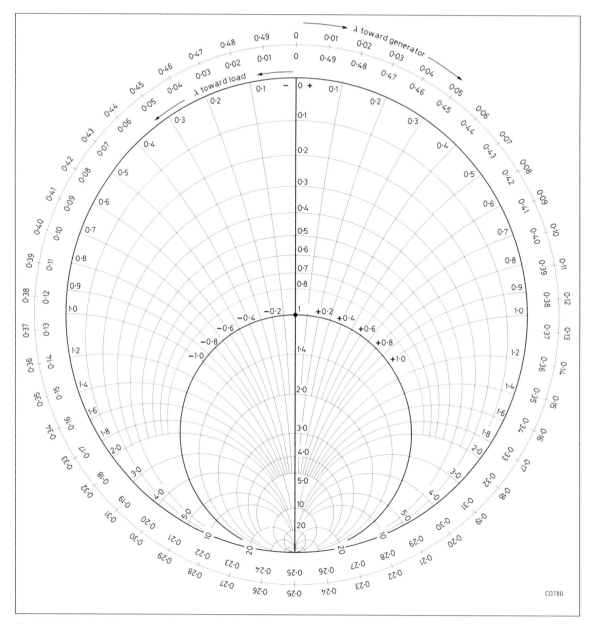

Fig A5.2. Smith chart for constructing normalised calculator

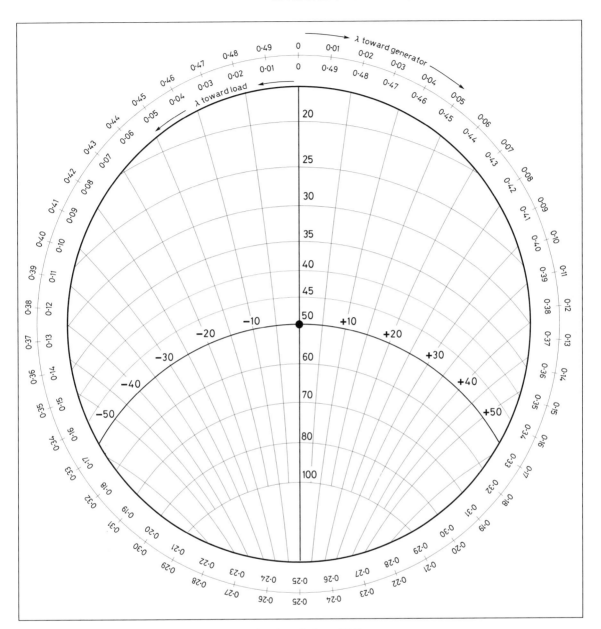

Fig A5.3. A restricted range Smith chart for constructing the calculator (50Ω)

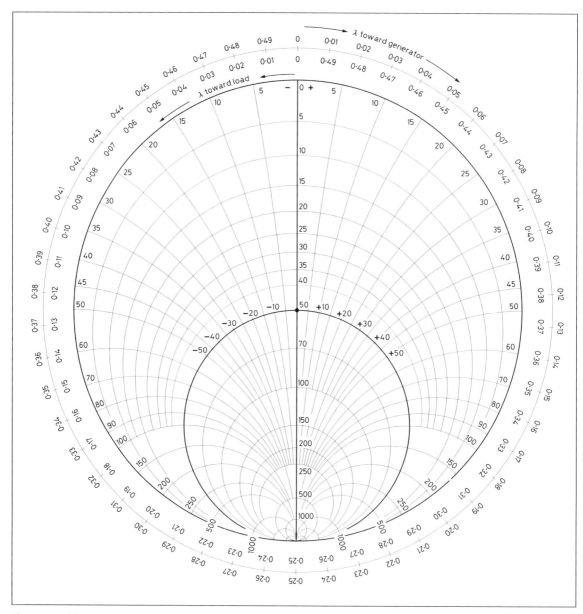

Fig A5.4. Smith chart for constructing the calculator (50Ω)

Index

Some other RSGB publications . . .

❏ **HF ANTENNA COLLECTION**

An invaluable collection of outstanding articles and short pieces which were published in *Radio Communication* during the period 1968–89. As well as ingenious designs for single-element, beam and miniature antennas, there is a wealth of information on ancillary topics such as feeders, tuners, baluns, testing, modelling, and the mechanics of mounting an antenna safely.

❏ **HF ANTENNAS FOR ALL LOCATIONS**

This book explains the 'why' as well as the 'how' of HF antennas, and takes a look at existing designs in the light of the latest developments. A wealth of practical information on the choice and construction of antennas to suit most locations and requirements is also presented. An essential reference for the experimenter and enthusiast.

❏ **PRACTICAL WIRE ANTENNAS**

Wire antennas offer one of the most cost-effective ways to put out a good signal on the HF bands, and this practical guide to their construction has something to interest every amateur on a budget. Theory has been kept to a minimum – instead the author has shared his years of experience in this field.

❏ **RADIO COMMUNICATION HANDBOOK**

First published in 1938 and a favourite ever since, this large and comprehensive guide to the theory and practice of amateur radio takes the reader from first principles right through to such specialised fields as packet radio, slow-scan television and amateur satellite communication.

❏ **TECHNICAL TOPICS SCRAPBOOK 1985–89**

Contains the complete 'Technical Topics' columns from 1985 to 1989 inclusive, reprinted from *Radio Communication* magazine, together with a new index. No amateur experimenter or constructor should be without this information at his or her fingertips.

❏ **TEST EQUIPMENT FOR THE RADIO AMATEUR**

Describes a range of test instruments and measurement methods which should satisfy the requirements of most anateur stations. The theory behind the methods is given, and

 RADIO SOCIETY OF GREAT BRITAIN
Lambda House, Cranborne Road,
Potters Bar, Herts EN6 3JE, England
Visit our Web site for more details at http://www.rsgb.org.uk

Get more out of amateur radio . . . as an RSGB member!

Radio Communication

An outstanding magazine, sent free of charge to all members, which covers a wide range of interests and which features the best and latest amateur radio news. There's technical articles, equipment reviews, and the famous 'Technical Topics' column to keep you up to date with technical matters. There are also regular news columns for HF, VHF/UHF, microwaves, SWL, satellites, data and contests. And, if you're after equipment, the Members' Ads offer the best bargains around.

QSL Bureau

Members enjoy the use of the QSL Bureau free of charge for both outgoing and incoming cards. This can save you a good deal of postage.

Specialised Equipment Insurance

Insurance for your valuable equipment which has been arranged specially for members. The rates are very advantageous.

Government Liaison

One of the most vital features of the work of the RSGB is the ongoing liaison with the UK Licensing Authority – presently the Radiocommunications Agency of the Department of Trade and Industry. Setting and maintaining the proper framework in which amateur radio can thrive and develop is essential to the well-being of amateur radio. The Society spares no effort in defence of amateur radio's most precious assets – the amateur bands.

Operating Awards

A wide range of operating awards are available via the responsible officers: their names can be found in the front pages of *Radio Communication* and in the Society's *Amateur Radio Call Book*.

Contests (HF/VHF/Microwave)

The Society has two contest committees which carry out all work associated with the running of contests. The HF Contests Committee deals with contests below 30MHz, whilst events on frequencies above 30MHz are dealt with by the VHF Contests Committee.

Morse Testing

In April 1986 the Society took over responsibility for morse testing of radio amateurs in the UK. If you wish to take a morse test, write direct to RSGB HQ (Morse tests) for an application form.

Slow Morse

Many volunteers all over the country give up their time to send slow morse over the air to those who are preparing for the 5 and 12 words per minute morse tests. The Society also produces morse instruction tapes.

RSGB Books

The Society publishes a range of books for the radio amateur and imports many others. RSGB members are entitled to a discount on all books purchased from the Society. This discount can offset the cost of membership.

Technical and EMC Advice

Although the role of the Society's Technical and Publications Advisory Committee is largely to vet material intended for publication, its members and HQ staff are always willing to help with any technical matters.

Breakthrough in domestic entertainment equipment can be a difficult problem to solve as well as having licensing implications. The Society's EMC Committee is able to offer practical assistance in many cases. The Society also publishes a special book to assist you. Additional advice can be obtained from the EMC Committee Chairman via RSGB HQ.

Planning Permission

There is a special booklet and expert help available to members seeking assistance with planning matters.

Send for our Membership Information Pack today and discover how you too can benefit from these services. Write to:

RADIO SOCIETY OF GREAT BRITAIN, Lambda House, Cranborne Road, Potters Bar, Herts EN6 3JE, England

or visit our Web site at http://www.rsgb.org.uk